MORE FAVORITE STORIES
OLD AND NEW

More Favorite Stories

Old and New

FOR BOYS AND GIRLS

Revised and Enlarged Edition

Selected by

Sidonie Matsner Gruenberg

Illustrated by Kurt Wiese

DOUBLEDAY & COMPANY, INC., GARDEN CITY, NEW YORK

FOR MY GRANDCHILDREN

Peter Barnard
Daniel Barnard
Nicholas Benjamin
Elisabeth Allée
Richard Joseph
Ann Matsner
Kathryn Mary
Jean Allée
Judith Sidonie
Joel William
Matthew Alan

Library of Congress Catalog Card Number 60–12997

Printed in the United States of America

ACKNOWLEDGMENTS

My warmest gratitude goes first of all to my husband, Benjamin C. Gruenberg, who is really co-editor of this collection.

And my special appreciations go

To Margaret H. Lesser, head of the Junior Books Department of Doubleday & Company, Inc., for her constant interest and many helpful suggestions;

To Helen Ferris, editor, Junior Literary Guild, for the inspiration to continue selecting "favorite stories" for the older children, and especially for her brilliant suggestion to combine under "Animals Around the World" a number of folk tales that have to do with animals;

To Flora Straus, chairman, and Josette Frank, staff consultant, of the Children's Literature Committee of the Child Study Association of America, Inc., for inspiring counsel out of their many years of experience with juvenile literature;

To Bella Koral, whose familiarity with the literature for boys and girls was invaluable in our search;

To Edna May Jones, my secretary, who managed so efficiently and graciously the many details involved in the project;

And to the following publishers and authors for permission to use the various stories as indicated:

D. Appleton-Century Company, Inc.—for "Waukewa's Eagle," by James Buckham, from *St. Nicholas Magazine*, copyright, 1900, 1928, and to Katherine Williams Watson for her version of "Waukewa's Eagle" in *Once upon a Time*, The H. W. Wilson Company, copyright, 1942.

Montgomery Atwater—for "Pure-Bred Pulls Through."

The Beacon Press—for "Thanksgiving Day," from *Nothing Ever Happens*, by Dorothy Canfield Fisher, copyright, 1940.

Margery Williams Bianco—for "Poor Mr. Fingle," from *A Street of Little Shops*, published by Doubleday & Company, Inc., copyright, 1932.

Claire Huchet Bishop—for "A Dust Rag for Easter Eggs," which first appeared in *Child Life*. Copyright, 1947, by Child Life, Inc.

Boy's Life—for "Rocket Rider" by Charles Coombs, reprinted by permission of the author and *Boy's Life*, published by the Boy Scouts of America.

The Caxton Printers, Ltd., Caldwell, Idaho—for "Johnnie Inkslinger and His Magic Pen," from *Paul Bunyan Swings His Axe*, by Dell J. McCormick, copyright, 1937. Used by special permission of the copyright owners.

Christy & Moore, Ltd., London—for "Billy, the Dog That Made Good," from *Wild Animal Ways*, by Ernest Thompson Seton. Published by Doubleday & Company, Inc., copyright, 1916.

Catherine C. Coblentz—for "The Horse That Came from Heaven," from *Animal Pioneers*, by Catherine C. Coblentz, copyright, 1936. Published by Little, Brown & Company.

Walter de la Mare—for "The Race Between the Hare and the Hedgehog."

Dodd, Mead & Company—for "How the Speckled Hen Got Her Speckles," from *Fairy Tales from Brazil*, by Elsie Spicer Eells, copyright, 1917.

Doubleday & Company, Inc.—for "Poor Mr. Fingle," from *A Street of Little Shops*, by Margery Williams Bianco, copyright, 1932; "Why the Dog and the Cat Are Not Friends," from *Tales of a Korean Grandmother*, by Frances Carpenter, copyright, 1947; "The Ghost of the Great White Stag," from *Skunny Wundy and Other Indian Tales*, by Arthur C. Parker, copyright, 1926; "Billy, the Dog That Made Good," from *Wild Animal Ways*, by Ernest Thompson Seton, copyright, 1916.

Ruth Sawyer Durand—for "Juan Cigarron."

E. P. Dutton & Co., Inc.—for "How Kari Saved Our Lives in the Jungle," from *Kari the Elephant*, by Dhan Gopal Mukerji, copyright, 1922.

Messrs. Faber & Faber, London—for "The Race Between the Hare and the Hedgehog," by Walter de la Mare.

Wells Gardner, Darton & Co., Ltd., London—for "The Marvel of the Sword" and "How Arthur Became King," from *Book of King Arthur and His Noble Knights*, by Mary Macleod. Published by J. B. Lippincott Company.

Elizabeth Enright Gilham—for *Kintu*, by Elizabeth Enright, copyright, 1935. Published by Rinehart & Company.

Mrs. George B. Grinnell—for "The First Corn," from *Punishment of the Stingy*, by George Bird Grinnell. Published by Harper & Brothers.

Harcourt, Brace and Company, Inc.—for "The Laughing Prince," adapted from *The Laughing Prince* by Parker Fillmore, copyright, 1921; "How They Bring Back the Village of Cream Puffs When the Wind Blows It Away," from *Rootabaga Stories* by Carl Sandburg, copyright, 1923; "A Race Against Death," from *Perilous Journeys*, by Irma Taylor, copyright, 1940; "The Dog of Pompeii," from *The Donkey of God and Other Stories*, by Louis Untermeyer, copyright, 1932.

Harper & Brothers—for "The First Corn," from *Punishment of the Stingy*, by George Bird Grinnell; "Brother Rabbit and the Mosquitoes," from *Brer Rabbit*, by Joel Chandler Harris adapted by Margaret Wise Brown, copyright, 1941; "Woman's Wit," from *Twilight Land*, by Howard Pyle, copyright, 1894, by Harper & Brothers, copyright, 1921, by Ann Poole Pyle; "The Glorious Whitewasher," from *Tom Sawyer*, by Mark Twain.

Hartsdale House—for Chapter 4 of *The Adventures of Baron Munchausen* ("The Stag and the Cherry Stones").

Holiday House—for "Whitey's Sunday Horse," by Glen Rounds.

Henry Holt and Company, Inc.—for "Hungry Spider and the Turtle," from *The Cow-Tail Switch*, by Harold Courlander and George Herzog, copyright, 1947; "The Barmecide Feast," from *More Tales from the Arabian Nights*, by Frances J. Olcott, copyright, 1915.

Houghton Mifflin Company—for "William Tell," from *The Book of Legends*, by Horace E. Scudder, copyright, 1927.

Alfred A. Knopf, Inc.—for "Against the Wind," reprinted from *The Adventures of Don Quixote*, adapted by Leighton Barrett, copyright, 1939, by Warren Chappell; "Father Teaches Me to Be Prompt," reprinted from *Life with Father*, by Clarence Day, copyright, 1934, 1935, by Clarence Day; "The Windbird and the Sun," reprinted from *Koos the Hottentot*, by Josef Marais, copyright, 1945, by Alfred A. Knopf, Inc.

Lantern Press, Inc.—for "Danger in the Deep" by Charles Coombs, reprinted from *Young Readers Water Sports Stories*, copyright 1952.

Longmans, Green and Co.—for "How Cats Came to Purr," from *The Pigtail of Ah Lee Ben Loo*, by John Bennett, copyright, 1928; "The Forty Thieves," from *Arabian Nights*, by Andrew Lang, copyright, 1946; "The Two Frogs," from *Violet Fairy Book*, by Andrew Lang, copyright, 1901, 1947.

The Macmillan Company—for "The Home on Wheels," from *America Travels*, by Alice Dalgliesh, copyright, 1933; "Mr. Crow Takes a Wife," from *Beyond the Clapping Mountains*, by Charles Gillham, copyright, 1943; "The Big Bear," from *The Bears of Blue River*, by Charles Major.

David McKay Company—for "The Sword of Damocles," "Archimedes and the Crown" ("Eureka!"), and "Damon and Pythias," from *A Book of Great Old Stories*, by Frederick S. Hoppin, copyright, 1931.

Thomas Nelson & Sons—for "The Cat Who Became Head-Forester," from *Old Peter's Russian Tales*, by Arthur Ransome.

Oxford University Press—for *Johnny and His Mule*, by Ellis Credle, copyright, 1946; "Comanche," by Alice Gall and Fleming Crew, and Katherine Williams Watson for her version of "Comanche" in *Once upon a Time*, The H. W. Wilson Company, copyright, 1942; "Steppin's First

Public Appearance," from *Steppin and Family*, by Hope Newell, copyright, 1942.

Rand McNally & Company—for "No Land in Sight" from *Kon-Tiki* by Thor Heyerdahl, reprinted by permission of the publisher.

Rinehart & Company, Inc.—for "How Pecos Bill Won and Lost His Bouncing Bride," from *The Hurricane's Children*, by Carl Carmer, copyright, 1937; *Kintu*, by Elizabeth Enright, copyright, 1935.

Charles Scribner's Sons—for *Hi Guy—The Cinderella Horse*, by Paul Brown, copyright, 1944; "How Horatius Held the Bridge," from *The Book of Bravery*, by Henry W. Lanier.

Story Parade, Inc.—for "Fleet-Foot Ann," by Elizabeth Coatsworth; "High Water in Arkansas!" by Charles J. Finger; "How Pat Got Good Sense," by Charles J. Finger, copyright, 1940; "Mother Makes Christmas," by Cornelia Meigs, copyright, 1937; "Storm Flight," by Rutherford G. Montgomery, copyright, 1939; *Whitey's Sunday Horse*, by Glen Rounds, copyright, 1941; "Journey into Space," by Katherine B. Shippen, copyright, 1944.

James Thurber—for "The Great Quillow," copyright, 1944 by James Thurber and reprinted by permission.

The Viking Press, Inc.—for "The Doughnuts," from *Homer Price*, by Robert McCloskey, copyright, 1943, by Robert McCloskey.

Whitman Publishing Company—for "The Wooden Horse," by Bella Koral. Used by permission of Whitman Publishing Company.

The H. W. Wilson Company—for the version of "Waukewa's Eagle" (by James Buckham), and of "Comanche" (by Alice Gall and Fleming Crew), by Katherine Williams Watson in *Once upon a Time*, copyright, 1942.

The John C. Winston Company—for "Oscar on Roller Skates," from *All About Oscar*, by Mabel Neikirk, copyright, 1943.

Omitted from this list are items that are acknowledged in separate footnotes.

FOREWORD TO REVISED EDITION

To Boys and Girls:

Very few of the things I have done have given me as much satisfaction as this opportunity of introducing to thousands of boys and girls some of the older stories as well as treasures of the present.

MORE FAVORITE STORIES was first published in 1948, and everything around us has changed so much that new kinds of stories had to be written. In this new edition I have a chance to include stories that could not have been written a dozen years ago—stories that come right out of our modern, wonderful new world such as a skin diving story, "Danger in the Deep" and a story of a boy's courage called "Rocket Rider." "The Fun They Had" set in the year 2000 looks back to the time when children had fun learning from teachers instead of machines. I think we are all very fortunate that we could get one of the only two stories for young people that James Thurber wrote, the whole book called "The Great Quillow."

I have also included an exciting episode called "No Land in Sight" from the epoch-making trip of "Kon-Tiki" and a tale, "Hawaiian Myth" from our newest state, by Padraic Colum.

I know you'll have fun reading and re-reading these wonderful stories.

Sidonie Matsner Gruenberg

New York, 1960

To Boys and Girls

[illegible]

FOREWORD TO FIRST EDITION

To Boys and Girls:

When I was collecting stories for *Favorite Stories, Old and New*, I was hoping that boys and girls would be pleased with it. After the book was published I was very glad to learn that my hope had come true.

In a few years I began to think that some of my graduates must be going on toward nine or ten or eleven years, and that I might help them to move on to "older" stories. So I decided to make another collection. And this is it.

In getting up this book I had about the same plan in mind as I had for the *Favorite Stories*. That is, I wanted some of the best of the old stories and some of the best of the new stories, for each particular *kind* of story in the collection. I wanted tales about real boys and girls in different parts of the world, some make-believe stories, and also a few that could never be true anywhere. Then I wanted some stories about remarkable things that did happen, about adventures and heroes and humor.

Of course we had to have some stories about horses and dogs, "man's best friends." Everybody loves folk tales, homey stories about how folks live and think and act in different countries. These stories should be especially interesting at this time, when all people are hoping that we can learn to live together in peace in one world. Perhaps the section "Animals Around the World" will tell us as much about people as about the animals.

I thought it would be fun if boys and girls could get acquainted with a few stories that I selected for a rather special reason. Some stories have been told over and over again and in all languages so many times that they have left their marks in the common speech. Nearly everybody has heard the expression "Open Sesame" as a magic word for fulfilling wishes, for example; but many of us use it without knowing that it came out of the story of Ali Baba and the Forty Thieves, from the *Thousand-and-One Nights.* Nearly all of us have heard about "Fighting Windmills" or "Eureka!" or "An Ax to Grind," with its very special meaning. I think you will be interested in these and other common expressions when you see how they have come to be used so widely.

Well, that was my plan.

Then my search for suitable stories began, chiefly in libraries.

Of course I remembered some of the stories I intended to include. When I came to read them over, some were even better than I had remembered them. Some, however, were disappointing. Many friends suggested stories that I had once known but had forgotten, as well as others I had never known. A great many of these were just the kind that I knew you would like. Indeed, I found a far greater treasure than I had expected. So the very hardest part of my task was to decide which stories I would have to leave out, because there just wasn't room for all the excellent ones.

However, as I look over the ones I have saved, I feel quite satisfied. Since I did not write any of these stories (I only picked them out for you) I do not have to restrain my enthusiasm, for I can almost share the thrill you will get when you read them for the first time.

As this collection is only a small sample of the many, many lovely stories of all kinds I hope that when you like any of these you will go out and try to get some of those that I wasn't able to put into this book. Whether you find any of those particular stories or not, I think that these samples will help you to discover more and more of the great adventures and dreams and make-believe and fun and struggles that men and women have been recording in books for more years than anyone can remember.

Sidonie Matsner Gruenberg

CONTENTS

1 Boys and Girls Here and There

2 Of Courage and Adventure

3 Folk Tales: Animals Around the World

4 When America Was Younger

5 Enchantment and Wonder

6 Humor and Tall Tales

7 Of Man's Best Friends: Horses and Dogs

8 From Myths and Fables to Legend and History

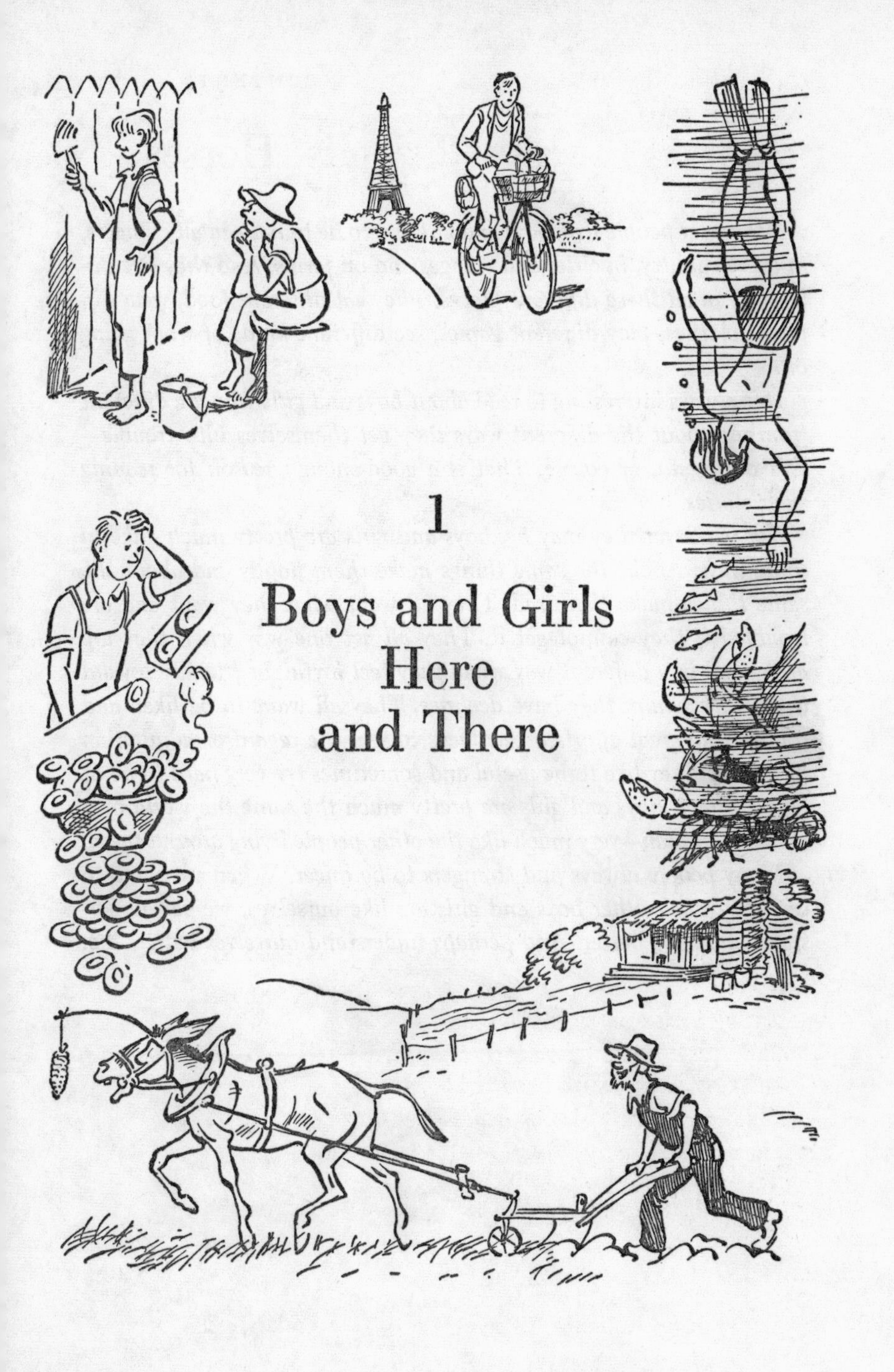

1

Boys and Girls Here and There

Wherever people live, boys and girls are to be found—in all climates, in every country, in cities and villages and on farms. And they live differently in all these different places. They eat different food, wear different clothes, play different games, see different kinds of work going on.

It is always interesting to read about boys and girls who are different from us, about the different ways they get themselves into trouble—and out again, of course. That is a good-enough reason for reading such stories.

Yet wherever they may be, boys and girls are pretty much alike in some ways. About the same things make them happy and about the same things make them sad. They all want what they want and are troubled if they cannot get it. They all act one way when they are angry and in a different way when they feel joyful, or friendly toward those with whom they have dealings. They all want to be liked and often make great efforts or sacrifices to win the regard or admiration of others. They like to be useful and sometimes try very hard to be of help. In fact, boys and girls are pretty much the same the world over and very human—very much like the other people living around them.

Many people always find strangers to be queer. When we come to see how much other boys and girls are like ourselves, we can understand strangers better. And perhaps understand ourselves better, too.

JOHNNY AND HIS MULE

by Ellis Credle

Away up in the Great Smoky Mountains there is a town called Horny Hollow. It is not a very large town and the great mountains standing up all around make it seem very small indeed. There are no more than twenty dwellings there, a courthouse, several stores, a church and a schoolhouse.

To this little schoolhouse came all the children in the town and a little mountain boy named Johnny. Johnny lived far back in the hills, a long, long way from town.

He had to get up very early, when the cocks were crowing for the sunrise, to get to school on time. But in spite of the long walk over the mountains, he was never late for school.

The town children might bustle into the school yard as the last bell was ringing, they might catch the end of the line as it was marching into the building, they might even tiptoe fearfully into the room after classes had started—but never Johnny! He was always in his place as the line marched in and in his proper seat when classes began. In the fall, in the winter, and in the spring, it was always the same. Johnny was always on time.

But one day, toward the end of the school year, Johnny was late! The last bell rang—Johnny was not there! Nine o'clock came —and still no Johnny. Ten o'clock rolled around, half past ten, and not a sign of Johnny.

It was so very late now, the children and the teacher began to wonder what had happened. Perhaps Johnny was sick or perhaps he had fallen over the steep mountainside on the way to school. But a half hour later, at eleven o'clock, there was a shuffle-shuffle outside the door. It opened slowly and Johnny creaked guiltily into the room.

"Why, Johnny!" cried the teacher. "It's eleven o'clock! Why are you so late?"

"I just couldn't help it, Miss Mary!" stammered Johnny and he looked as though he might cry at any moment.

"But tell me, what happened?" urged Miss Mary.

"I got into town early this morning, Miss Mary," began Johnny, "in plenty of time for school, but I stopped for a minute in the town square to watch the auction sale."

Everyone knew about the auction. It was held every Friday and the mountaineers called it "Trade Day." They came in from all the surrounding hills and ranges bringing anything they had on hand which they wanted to swap or sell. Handmade chairs, baskets, turkeys, jackknives, horses, preserves, feather pillows, anything and everything went on sale in the town square on Friday.

"And so," continued Johnny, "while I was standing there, an old mule was put up to be sold. The auctioneer began shouting, 'What am I offered for this mule? What am I bid? What am I bid?'

"Nobody would begin the bidding, and so, just to get the sale started, I hollered out, 'I bid five cents!' I thought sure somebody would bid higher because mules usually cost a lot of money. But nobody did, and so they gave me the mule!

"And there I stood, Miss Mary, holding the mule by the halter. I didn't know what to do with him. About the only thing I could think of was to take him along to school with me. So I started toward the schoolhouse leading the mule.

"I soon found out why nobody wanted that mule. After we had gone about a block he stopped stock still. I tried every way to get him to go along, but he wouldn't budge an inch. He was a balker! Lots of other people tried to make him go, but no sir! That mule wouldn't go until he felt like it. After a while, all by himself, he took a notion to start. He walked another block and then he balked again. Miss Mary, honest-to-goodness, it took me two hours to get that critter four blocks to the schoolhouse! That's why I'm late, honest-to-goodness!"

"Why Johnny!" exclaimed Miss Mary. "I never heard such a tale!"

"If you don't believe it, Miss Mary, just look out the window," replied Johnny.

The teacher gazed through the window and so did all the pupils. There, tied to a tree, was a mule. His head hung down and his large ears flopped sadly. There was no doubt about it, Johnny's tale was true.

Lessons began again and the day wore on. Johnny did not pay much attention to his lessons. The thought of his mule lay heavy on his mind. What could he do with him?

When the bell rang for closing time, all the children rushed into the school yard and gathered 'round the mule. They were in a jolly mood, laughing and joking and poking fun at Johnny and his animal.

"Such a sad looking critter! What are you going to do with him, Johnny?" asked his little friend, Matthey.

Johnny did not feel very gay. "I don't know what to do with him," he said wretchedly. "If it took me two hours to get him a few blocks to school, how long will it take me to get him home? I live five miles over the mountain. It will be black night and the owls a-hooting before I could get him half way there!"

Johnny leaned against the tree beside his mule and began to cry.

The children stopped laughing and looked solemnly at each other.

"Hold on there, Johnny, you never can tell about a balking mule," comforted Matthey. "He may be ready to go by now. Maybe he'll start right off!"

Johnny brightened. He untied the mule's rope and tried to lead him forward. But the mule was *not* ready to go and he did *not* start right off. Johnny braced himself and pulled. But the mule was not in the notion.

"Give me a hand-hold and I'll help you pull," said Matthey.

"I'll help too," said Nancy Belle. Both children threw their weight against the mule. But he did not budge.

"Make room for us. We'll all pull!" said Hetty and Hank. They grasped the mule's halter and hauled with all their might. But the mule only braced himself and stood in his tracks.

While the children were pulling and straining and puffing and blowing, the teacher came out of the schoolhouse. "Let me get a hold. I'll pull too!" she said. But one more made no difference to the mule. His mind was made up.

"My father once had a balking mule," piped up Nancy Belle, "and he used to get him to go by twisting his ear."

"Twisting his ear?" echoed Hezekiah. "Whoever heard of making a mule go by twisting his ear?"

"Well, it's true," insisted the little girl. "That made him go."

"It wouldn't hurt to try it," said the teacher. "Go ahead. Nancy Belle, you are the one who knows how. You twist his ear."

Nancy Belle grasped the long droopy ear and twisted.

The mule stood pat.

"Twist again, twist harder!" said the children and Nancy twisted, but it was no good. The mule did not care to move and twisting his ear did not make him change his mind. He only rolled his eyes and wiggled his ear to make sure that it was all in a piece.

"My uncle once had a balking mule," offered Hetty, "and he used to get behind him with a plank and push him."

"That's right," added Hank. "They used to push the mule a few steps forward and after that he would go all by himself."

"Maybe that's just what this mule needs," said Miss Mary. "Where can we find a plank?"

The children hustled around and underneath the edge of the schoolhouse, they found a long plank. They put it behind the mule's haunches and pushed. They huffed and they puffed, but the mule stood pat! They stopped for breath.

"Maybe the mule's hungry," spoke up Nancy Belle. "If we got

a piece of corn and held it out to him, maybe he'd follow after it."

Johnny ran to the nearest house and brought back an ear of corn. He held it out to the mule. Yes, the mule *was* hungry. He stretched his neck toward the corn.

The children held their breath. The mule took one step forward. Johnny backed away, holding the corn just out of reach. The mule took another step forward, then another and another. A loud shout rose from the children.

"Hurrah! Hurrah! He's going!" they yelled.

The teacher held the mule's halter while Johnny danced ahead with the corn. Through the town they went, clip-clop, clip-clop. Over the mountain trail they started as fast as they could go. But still Johnny did not seem very happy.

"A balking mule is no good to anybody," he grieved. "I'm afraid my Pappy will be as mad as fire when he sees this critter. Like as not he'll give me a good licking."

"No use borrowing trouble," said the teacher. "Let's sing a song and forget all about the mule."

Johnny struck up an old mountain hunting song and along they went singing.

Moon's a-rising on Thunderhead Mountain,
Heigh! Heigh! Step and go lightly!
Hound dog's baying and we're a-going hunting,
Heigh! Heigh! Step and go lightly!

Chased a coon into a gum tree,
Heigh! Heigh! Step and go lightly!
Shot at the coon and hit a froggie.
Heigh! Heigh! Step and go lightly!

Thought I had a possum up in a tree there,
Heigh! Heigh! Step and go lightly!
Shook that tree and down come a he-bear!
Heigh! Heigh! Step and go lightly!

Oh, Mr. Bear, please don't ketch me, sir!
Heigh! Heigh! Step and go lightly!
Ketch that fellow behind the tree, sir!
Heigh! Heigh! Step and go lightly!

Moon's going down, my song is ended,
Heigh! Heigh! Step and go lightly!
Mighty good thing for I'm pretty nigh winded!
Heigh! Heigh! Step and go lightly!

After that Johnny felt better. "You never can tell," he said cheerfully, "maybe Pappy'll be pleased to have a mule. He needs some kind of a critter to help him plow his potatoes. He has to do it now all by himself with an old hand plow."

"Why yes, of course," agreed the teacher. "It's likely that he'll be glad to get him."

"If only he wasn't a balker," said Johnny, wrinkling his forehead again. "Hardly anybody would want a balker."

"Oh don't think about that," the teacher tried to cheer him up. "It's too beautiful on the mountains to get a head full of worry."

"Yes, it *is* pretty on the mountains." Johnny looked all around and forgot to worry about the mule. The air was full of the nice smell of pine and balsam and the pink rhododendron was blooming everywhere.

But the mule did not care for anything except the ear of corn that was always just out of reach. He kept his eyes upon it and went clop-clopping along.

Johnny and the teacher felt cheerful until they came opposite Aunt Betsy's house.

Aunt Betsy was sitting on the porch busily spinning some yarn to weave into a bedspread.

"My me! Whatever have you got there?" she cried when she saw Johnny and the teacher and the mule.

"It's a mule," Johnny replied. "I bought him at the auction for five cents."

"Five cents!" Aunt Betsy threw back her hands and laughed. Then she grew sober. "But he's not a balker, is he? I never heard of a mule's going that cheap unless he was a balker."

"Yes'm," Johnny admitted uneasily. "He's a balker, all right."

"Oh my, my," Aunt Betsy shook her head dolefully. "I don't know what in the name of goodness you'll ever do with a balker."

After that there was hardly anything the teacher could say to comfort Johnny. They walked gloomily along.

A little farther along they came upon Uncle Boogermore Bennet sitting on his cabin steps, picking merrily at his old banjo. "Land o' the livin'," he cried when he looked up and saw the mule. "You haven't got that old balking mule now have you Johnny?"

"Yes, sir, Uncle Boogermore," replied Johnny unhappily. "I bought him at the auction for five cents and now I don't know what to do with him."

"Treat him like I do my wife when *she* gets a balky notion."

"How's that, Uncle Boogermore?" inquired Johnny.

"Why I just leave her be until she gets a better one! Ha! Ha! Ha!" Uncle Boogermore laughed and slapped his leg as though he thought it a great joke.

On up the trail trudged Johnny feeling more dismal every minute. "The worst of it is: a mule has got a terrible appetite," he worried. "Why, that old mule could probably eat us out of house and home in no time. Miss Mary, I'm going to get that licking as sure as shooting. I wish I didn't have to go home at all."

But the mule took them there in a hurry.

Mammy and Pappy were waiting in front of the cabin looking down the road, wondering what kept Johnny so long.

When they saw him tolling the mule along, and the teacher holding the rope, their eyes popped open.

"Dog-gone my time!" exclaimed Pappy.

"What in the name of the land have you got there?" cried Mammy, laughing.

"It's a mule," replied Johnny nervously. "I bought him at the auction for five cents."

"For five cents! Then there must be something wrong with him," said Mammy.

"Yes'm, there is—a little something wrong. He's a balker, I reckon."

"A balking mule!" exclaimed Mammy. "Whatever could we do with a balking mule?"

"I—I—don't know, ma'am," stammered Johnny, glancing at Pappy uneasily.

Pappy did not say anything at all. He just rubbed his chin and looked thoughtfully at the mule.

The sun was setting by this time. It was much too late for the teacher to return to town. She decided to spend the night with Johnny and his parents.

Mammy set a chicken on to stew in a big iron pot and later on they had supper, chicken-and-dumplings, hot biscuits and nice cold buttermilk. For dessert, there was honey from their own beehives and a pot full of sassafras tea.

It was a fine supper, but Johnny could not enjoy it. What was his Pappy thinking about that old balking mule? What was he going to do with him?

After the meal, everyone sat around the fire which leaped brightly in the old stone fireplace. Pappy got out his fiddle and played some merry jigs. Mammy sang some old mountain ballads for the teacher.

Johnny sat in the chimney corner. He did not feel very happy because he kept wondering if his Pappy felt angry about the mule. At last he screwed up his courage and asked him.

"Pappy," he said timidly. "That balking mule is going to be sort of a nuisance, I reckon."

"Nuisance!" cried Pappy. "Why, I know how to make that old mule do all my plowing and hauling and turning of my sorghum mill!" He winked at Miss Mary. "Yes, siree! I know a little trick that will make a balking mule work harder than a hornet!"

"What's that?" cried Johnny and Miss Mary in a breath.

"Wait until the morning," laughed Pappy. "Look out the window when you first wake up and you'll find out!"

The teacher went to bed in the spare room and Johnny climbed the ladder to his little room in the loft.

In the morning, he woke up early and looked out the window. There, pulling a plow briskly through the potato patch, was the balking mule. Hanging on to the handles of the plow was Pappy. He looked up and caught sight of Johnny.

"He's a fine, strong mule!" cried Pappy. "I'm much obliged to you!"

But the mule did not look up, nor to the right nor to the left. He was gazing greedily straight ahead at the ear of corn that dangled on the end of a stick in front of his nose!

MOTHER MAKES CHRISTMAS

by Cornelia Meigs

Just because it was a dull gray afternoon, with low skies and a soft chill in the air, Sally Gilbertson had let the school bus rumble away and had chosen to walk home. Now it was not so very far from Christmas and still the first snow to come. It would begin this very afternoon, Sally felt sure, for people who live on Vermont farms are always weather-wise. Snow would make everything perfect for the Christmas feast they were going to spread at her house—the white farmhouse at the top of the hill. It had been a hard year, she knew, with her father working harder and harder, and her mother trying not to look anxious. But only last week her father, George Gilbertson, had come in smiling to say,

"I've sold all the extra hay and the two colts, both to the same buyer from up north. So now we can feel a little easy again."

And her mother's prompt answer was, "Then I'm going to make Christmas."

In Vermont, if you say you will make Christmas, it means that you will hold the Christmas feast at your house and all the family from round about will come to it. Sally jumped up and down with delight. She was eleven years old, and as full of spirit and enterprise as one of the striped chipmunks that ran up and down the pasture stone wall.

As she came out of school and walked down the one short street of the town her mind was so full of plans that she hardly noticed anything about her. She passed the railroad station with scarcely a glance; the afternoon train was in and there was nothing to watch for. But suddenly she heard feet running after her and looked around to see a tall boy, a little older than herself. He spoke rather breathlessly,

"I think you're the cousin I met five years ago. I'm Hugh Evans. Father and mother are traveling, so I came up to spend the vacation with Uncle Silas. He is——"

Just then Great-Uncle Silas came rattling down the street in his loose-jointed old buggy with the stout gray mare, Bess. He pulled up with a great whoa and motioned Hugh to get in, saying gruffly,

"Well, you got here, I see. I've got errands to do before I go out home. Get up, Bess." They clattered away.

How would a boy feel, Sally thought hotly, who came for his Christmas vacation and was given so brief a greeting? Oh, dear, why must Uncle Silas be like that! But as she set out on the long tramp home her heart lightened and her feet scarcely knew they were on the ground as she went up the hill.

There are few things that one learns to love more than one's own home road. Sally loved hers, with its loop at the edge of the village, its curves around the head of Mr. Hopkins' little stream, its long straight uphill stretch with the valley lying ever wider and more distant below. She loved it at all seasons but perhaps most of all when the smooth slopes of brown and yellow fields began to show the first powdering of snow. A soft aimless flake wandered down, touched her cheek and melted and was followed by another. Then there was a thin veil of falling white which spread slowly over the whole hillside and hid the dark bulk of the mountains looming above. Nothing was ever so mysterious, so exciting or so curiously satisfying as this first downfall of snow. She lifted her face to the cool touch of the flakes as she walked along.

Sally was halfway up the hill when she heard the sound of wheels and the trot, trot of a horse's feet. She knew the thin rattle of those wheels, this was Great-Uncle Silas again, with his errands finished, jogging home. He drew up to offer her a ride. She felt shy and looked down as she climbed in. The boy with him seemed subdued by Uncle Silas' presence, too, for he gave her one quick, friendly look and did not say anything. At last Uncle Silas brought out the remark that Sally had been waiting for.

"Well, all the children look forward to the first snow. Now they have it." He said that every year.

Her house was beginning to show at the top of the hill, white behind the row of tall maples. She would get down at her own door, but before she did so she must give Uncle Silas his invitation.

"You must come for Christmas dinner at our house. Mother told me to ask you."

"Going to make Christmas, air ye?" Uncle Silas returned sourly. "And I'd like to know what you think you're going to make it on. Your father may think he sold his hay and his colts, but you can never be sure of such things until the money has passed. If I was as bad off as George Gilbertson, I wouldn't be making Christmas for nobody."

Sally's cheeks flamed. Her mother had told her often that she was too hasty, but she forgot it completely now.

"Of course we're going to do it. My father and mother both said so and they're never wrong. So you're to come. Both of you."

Uncle Silas said nothing; Bess heaved herself into motion again and they rolled away. Sally thought that Hugh looked back over his shoulder at her as they turned into the road.

The big farm kitchen was warm and bright as they sat down to supper. Her father had driven the car to town and came in late, with snow all over his coat.

"It's really coming down," he said as he took his place at the table. Sally's younger brother, Billy, settled himself in his chair.

"Gee, but I'm hungry," he said happily.

They had nearly finished supper when Sally's father pushed back his chair. "There is word going around town that the man who was here buying grain and horses has gone back on every bargain he made. So I guess I haven't sold the colts and the hay."

Sally saw her mother's face change, saw it look almost frightened. It is so easy to step from good fortune to bad, all in a minute, when you live on a farm. The same thought was in every mind, even Billy's, when Mary Gilbertson put it into words.

"Then we have hardly anything to go on with. And we've asked at least twenty people to Christmas dinner."

"Twenty-two," said Sally in a little voice, but no one seemed to hear her.

On the wall opposite her place hung the round, gold-framed mirror with an eagle on it which had belonged to her grandmother. Sally was growing so big that she was beginning to be able to catch sight of herself in it, though for all the years before it had hung too high. Now, by a very little stretching she could see her whole head and shoulders, her flyaway hair, her sturdy chin, her dark eyes. Why, she was a big girl now, she was able to do all sorts of things she had not thought possible.

"I'll help you, mother, I can help. And Billy and I can help with the colts, they can eat up the hay, and in the spring they will be big horses. Oh, surely we can have Christmas. We have to." Her voice was desperate. She had told Uncle Silas and the new cousin that they would.

"I think we can manage," Mary Gilbertson said slowly. "Yes, we'll do it somehow."

It was a busy two weeks, so busy that Sally began to think that she had never before known what real work meant. But the work was fun because she knew she could do it. It was not for nothing that she had grown big enough to see herself in Granny's looking glass.

There was first of all the great problem of the Christmas dinner. What they would make it out of seemed at first a complete mystery. They had some young guinea hens.

"But they're so slim and small," her mother said. "People say they are choice eating, but they never would go around twenty hungry guests." But only the next day Mrs. Haskins, who raised poultry below the hill, came up to get some eggs and admired the guineas.

"I never seem to have enough to supply my customers down in the town," she said.

It was Sally's grand and sudden idea that they should trade the guineas for two of Mrs. Haskins' turkeys, to be collected the day before Christmas. The plan was good. Mrs. Haskins thought she had a mite too many turkeys and would be glad of the exchange. She went home with the basket of loud-voiced guineas in the back of her bumpy old car and the main dish for Christmas dinner was settled. The makings of the plum pudding were not so hard to find; the Corners store would give them raisins and citron and flour when they took in their pumpkins and squash. Things began to look hopeful, but there would be plenty of work to do.

Besides this the colts were Sally's job, hers and Billy's. It was surprising how much waiting on young colts needed, water and grain brought to them in the morning, bedding down and feeding at night, turning out when the weather was good, bringing in when storms threatened. Sally loved to see the colts scamper down the pasture, stepping high in the crisp frozen snow, the breath from their noses going up in columns in the frosty air. They seemed to grow every day, turning from awkward, lanky babies into real horses. She and Billy were very proud of them.

There was one afternoon when Sally got home, a little tired after the long day in school, to be met at the door by her mother. "Billy came home early, with a cold. Can you tend the colts?"

It was not so easy to go alone into the dark barn, to hang up the lantern, to get the hay fork and clamber up into the loft. The colts were stamping in their stalls and nickering for their supper. The hay was low in the part of the mow where they were used to getting it. She had to move the heavy ladder, but finally got it into a new place. It was not very steady—"But it will do—it will have to do," she said impatiently.

She began to climb up, but suddenly the foot of the ladder slid outward. She caught at a beam and held herself, but she could get neither up nor down. She hung there, wondering what she should do when all at once a voice spoke in the gloom below her, a voice she did not recognize.

"I came out to help you. Steady, I'll hold the ladder and you can get down." She scrambled down safely and saw in the lantern light that it was the visiting cousin, Hugh Evans. He took the fork from her hand and clambered up.

"Let me know when I have thrown down enough," he said. The hay began swishing down in great forkfuls. How good it was to have some real help!

Sally heard an odd sound, and saw her mother standing in the barn doorway, holding something white in her arms, something that struggled and quacked.

"Why, it's Uncle Silas' Josiah," she exclaimed. Josiah was a white duck so old that everyone knew him. Hugh leaned over to explain, a little unwillingly.

"Uncle Silas said it was to help out with the Christmas dinner," he said. "I wish—I wish a little you could keep him somewhere for the few years he will last. Josiah is a noble old bird, but I'll bet he would make tough eating."

Sally's mother nodded and laughed. "Certainly, we will give him a home," and she added what was in Sally's mind too. "You know how to pitch hay well for a city boy."

"Oh, I've learned to do it since I've been with Uncle Silas. May I come help you again?"

He came again and again, to help Sally and Billy and their father in the barn, and, when the work was done, to have a wild romp with his cousins all over the mountains of hay in the loft. But he always walked away looking serious and dignified. That was how one had to look when one stayed in Uncle Silas Evans' house.

On Christmas morning everyone was up at sunrise, a glowing red sunrise behind the still, snow-wrapped mountains. There were gay gifts for the children; for Sally a red hood with rabbit's fur around the face, for Billy a small axe, shiny and sharp, a sign that he was a big boy and could be trusted with a keen edge. Then everyone began to "fly around." The two turkeys were ushered into the oven, the dried corn and squash and pickles and cake were made ready. The sauce for the plum pudding was a morning's occupation in itself. Sally felt very proud as she stirred and stirred. The kitchen was full of steam, of delicious smells, of bubbling and popping sounds coming from under every cover.

"Mother," said Sally suddenly, "what will Uncle Silas say about Josiah?"

"Uncle Silas will be glad enough to eat turkey, he won't ask about Josiah."

Guests began to arrive long before noon, Cousin Miranda Betts with her three small children, Cousin Tom Howe with his wife and his big son and bigger daughter. More came and more. All the women and most of the young girls put on aprons at once and began to help, or gave their assistance to Sally who was setting the table in the long living room. The work went forward steadily in a loud buzz of talk. Uncle Silas came in last, wrapped in half a dozen scarfs and two pairs of big mittens.

"The rest of you don't seem to be taking much notice, but it's going to storm before the day is over. This Christmas-card weather is too good to last."

Hugh came in behind him. He had brought a big bunch of arbor vitae and red berries to add to the other Christmas greens.

The oven was opened for the last time and the turkeys were brought out. Everything was ready. Suddenly the outer door of the kitchen was flung back and Billy stood on the threshold, his cheeks scarlet, his eyes wide with excitement.

"There's a big wind coming up. It blew the stable door open and the colts got out." The wind was big indeed, for it slammed the door behind him with a crash.

One of the women screamed, all the men jumped up, grabbed their wraps and ran out, Sally and Billy at their father's heels. The great pile of clouds, sweeping up the sky, spoke the truth of the storm which Uncle Silas had prophesied. Two dots, racing wildly across the pasture, told which way the excitable colts had dashed to freedom. Hugh plunged into the stable and came out leading Bess. Uncle Silas raised a shout of protest, but Tom Howe silenced him.

"Let the boy alone. He knows what he is about."

The colts had tried to run down the long slippery slope, but headed off by Hugh and the galloping Bess, they turned about and plunged into the woods.

"That's no place for them in this wind," George Gilbertson cried. "We'll have to drive them out."

Sally and Billy kept close behind their father as they dashed for the wood. The wind was screaming overhead now, filling the air with a cloud of dry snow. She saw Hugh slide off the back of the horse; she thought he motioned to her to go back, but she could not be stopped. The colts were standing, undecided, for an instant, and she and Billy ran up to them. She had caught hold of the forelock of the black one when, all at once, a great shattering crash almost stunned her and a whiff of snow blinded her.

When Sally opened her eyes, she and Billy and the two colts were tangled in a great tent of broken branches. One big maple had crashed down, carrying two others with it. They were sheltered by the tilt of the huge trunk, but were so fenced in that they could scarcely move.

"Hold him, Billy, don't let him plunge and hurt himself." She had caught the broken halter of the brown colt and put the end into Billy's hand. Then she raised a call, "Here we are. We're safe."

"Thank God for that," she heard her father's voice outside. "Now keep as still as you can. We'll chop a way in."

They stood very still, trying to soothe the horses, Billy as valiant as Sally, but his face a little pale. The noise of the driving axes sounded all about them. Sally heard Hugh's voice, knew that the fastest, fiercest strokes were his, heard him say, "Can you hold out?" Then a trunk beside them suddenly fell in two and Hugh stepped through the opening. He was so breathless that he could scarcely speak, but he took hold of the black colt. "I'll hold him now, Sally."

Yes, Sally was willing that he should. Her arm ached and her knees were weak. Another log rolled aside and her father pushed through to put his arm around her.

Christmas dinner was a little late, but it was a grand feast just the same. Sally was not allowed to help wait on the others as she had expected. The younger cousins took over that task and kept coming to her to ask, "Shall we do this, Cousin Sally? Is it right to do that?" It made her feel very grown up and proud.

When Uncle Silas was asked if he would prefer duck or turkey, he answered promptly, "Turkey, Mary. Leave the duck for the young ones," so that no questions were asked about Josiah. Cousin Tom Howe said the two colts were the likeliest-looking pair he had ever seen and were on the way to being valuable horses.

When they got up from the table, Uncle Silas, in the midst of a silence, said solemnly,

"Your mother knows how to make Christmas, Sally." And Hugh behind him whispered to her,

"And so do you. I'm coming again, next year."

STEPPIN'S FIRST PUBLIC APPEARANCE

by Hope Newell

To see Steppin Stebbins racing down the street one warm afternoon in June, no one would have believed that he was on his way to school. Every other school day in the whole year it had needed his mother's warning, "You'll be late," and his little sister Mary Ellis' constant scolding to get Steppin through his lunch and back to his desk before the tardy bell rang. But this day was different.

It was the last day of school. No more lessons, no more homework, no more scrambling out of bed in a hurry, nothing but fun for two blessed months! But it was not so much the thought of freedom to come as the great event of that very afternoon that made Steppin hurry. For he was to do a solo tap dance at the closing exercises of his class. "My first public appearance," he thought proudly as he ran down the street.

A changing traffic light on Eighth Avenue brought him to an abrupt halt. Hopping up and down on the curb, Steppin stared impatiently at the stream of automobiles, trucks and street cars roaring by. The thunder of the elevated trains overhead, the clank and clatter of street cars and honks of taxis went unnoticed. His ears were tuned to city din.

"School is out
Hear me shout,"

he crooned under his breath, while his feet beat out a tap in the same rhythm. Brush, brush, hop with his right foot, and brush, brush, hop with the left foot, over and over. While he danced Steppin kept an eye on the green signal light. Was it going to stay that way all day? Wouldn't it ever turn red?

At last it changed and Steppin darted across the street like a flash and scurried down the street. Out of habit he looked up at the street clock which generally told him he was in danger of being late. But today he saw that it had taken him only five minutes to come this far. As school was only two blocks away, Steppin slowed down to a walk and stopped before his favorite window, the pawn shop.

Treasures of all kinds were heaped together in the dusty shop window; guns, tennis rackets, telescopes, banjos, roller skates and jackknives. Steppin always played a game before that window. He picked out the thing he would most like to buy if he had all the money he wanted. He usually spent a long time over that choice, weighing values carefully. But this day he paid no attention to the wonderful display. He had caught sight of his reflection in the gilt mirror that stood at the back of the show case.

He eyed himself proudly. "Boy, I sure do look like a professional," he murmured, strutting a little and grinning broadly. His coffee-brown face, shining with the scrubbing he had given it, grinned back at him, showing all of his ivory white teeth. His hair under the tight skull cap he wore was slicked so close to his skull that it looked as if it was painted on. His big black eyes took in the navy blue coat of his Sunday suit, the stiffly starched white shirt with a little black bow tie, and the white duck trousers which his friend Charley Kee, the Chinese laundry man, had pressed for him in exchange for errands. Steppin sighed with satisfied approval.

Steppin had pored over the pictures of Negro celebrities who performed in night clubs and theatres, and this costume was the best imitation of his idols that he could manage. Except for one thing Steppin was greatly pleased with the elegant entertainer he saw reflected in the mirror. His shoes were all wrong. He had no soft flexible slippers with metal taps on their tips like a real dancer. He wore a pair of old sneakers and had stuck a cluster of thumbtacks in the tip of each sole to use for taps. They did pretty well, but Steppin was not satisfied with them.

"Oh, well, you can't have everything at once, I suppose," he consoled himself. "Anyway when I get to be a professional I'm going to have six dozen pairs of dancing shoes at a time, with solid silver taps on every single one of them. Even platinum, maybe, if I want to."

Steppin's dreams of the future carried him happily on to school. A few boys were playing ball in the playground. They called to Steppin to join them. "Not a chance," thought Steppin, not when he was about to make his first public appearance as a dancer. He must keep his clothes in order for an occasion like this. So he entered the large brick building and ran up the stairs to his class room.

Steppin hardly recognized the familiar room, it looked so festive with garlands of evergreens on the walls and bowls of flowers on the window sills. Some of the girls, who were helping the teacher, Miss Blair, decorate the room, looked festive too, in their frilly dresses of pink and blue and white, their hair gay with bows of bright ribbons. Miss Blair herself, in a blue silk dress, with her blond hair fluffed out around her face, looked young as a girl, Steppin thought.

Miss Blair's desk had been taken away, and two big jars of lilacs stood one on each side of the platform. A bright poster painted by some of the children served as a back drop. Steppin surveyed the room with approval. It looked almost like a stage.

But suddenly he thought of the moment when he would have to step up there before all the boys and girls. Cold shivers went up his spine. A strange sinking feeling gripped him in the stomach. He was scared! Steppin had never thought of that.

"Oh my gosh, I've got to make good, and here I am as jumpy as a cat," he thought as he slid into his seat. His own name, Stephen A. Stebbins, seemed to jump at him from the neatly printed program on his desk. He stared at it and clenched his clammy hands under the desk.

While the other boys and girls, demure and solemn in their best clothes, took their seats, Steppin anxiously went over in his mind the dance routine he had so carefully worked out. He counted out the steps to the tune of *Marching Through Georgia* which his sister, Mary Ellis, was to play for his accompaniment. Brush, brush, hop and brush, brush, hop; and heel and toe and break. "Gee, I wish I could have a tune with some snap to it," he thought. But the few selections which Mary Ellis could play by ear on the wheezy old organ at home did not include pieces with snap.

In a daze Steppin heard Miss Blair make her little opening speech and then announce: "And now we will have the first number on our program, a recitation of Kipling's poem *If* by Martin Burns, Junior." Martin had been speaking that piece on every school program since he was in the fourth grade and never yet had been able to get through all the "ifs" without help. Steppin had never before felt the slightest interest in his struggles, but now he found himself waiting in an agony of suspense every time Martin hesitated. When for the fourth time he began "Eff you can" and stopped, open mouthed, with imploring eyes fixed on Miss Blair, Steppin knew how he felt. Suppose I forget my dance steps! But Miss Blair, with whispered prompting, urged Martin on to the final line which he knew by heart and which he spoke in ringing tones. "AND WHAT IS MORE, YOU'LL BE A MAN, MY SON."

Steppin's place was fifth on the program. It had seemed a long way down the list, but now the time was coming, quickly, surely, when he would have to get up on the platform and dance. He saw Mary Ellis come in quietly and take a seat. She had been excused early from her class so that she might play for him. Oh, if only something had happened to keep her from coming! But there she was, smiling at him as calmly as though he were not crazy with stage fright and about to be disgraced before the whole school.

The sweet, clear notes of a cornet recalled Steppin from his miserable thoughts. That was David Harmon and he was playing the Schubert *Serenade*. David played in the school orchestra and was an old hand at public appearances. Watching him standing there so easy and calm, Steppin felt sick with envy and fright. "I would have to be billed next to him," he thought unhappily. "Oh my gosh, why didn't I practice more on cartwheels, so I could do a cartwheel, then go into a split to finish the act? I could try, maybe, but like as not I'd land on my head and a fine finale that would be."

The last soft note of the *Serenade* died away. David bowed gracefully and returned to his seat. "That was lovely, David." Miss Blair rose and beamed on him, then, still smiling, she glanced kindly at Steppin. "The next number will be a tap dance by Stephen A. Stebbins, and"—she smiled at Mary Ellis—"his little sister will play his accompaniment."

Like one in a dream Steppin found himself getting to his feet, while before him the big yellow bow on Mary Ellis' hair bobbed up as she rose and went to the piano. His knees trembled and his legs felt like cooked noodles, thought Steppin miserably, but somehow he mounted the platform and bowed gravely. This wasn't a bit the way he had dreamed it—this horrible nightmare. Mary Ellis struck the first chord. To his surprise his feet responded, although they felt like solid blocks of wood. Mechanically he went through the simple steps of his dance. In a few moments he forgot the staring boys and girls in front of him and began to dance as though his life depended on it. He thought of nothing but the rhythm and the beat of his dancing feet. He varied his few steps with pantomime, making himself very tall, then letting his arms hang perfectly limp from his shoulders so that they flapped queerly with every step. Someone giggled. Then a chuckle swept over the room. That did it. It was all fun now. Joyously he hopped and whirled. No longer afraid, he varied his pantomime, now grinning at his audience, now looking very solemn.

He had just completed a quick whirl on one foot and was finishing with a split when he felt a stinging in the soles of his feet. Steppin knew very well what that meant. The thumbtacks were working through the soles of his shoes! Every time he hopped the pain grew worse. Brush, brush, tap; brush, brush, tap, ouch! Steppin nearly yelled out with pain. "I can't give up, the show has got to go on," he reminded himself, like an old trouper. And all the while his feet tapped and his face wore a stiff frozen smile.

Then one of the boys began clapping in time to the music. Soon others joined in, marking the beat. "Boy, they're with me. I got to go on if it kills me." Steppin flashed his white teeth in a bright agonized grin and spread out his hands in an inviting gesture to his friends. The whole room broke into clapping. Almost over now, thought Steppin. Mary Ellis was pounding out the last chorus—"Hurrah, hurrah, the flag that makes us free."

Suddenly Steppin tripped! The thumbtacks in his shoes had caught on a rough spot of the floor. Quick as a flash, even as he stumbled, Steppin knew there was only one thing to do. He threw out his arms, and, hurling himself forward with all his might, tried to turn his fall into a cartwheel. He felt himself flying through space and in the next instant he was teetering on his feet, gasping for breath as he slid to the floor in a fast split.

In a daze he heard the loud applause and suddenly he realized that in his cartwheel he had flung himself right off the platform. A pleased grin spread from ear to ear. "Well, tie my shoes! I didn't know I had it in me."

Just then Mary Ellis, who had gone placidly on with her piece, struck the last chord with a resounding thump. Steppin scrambled to his feet, bowed politely as Miss Blair had taught him, and limped to his seat. The continued clapping was music in his ears. He looked over at Miss Blair who smiled and nodded encouragingly. Steppin rose and bowed again with a flourish, glowing with pride and happiness.

The program continued, but Steppin hardly heard or saw what was going on, though he clapped heartily for each performer. He was lost in a haze of glory and triumph. "Boy, applause sure is jam on my bread," he chuckled while he slyly removed the torturing thumbtacks from his shoes. "From now on, nothing is going to stop me. I'm going to be a first class dancer or bust."

THE DOUGHNUTS

by Robert McCloskey

One Friday night in November Homer overheard his mother talking on the telephone to Aunt Agnes over in Centerburg. "I'll stop by with the car in about half an hour and we can go to the meeting together," she said, because tonight was the night the Ladies' Club was meeting to discuss plans for a box social and to knit and sew for the Red Cross.

"I think I'll come along and keep Uncle Ulysses company while you and Aunt Agnes are at the meeting," said Homer.

So after Homer had combed his hair and his mother had looked to see if she had her knitting instructions and the right size needles, they started for town.

Homer's Uncle Ulysses and Aunt Agnes have a very up and coming lunch room over in Centerburg, just across from the courthouse on the town square. Uncle Ulysses is a man with advanced ideas and a weakness for labor saving devices. He equipped the lunch room with automatic toasters, automatic coffee maker, automatic dish washer, and an automatic doughnut maker. All just the latest thing in labor saving devices. Aunt Agnes would throw up her hands and sigh every time Uncle Ulysses bought a new labor saving device. Sometimes she became unkindly disposed toward him for days and days. She was of the opinion that Uncle Ulysses just frittered away his spare time over at the barber shop with the sheriff and the boys, so, what was the good of a labor saving device that gave you more time to fritter?

When Homer and his mother got to Centerburg they stopped at the lunch room, and after Aunt Agnes had come out and said, "My, how that boy does grow!" which was what she always said, she went off with Homer's mother in the car. Homer went into the lunch room and said, "Howdy, Uncle Ulysses!"

"Oh, hello, Homer. You're just in time," said Uncle Ulysses. "I've been going over this automatic doughnut machine, oiling the machinery and cleaning the works . . . wonderful things, these labor saving devices."

"Yep," agreed Homer, and he picked up a cloth and started polishing the metal trimmings while Uncle Ulysses tinkered with the inside workings.

"Opfwo-oof!!" sighed Uncle Ulysses and, "Look here, Homer, you've got a mechanical mind. See if you can find where these two pieces fit in. I'm going across to the barber shop for a spell, 'cause there's somethin' I've got to talk to the sheriff about. There won't be much business here until the double feature is over and I'll be back before then."

Then as Uncle Ulysses went out the door he said, "Uh, Homer, after you get the pieces in place, would you mind mixing up a batch of doughnut batter and put it in the machine? You could turn the switch and make a few doughnuts to have on hand for the crowd after the movie . . . if you don't mind."

"O. K." said Homer, "I'll take care of everything."

A few minutes later a customer came in and said, "Good evening, Bud."

Homer looked up from putting the last piece in the doughnut machine and said, "Good evening, Sir, what can I do for you?"

"Well, young feller, I'd like a cup o' coffee and some doughnuts," said the customer.

"I'm sorry, Mister, but we won't have any doughnuts for about half an hour, until I can mix some dough and start this machine. I could give you some very fine sugar rolls instead."

"Well, Bud, I'm in no real hurry so I'll just have a cup o' coffee and wait around a bit for the doughnuts. Fresh doughnuts are always worth waiting for is what I always say."

"O. K.," said Homer, and he drew a cup of coffee from Uncle Ulysses' super automatic coffee maker.

"Nice place you've got here," said the customer.

"Oh, yes," replied Homer, "this is a very up and coming lunch room with all the latest improvements."

"Yes," said the stranger, "must be a good business. I'm in business too. A traveling man in outdoor advertising. I'm a sandwich man, Mr. Gabby's my name."

"My name is Homer. I'm glad to meet you, Mr. Gabby. It must be a fine profession, traveling and advertising sandwiches."

"Oh no," said Mr. Gabby, "I don't advertise sandwiches, I just wear any kind of an ad, one sign on front and one sign on behind, this way . . . Like a sandwich. Ya know what I mean?"

"Oh, I see. That must be fun, and you travel too?" asked Homer as he got out the flour and the baking powder.

"Yeah, I ride the rods between jobs, on freight trains, ya know what I mean?"

"Yes, but isn't that dangerous?" asked Homer.

"Of course there's a certain amount a risk, but you take any method a travel these days, it's all dangerous. Ya know what I mean? Now take airplanes for instance . . ."

Just then a large shiny black car stopped in front of the lunch room and a chauffeur helped a lady out of the rear door. They both came inside and the lady smiled at Homer and said, "We've stopped for a light snack. Some doughnuts and coffee would be simply marvelous."

Then Homer said, "I'm sorry, Ma'm, but the doughnuts won't be ready until I make this batter and start Uncle Ulysses' doughnut machine."

"Well now aren't *you* a clever young man to know how to make *doughnuts!*"

"Well," blushed Homer, "I've really never done it before but I've got a receipt to follow."

"Now, young man, you simply must allow me to help. You know, I haven't made doughnuts for years, but I know the best receipt for doughnuts. It's marvelous, and we really must use it."

"But, Ma'm . . ." said Homer.

"Now just *wait* till you taste these doughnuts," said the lady. "Do you have an apron?" she asked, as she took off her fur coat and her rings and her jewelry and rolled up her sleeves. "Charles," she said to the chauffeur, "hand me that baking powder, that's right, and, young man, we'll need some nutmeg."

So Homer and the chauffeur stood by and handed things and cracked the eggs while the lady mixed and stirred. Mr. Gabby sat on his stool, sipped his coffee, and looked on with great interest.

"There!" said the lady when all of the ingredients were mixed. "Just *wait* till you taste these doughnuts!"

"It looks like an awful lot of batter," said Homer as he stood on a chair and poured it into the doughnut machine with the help of the chauffeur. "It's about *ten* times as much as Uncle Ulysses ever makes."

"But wait till you taste them!" said the lady with an eager look and a smile.

Homer got down from the chair and pushed a button on the machine marked, "*Start.*" Rings of batter started dropping into the hot fat. After a ring of batter was cooked on one side an automatic gadget turned it over and the other side would cook. Then another automatic gadget gave the doughnut a little push and it rolled neatly down a little chute, all ready to eat.

"That's a simply *fascinating* machine," said the lady as she waited for the first doughnut to roll out.

"Here, young man, *you* must have the first one. Now isn't that just *too* delicious!? Isn't it simply marvelous?"

"Yes, Ma'm, it's very good," replied Homer as the lady handed doughnuts to Charles and to Mr. Gabby and asked if they didn't think they were simply divine doughnuts.

"It's an old family receipt!" said the lady with pride.

Homer poured some coffee for the lady and her chauffeur and for Mr. Gabby, and a glass of milk for himself. Then they all sat down at the lunch counter to enjoy another few doughnuts apiece.

"I'm so glad you enjoy my doughnuts," said the lady. "But now, Charles, we really must be going. If you will just take this apron, Homer, and put two dozen doughnuts in a bag to take along, we'll be on our way. And, Charles, don't forget to pay the young man." She rolled down her sleeves and put on her jewelry, then Charles managed to get her into her big fur coat.

"Good night, young man, I haven't had so much fun in years. I *really* haven't!" said the lady, as she went out the door and into the big shiny car.

"Those are sure good doughnuts," said Mr. Gabby as the car moved off.

"You bet!" said Homer. Then he and Mr. Gabby stood and watched the automatic doughnut machine make doughnuts.

After a few dozen more doughnuts had rolled down the little chute, Homer said, "I guess that's about enough doughnuts to sell to the after theater customers. I'd better turn the machine off for a while."

Homer pushed the button marked "*Stop*" and there was a little click, but nothing happened. The rings of batter kept right on dropping into the hot fat, and an automatic gadget kept right on turning them over, and another automatic gadget kept right on giving them a little push and the doughnuts kept right on rolling down the little chute, all ready to eat.

"That's funny," said Homer, "I'm sure that's the right button!" He pushed it again but the automatic doughnut maker kept right on making doughnuts.

"Well I guess I must have put one of those pieces in backwards," said Homer.

"Then it might stop if you pushed the button marked *Start*," said Mr. Gabby.

Homer did, and the doughnuts still kept rolling down the little chute, just as regular as a clock can tick.

"I guess we could sell a few more doughnuts," said Homer, "but I'd better telephone Uncle Ulysses over at the barber shop." Homer gave the number and while he waited for someone to answer he counted thirty-seven doughnuts roll down the little chute.

Finally someone answered "Hello! This is the sarber bhop, I mean the barber shop."

"Oh, hello, sheriff. This is Homer. Could I speak to Uncle Ulysses?"

"Well, he's playing pinochle right now," said the sheriff. "Anythin' I can tell 'im?"

"Yes," said Homer. "I pushed the button marked *Stop* on the doughnut machine but the rings of batter keep right on dropping into the hot fat, and an automatic gadget keeps right on turning them over, and another automatic gadget keeps giving them a little push, and the doughnuts keep right on rolling down the little chute! It won't stop!"

"O. K. Wold the hire, I mean, hold the wire and I'll tell 'im." Then Homer looked over his shoulder and counted another twenty-one doughnuts roll down the little chute, all ready to eat. Then the sheriff said, "He'll be right over. . . . Just gotta finish this hand."

"That's good," said Homer. "G'by, sheriff."

The window was full of doughnuts by now so Homer and Mr.

Gabby had to hustle around and start stacking them on plates and trays and lining them up on the counter.

"Sure are a lot of doughnuts!" said Homer.

"You bet!" said Mr. Gabby. "I lost count at twelve hundred and two and that was quite a while back."

People had begun to gather outside the lunch room window, and someone was saying, "There are almost as many doughnuts as there are people in Centerburg, and I wonder how in tarnation Ulysses thinks he can sell all of 'em!"

Every once in a while somebody would come inside and buy some, but while somebody bought two to eat and a dozen to take home, the machine made three dozen more.

By the time Uncle Ulysses and the sheriff arrived and pushed through the crowd, the lunch room was a calamity of doughnuts! Doughnuts in the window, doughnuts piled high on the shelves, doughnuts stacked on plates, doughnuts lined up twelve deep all along the counter, and doughnuts still rolling down the little chute, just as regular as a clock can tick.

"Hello, sheriff, hello, Uncle Ulysses, we're having a little trouble here," said Homer.

"Well, I'll be dunked!!" said Uncle Ulysses.

"Dernd ef you won't be when Aggy gits home," said the sheriff. "Mighty fine doughnuts though. What'll you do with 'em all, Ulysses?"

Uncle Ulysses groaned and said, "What will Aggy say? We'll never sell 'em all."

Then Mr. Gabby, who hadn't said anything for a long time, stopped piling doughnuts and said, "What you need is an advertising man. Ya know what I mean? You got the doughnuts, ya gotta create a market . . . Understand? . . . It's balancing the demand with the supply . . . That sort of thing."

"Yep!" said Homer. "Mr. Gabby's right. We have to enlarge our market. He's an advertising sandwich man, so if we hire him, he can walk up and down in front of the theater and get the customers."

"You're hired, Mr. Gabby!" said Uncle Ulysses.

Then everybody pitched in to paint the signs and to get Mr. Gabby sandwiched between. They painted "SALE ON DOUGHNUTS" in big letters on the window too.

Meanwhile the rings of batter kept right on dropping into the hot fat, and an automatic gadget kept right on turning them over, and another automatic gadget kept right on giving them a little push, and the doughnuts kept right on rolling down the little chute, just as regular as a clock can tick.

"I certainly hope this advertising works," said Uncle Ulysses, wagging his head. "Aggy'll certainly throw a fit if it don't."

The sheriff went outside to keep order, because there was quite a crowd by now—all looking at the doughnuts and guessing how many thousand there were, and watching new ones roll down the little chute, just as regular as a clock can tick. Homer and Uncle Ulysses kept stacking doughnuts. Once in a while somebody bought a few, but not very often.

Then Mr. Gabby came back and said, "Say, you know there's not much use o' me advertisin' at the theater. The show's all over, and besides almost everybody in town is out front watching that machine make doughnuts!"

"Zeus!" said Uncle Ulysses. "We must get rid of these doughnuts before Aggy gets here!"

"Looks like you will have ta hire a truck to waul 'em ahay, I mean haul 'em away!!" said the sheriff who had just come in. Just then there was a noise and a shoving out front and the lady from the shiny black car and her chauffeur came pushing through the crowd and into the lunch room.

"Oh gracious!" she gasped, ignoring the doughnuts, "I've lost my diamond bracelet, and I know I left it here on the counter," she said, pointing to a place where the doughnuts were piled in stacks of two dozen.

"Yes, Ma'm, I guess you forgot it when you helped make the batter," said Homer.

Then they moved all the doughnuts around and looked for the

diamond bracelet, but they couldn't find it anywhere. Meanwhile the doughnuts kept rolling down the little chute, just as regular as a clock can tick.

After they had looked all around the sheriff cast a suspicious eye on Mr. Gabby, but Homer said, "He's all right, sheriff, he didn't take it. He's a friend of mine."

Then the lady said, "I'll offer a reward of one hundred dollars for that bracelet! It really *must* be found! . . . it *really* must!"

"Now don't you worry, lady," said the sheriff. "I'll get your bracelet back!"

"Zeus! This is terrible!" said Uncle Ulysses. "First all of these doughnuts and then on top of all that, a lost diamond bracelet . . ."

Mr. Gabby tried to comfort him, and he said, "There's always a bright side. That machine'll probably run outta batter in an hour or two."

If Mr. Gabby hadn't been quick on his feet Uncle Ulysses would have knocked him down, sure as fate.

Then while the lady wrung her hands and said, "We must find it, we *must!*" and Uncle Ulysses was moaning about what Aunt Agnes would say, and the sheriff was eyeing Mr. Gabby, Homer sat down and thought hard.

Before twenty more doughnuts could roll down the little chute he shouted, "SAY! I know where the bracelet is! It was lying here on the counter and got mixed up in the batter by mistake! The bracelet is cooked inside one of these doughnuts!"

"Why . . . I really believe you're right," said the lady through her tears. "Isn't that *amazing*? Simply *amazing!*"

"I'll be durn'd!" said the sheriff.

"OhH-h!" moaned Uncle Ulysses. "Now we have to break up all of these doughnuts to find it. Think of the pieces! Think of the *crumbs!* Think of what *Aggy* will say!"

"Nope," said Homer. "We won't have to break them up. I've got a plan."

So Homer and the advertising man took some cardboard and

some paint and printed another sign. They put this sign in the window, and the sandwich man wore two more signs that said the same thing and walked around in the crowd out front.

FRESH DOUGHNUTS
2 for 5¢
While They Last
$100.00 PRIZE
A BRACELET
INSIDE A DOUGHNUT
P.S. YOU HAVE TO GIVE THE
BRACELET BACK

THEN . . . The doughnuts began to sell! *Everybody* wanted to buy doughnuts, *dozens* of doughnuts!

And that's not all. Everybody bought coffee to dunk the doughnuts in too. Those that didn't buy coffee bought milk or soda. It kept Homer and the lady and the chauffeur and Uncle Ulysses and the sheriff busy waiting on the people who wanted to buy doughnuts.

When all but the last couple of hundred doughnuts had been sold, Rupert Black shouted, "I GAWT IT!!" and sure enough . . . there was the diamond bracelet inside of his doughnut!

Then Rupert went home with a hundred dollars, the citizens of Centerburg went home full of doughnuts, the lady and her chauffeur drove off with the diamond bracelet, and Homer went home with his mother when she stopped by with Aunt Aggy.

As Homer went out of the door he heard Mr. Gabby say, "Neatest trick of merchandising I ever seen," and Aunt Aggy was looking sceptical while Uncle Ulysses was saying, "The rings of batter kept right on dropping into the hot fat, and the automatic gadget kept right on turning them over, and the other automatic gadget kept right on giving them a little push, and the doughnuts kept right on rolling down the little chute just as regular as a clock can tick—they just kept right on a comin', an' a comin', an' a comin', an' a comin'."

THANKSGIVING DAY

by Dorothy Canfield Fisher

A new girl came into the Winthrop Avenue public school about the beginning of November, and this is how she looked to the other boys and girls in the seventh grade. She couldn't understand English, although she could read it enough to get her lessons. (This was a small public school in a small inland American town where they seldom saw any foreigners, and people who couldn't speak English seemed outlandish.) She wore the queerest looking clothes you ever saw, and clumping shoes and great, thick, woolen stockings. (All the children in that town, as in most American towns, dressed exactly like everybody else, because their mothers mostly bought their clothes at Benning and Davis' department store on Main Street.) Her hair wasn't bobbed and curled, neither a long nor short bob; it looked as though her folks hadn't ever had sense enough to bob it. It was done up in two funny-looking pig-tails. She had a queer expression on her face, like nothing anybody had ever seen—kind of a smile and yet kind of offish. She couldn't see the point of wisecracks but she laughed over things that weren't funny a bit, like the way a cheer leader waves his arms. She got her lessons *terribly* well, (the others thought somebody at home must help her more than the teachers like) and she was the dumbest thing about games—didn't even know how to play duck-on-a-rock or run-sheep-run. And queerest of all, she wore *aprons!* Can you beat it!

That's how she looked to the school. This is how the school looked to her. They had come a long way, she and her grandfather, from the town in Austria where he had a shop in which he repaired watches and clocks and sold trinkets the peasant boys bought for their sweethearts. Men in uniforms and big boots had come suddenly one day—it was in vacation and Magda was there —and had smashed in the windows of the shop and the showcase with the pretty things in it, and had thrown all the furniture from their home back of the shop out into the street and made a bonfire of it. And although Grandfather had not said a word to them, they had knocked him down, and hit him with their sticks till his white hair was all wet and scarlet with blood. Magda had been hiding in a corner and saw this; and now, after she had gone to sleep, she sometimes saw it again and woke up with a scream, but Grandfather always came quickly to say smilingly, "All right, Magda child. We're safe in America with Uncle Harry. Go to sleep again."

He had said she must not tell anybody about that day. "We can do something better in the New World than sow more hate," he said seriously. She was to forget about it if she could, and about the long journey afterwards, when they were so frightened, and had so little to eat; and, worst of all, when the man in the uniform in New York thought for a minute that something was wrong with their precious papers, and they might have to go back. She tried not to think of it, but it was in the back of her mind as she went to school every day, like the black cloth the jewelers put down on their counters to make their pretty gold and silver things shine more. The American school (really a rather ugly old brick building) was for Magda made of gold and silver, shining bright against what she tried to forget.

How kind the teachers were! Why, they *smiled* at the children. And how free and safe the children acted! Magda simply loved the sound of their chatter on the playground, loud and gay and not afraid even when the teacher stepped out for something. She did wish she could understand what they were saying. She had studied English in her Austrian school, but this swift birdlike twittering didn't sound a bit like the printed words on the page. Still, as the days went by she began to catch a word here and there, short ones like "down" and "run" and "back." And she soon found out what *hurrah!* means, for the Winthrop Avenue School made a specialty of mass cheering and every grade had a cheer leader, even the first-graders. Magda thought nearly everything in America was as odd and funny as it was nice. But the cheer leaders were the funniest with their bendings to one side and the other and then jumping up straight in the air till both feet were off the ground. But she loved to yell, "Hurrah!" too, although she couldn't understand what they were saying!

This is what they were saying—at least the six or seven girls who tagged after Betty Woodworth. Most of the seventh-graders were too busy studying and racing around at recess time to pay much attention to the queer new girl. But some did. They used to say, "My goodness, look at that dress! It looks like her grandmother's—if she's got one."

"Of all the dumb clucks. She doesn't even know enough to play squat tag. My goodness, the first-graders can play *tag*."

"My father told my mother this morning that he didn't know why *our* country should take in all the disagreeable folks that other countries can't stand any more."

"She's Jewish. She must be. Everybody that comes from Europe now is Jewish. We don't want our town all filled up with Jews!"

"My Uncle Peter saw where it said in the paper we ought to keep them out. We haven't got enough for ourselves, as it is."

Magda could just catch a word or two, "country" and "enough" and "uncle." But it wouldn't be long now, she thought happily, till she could understand everything they said, and really belong to seventh grade.

About two weeks after Magda came to school Thanksgiving Day was due. She had never heard of Thanksgiving Day, but since the story was all written out in her history book she soon found out what it meant. She thought it was perfectly lovely! She read the story of the Pilgrim Fathers and their long hard trip across the ocean (she knew something about that trip) and their terrible first winter, and the kind Indian whose language they couldn't understand, who taught them how to cultivate the fields, and then —oh, it was poetry, just *poetry*, the setting aside of a day forever and forever, every year, to be thankful that they could stay in America! How could people (as some of the people who wrote the German textbooks did) say that Americans didn't care about anything but making money? Why here, more than three hundred years after that day, this whole school and every other school, everywhere all over the country, was turning itself upside down to celebrate with joy their great-grandfathers' having been brave enough to come to America and to stay here, even though it was hard, instead of staying in Europe, where they had been so badly treated. (Magda knew something about that, too.)

Everybody in school was to do something for the celebration. The first-graders had funny little Indian clothes, and they were going to pretend to show the second-graders (in Puritan costumes) how to plant corn. Magda thought they were delightful, those darling little things, being taught already to be thankful that they could go on living in America. Some grades had songs, others were going to act in short plays. The children in Magda's own seventh grade that she loved so, were going to speak pieces and sing. She had an idea all her own, and because she couldn't be sure of saying the right words in English she wrote a note to the teacher about it. She would like to write a thankful prayer, (she could write English pretty well now) and learn it by heart and say it, as her part of the celebration. The teacher, who was terrifically busy with a bunch of boys who were to build a small "pretend" log-cabin on the stage, nodded that it would be all right. So Magda went away happily to write and learn it by heart.

"Kind of nervy, if you ask me, of that little Jew girl to horn in on *our* celebration," said Betty.

"Who asked her to come to America, anyhow?" said another.

"I thought Thanksgiving was for *Americans!*" said another.

Magda, listening hard, caught the word "American" and her face lighted up. It wouldn't be long now, she thought, before she could understand them.

No, no, they weren't specially bad children, no more than you or I—they had heard older people talking like that—and they gabbled along, thoughtlessly, the way we are all apt to repeat what we hear, without considering whether it is right or not.

On Thanksgiving Day a lot of those grown-ups whose talk Betty and her gang had been repeating, had come, as they always did, to the "exercises." They sat in rows in the assembly room listening to the singing and acting of the children and saying "the first-graders are too darling," and "how time flies," and "can you believe it that Betty is up to my shoulder now, seems like last week she was in the kindergarten."

The tall principal stood at one side of the platform and read off the different numbers from a list. By and by he said, "We shall now hear a prayer written by Magda Bensheim, and spoken by her. Magda has been in this country only five weeks and in our school only three."

Magda came out to the middle of the platform, a bright, striped apron over her thick, woolen dress, her braids tied with red ribbons. Her heart was beating fast. Her face was shining and solemn. She put her hands together and lifted them up over her head and said to God, "Oh thank you, thank you, dear God, for letting me come to America and nowhere else, when Grandfather and I were driven from our home. I learned out of my history book that Americans all came to this country just how Grandfather and I come, because Europe treat them wrong and bad. Every year they gather like this—to remember their brave grandfathers who come here so long ago and stay on, although they had such hard times. American hearts are so faithful and true that they forget never how they were all refugees, too, and must thankful be that from refugees they come to be American citizens. So thanks to you, dear, dear God, for letting Grandfather and me come to live in a country where they have this beautiful once-a-year Thanksgiving, for having come afraid from Europe to be here free and safe. I, too, feel the same beautiful thank-you-God, that all we Americans say here today."

Magda did not know what is usually said in English at the end of a prayer, so did not say anything when she finished, just walked away back where the other girls of her class were. But the Principal said it for her—after he had given his nose a good blow and wiped his eyes. He looked out over the people in the audience and said in a loud, strong voice, "Amen! I say Amen, and so does everybody here, I know."

And then—it was sort of queer to applaud a prayer—they all began to clap their hands loudly.

Back in the seventh-grade room the teacher was saying, "Well, children, that's all. See you next Monday. Don't eat too much turkey." But Betty jumped up and said, "Wait a minute, Miss Turner. Wait a minute, kids. I want to lead a cheer. All ready?

"Three cheers for Magda!

"Hip! Hip!"—she leaned 'way over to one side and touched the floor and they all shouted, "Hurrah!"

She bent back to the other side, "Hurrah!" they shouted.

She jumped straight up till both feet were off the ground and clapped her hands over her head and "Hurrah" they all shouted.

The wonderful moment had come. The curtain that had shut Magda off from her schoolmates had gone. "Oh! Ach!" she cried, her eyes wide. "Why, I understood every word. Yes, now I can understand American!"

THE GLORIOUS WHITEWASHER

by Mark Twain

Saturday morning was come, and all the summer world was bright and fresh, and brimming with life. There was a song in every heart; and if the heart was young the music issued at the lips. There was cheer in every face and a spring in every step. The locust trees were in bloom and the fragrance of the blossoms filled the air. Cardiff Hill, beyond the village and above it, was green with vegetation, and it lay just far enough away to seem a Delectable Land, dreamy, reposeful, and inviting.

Tom appeared on the sidewalk with a bucket of whitewash and a long-handled brush. He surveyed the fence, and all gladness left him and a deep melancholy settled down upon his spirit. Thirty yards of board fence nine feet high. Life to him seemed hollow, and existence but a burden. Sighing he dipped his brush and passed it along the topmost plank; repeated the operation; did it again; compared the insignificant whitewashed streak with the far-reaching continent of unwhitewashed fence, and sat down on a tree-box discouraged. Jim came skipping out at the gate with a tin pail, and singing "Buffalo Gals." Bringing water from the town pump had always been hateful work in Tom's eyes, before, but now it did not strike him so. He remembered that there was company at the pump. White, mulatto, and Negro boys and girls were always there waiting their turns, resting, trading playthings, quarreling, fighting, skylarking. And he remembered that although the pump was only a hundred and fifty yards off, Jim never got back with a bucket of water under an hour—and even then somebody generally had to go after him. Tom said:

"Say, Jim, I'll fetch the water if you'll whitewash some."

Jim shook his head and said:

"Can't Mars Tom. Ole missis, she tole me I got to go an' git dis water and not stop foolin' roun' wid anybody. She say she spec' Mars Tom gwine to ax me to whitewash, an' so she tole me go 'long an' 'tend to my own business—she 'lowed *she'd* tend to de whitewashin'."

"Oh, never you mind what she said, Jim. That's the way she always talks. Gimme the bucket—I won't be gone only a minute. *She* won't ever know."

"Oh, I dasn't, Mars Tom. Ole missis she'd take an' tar de head off'n me. 'Deed she would."

"*She!* She never licks anybody—whacks 'em over the head with her thimble—and who cares for that, I'd like to know. She talks awful, but talk don't hurt—anyways it don't if she don't cry. Jim, I'll give you a marvel. I'll give you a white alley!"

Jim began to waver.

"White alley, Jim! And it's a bully taw."

"My! Dat's a mighty gay marvel, I tell you! But Mars Tom, I's powerful 'fraid ole missis—"

"And besides, if you will I'll show you my sore toe."

Jim was only human—this attraction was too much for him. He put down his pail, took the white alley, and bent over the toe with absorbing interest while the bandage was being unwound. In another moment he was flying down the street with his pail and a tingling rear, Tom was whitewashing with vigor, and Aunt Polly was retiring from the field with a slipper in her hand and triumph in her eye.

But Tom's energy did not last. He began to think of the fun he had planned for this day, and his sorrows multiplied. Soon the free boys would come tripping along on all sorts of delicious expeditions, and they would make a world of fun of him for having to work—the very thought of it burnt him like fire. He got out his worldly wealth and examined it—bits of toys, marbles, and trash; enough to buy an exchange of *work*, maybe, but not half enough to buy so much as half an hour of pure freedom. So he returned his straitened means to his pocket, and gave up the idea of trying to buy the boys. At this dark and hopeless moment an inspiration burst upon him! Nothing less than a great, magnificent inspiration.

He took up his brush and went tranquilly to work. Ben Rogers hove in sight presently—the very boy, of all boys, whose ridicule he had been dreading. Ben's gait was the hop-skip-and-jump—proof enough that his heart was light and his anticipations high. He was eating an apple, and giving a long, melodious whoop, at intervals, followed by a deep-toned ding-dong-dong, ding-dong-dong, for he was personating a steamboat. As he drew near, he slackened speed, took the middle of the street, leaned far over to starboard and rounded to ponderously and with laborious pomp and circumstance—for he was personating the *Big Missouri*, and considered himself to be drawing nine feet of water. He was boat and captain and engine-bells combined, so he had to imagine himself standing on his own hurricane-deck giving the orders and executing them:

"Stop her, sir! Ting-a-ling-ling!" The headway ran almost out and he drew up slowly toward the sidewalk.

"Ship up to back! Ting-a-ling-ling!" His arms straightened and stiffened down his sides.

"Set her back on the stabboard! Ting-a-ling-ling! Chow! ch-chow-wow! Chow!" His right hand, meantime, describing stately circles—for it was representing a forty-foot wheel.

"Let her go back on the labboard! Ting-a-ling-ling! Chow-ch-chow-chow!" The left hand began to describe circles.

"Stop the stabboard! Ting-a-ling-ling! Stop the labboard! Come ahead on the stabboard! Stop her! Let your outside turn over slow! Ting-a-ling-ling! Chow-ow-ow! Get out that head-line! *Lively* now! Come—out with your spring-line—what're you about there! Take a turn round that stump with the bight of it! Stand by that stage, now—let her go! Done with the engines, sir! Ting-a-ling-ling! Sh't s'h't! sh't!" (trying the gauge-cocks).

Tom went on whitewashing—paid no attention to the steamboat. Ben stared a moment and then said:

"Hi-*yi! You're* up a stump, ain't you!"

No answer. Tom surveyed his last touch with the eye of an artist, then he gave his brush another gentle sweep and surveyed the result, as before. Ben ranged up alongside of him. Tom's mouth watered for the apple, but he stuck to his work. Ben said:

"Hello, old chap, you got to work, hey?"

Tom wheeled suddenly and said:

"Why, it's you, Ben! I warn't noticing."

"Say—I'm going in a-swimming, I am. Don't you wish you could? But of course you'd druther *work*—wouldn't you? Course you would!"

Tom contemplated the boy a bit, and said:

"What do you call work?"

"Why, ain't *that* work?"

Tom resumed his whitewashing, and answered carelessly:

"Well, maybe it is, and maybe it ain't. All I know is it suits Tom Sawyer."

"Oh come, now, you don't mean to let on that you *like* it?"

The brush continued to move.

"Like it? Well, I don't see why I oughtn't to like it. Does a boy get a chance to whitewash a fence every day?"

That put the thing in a new light. Ben stopped nibbling his apple. Tom swept his brush daintily back and forth—stepped back to note the effect—added a touch here and there—criticized the effect again—Ben watching every move and getting more and more interested, more and more absorbed. Presently he said:

"Say, Tom, let *me* whitewash a little."

Tom considered, was about to consent; but he altered his mind:

"No—no—I reckon it wouldn't hardly do, Ben. You see, Aunt Polly's awful particular about this fence—right here on the street, you know—but if it was the back fence I wouldn't mind and *she* wouldn't. Yes, she's awful particular about this fence; it's got to be done very careful; I reckon there ain't one boy in a thousand, maybe two thousand, that can do it the way it's got to be done."

"No—is that so? Oh come, now—lemme just try. Only just a little—I'd let *you*, if you was me, Tom."

"Ben, I'd like to, honest injun; but Aunt Polly—well, Jim wanted to do it, but she wouldn't let him; Sid wanted to do it, and she wouldn't let Sid. Now don't you see how I'm fixed? If you was to tackle this fence and anything was to happen to it——"

"Oh, shucks, I'll be just as careful. Now lemme try. Say—I'll give you the core of my apple."

"Well, here—No, Ben, now don't. I'm afeared——"

"I'll give you *all* of it!"

Tom gave up the brush with reluctance in his face, but alacrity in his heart. And while the late steamer *Big Missouri* worked and sweated in the sun, the retired artist sat on a barrel in the shade close by, dangled his legs, munched his apple, and planned the slaughter of more innocents. There was no lack of material; boys happened along every little while; they came to jeer, but remained to whitewash. By the time Ben was fagged out, Tom had traded the next chance to Billy Fisher for a kite, in good repair; and when *he* played out, Johnny Miller bought in for a dead rat and a string to swing it with—and so on, and so on, hour after hour. And when the middle of the afternoon came, from being a poor poverty-stricken boy in the morning, Tom was literally rolling in wealth. He had beside the things before mentioned twelve marbles, part of a jews'-harp, a piece of blue bottle-glass to look through, a spool cannon, a key that wouldn't unlock anything, a fragment of chalk, a glass stopper of a decanter, a tin soldier, a couple of tadpoles, six firecrackers, a kitten with only one eye, a brass doorknob, a dog-collar—but no dog—the handle of a knife, four pieces of orange-peel, and a dilapidated old window-sash.

He had had a nice, good, idle time all the while—plenty of company—and the fence had three coats of whitewash on it! If he hadn't run out of whitewash, he would have bankrupted every boy in the village.

A DUST RAG FOR EASTER EGGS

by Claire Huchet Bishop

There were five children talking things over at the corner of the Street of the Cat-Who-Goes-Fishing and the Quai St. Michel in

Paris. They called themselves the Gang-of-the-Cat-Who-Goes-Fishing. They had spent countless nights in the same air raid shelter during the five years of occupation and even had managed, though they were only children, to play tricks on the Germans. And now they went to school together, came back together, played together on free days. At this time they were all surrounding ten-year-old Charles. Rémi, who was twelve and the oldest with his twin sister Louise, said: "What did the doctor say?"

"He said," answered Charles, "that it was all because she has not had the proper food for five years. Not since she was born."

Louise, Rémi's twin sister, said: "It's tough! With your father dying a year after he came back as a prisoner from Germany. And poor Zézette not knowing him. She came just after his death. I remember."

"I remember, too," said Rémi. "It was at the time of the first British air raid."

"No use speaking about *that*," said nine-year-old Jules. "It's what to do for Zézette, *now*."

"Sure," said Rémi. "It makes me sick. I wish we could give Zézette a beautiful Easter. When I think of all the festivals we used to have: Christmas, the New Year, Kings' Day, Mardi Gras, the Assumption, Bastille Day . . ."

"Oh! cut it out," said Jules sharply. "You and Louise are always talking of Before."

"Well," said Louise hotly, "please yourself. But it's true about oranges on the Christmas tree, and the Cake of the Kings on Kings' Day, and the crêpes for Mardi Gras, and the Chocolate Easter eggs."

Paul who was eight, said: "*Chocolate* Easter eggs! If only we could have just plain eggs."

"For Zézette," said Jules.

"That's it," said Charles. "For Easter."

And there was a silence. The circle broke, they all stepped back and leaned against the wall of a house. After a while Louise said, "You must have ration points to buy eggs."

"Yes," said Charles, "Zézette has. You know, being five years old. One egg a week. But you cannot find any. And the last one mother found, a month ago, she had to pay twenty-five cents for. She cannot afford it. She does not make enough at the factory."

Jules said: "There are eggs. In the country. If one can go there."

"Yes," said Charles, "that's what the doctor said. But he said you cannot buy in the country with money. You have to have things to exchange."

"Of course!" they all answered at once. They all knew about that. They were used to that Indian way of living. Barter, barter for everything.

"And to buy from country people," Jules went on, "you have to have the real thing to offer, like shoes, a wool blanket, a sweater . . ."

"Sure," said Rémi. "And nobody has any of those things any more."

"Except very rich people," said Paul.

"Come on," said Jules, "there is no use talking. Let's go to the Luxembourg."

"Good-by," said Charles, shaking hands with the gang. "Have to get home. It's only four-thirty and mother doesn't come back from work before seven. Have to keep Zézette company."

They said good-by a little sadly, but not too, because as Louise said, "Well, that's life."

And Charles, wishing he were going to the garden with the gang instead of going up the old stairway alone to take care of Zézette, shrugged his small shoulders and muttered, "That's life!"

Yes, they all knew. But Paul, who was the youngest of the four, on their way to the Luxembourg kept saying as he kicked a stray pebble in front of him, "Plain eggs for Zézette at Easter."

"Shut . . . Say," went on Jules, stopping the others on the Boulevard St. Michel, "the Gang-of-the-Cat-Who-Goes-Fishing should do something about this!"

"Sure," hastened Paul, who was very fond of Zézette. "Zézette belongs to the gang, too."

Rémi turned to Louise. "You are so good at knitting, Louise. Couldn't you knit something and we would sell it, that is, barter it for eggs?"

"Knit with what?" asked Louise, her eyes blazing. "Are you crazy? There isn't any yarn anywhere," she added bitterly.

They went on walking in silence.

No, there was no yarn to be had anywhere. What, what could the Gang-of-the-Cat-Who-Goes-Fishing find to barter for eggs? And Easter was only a month off. What? What? thought Louise lying awake that night. She and Rémi lived alone with their father. Her mother had caught a cold during the flight before the German army in 1940 and had died of pneumonia. Louise was the woman of the family now, just as Charles was the man of the family in his home.

Next day was Thursday. There was no school. It was cleaning house day for Louise. She washed, she swept, she ran the dust rag on the floor. She picked up the old wool rag to shake it outside . . . and nearly dropped it in the street. The old dirty rag was a discarded wool sweater of her mother's, so worn out and so full of holes that Louise had never noticed it before, not really. Carefully Louise spread the rag on the floor. No, she thought, it's hopeless. Even if I could wash it, it could not possibly be of any use. She sat there on the floor fingering the dirty old rag. Suddenly she picked up the piece, shook it out the window a long time, then brushed it . . . and set it to soak in a pan of water. She could not spare any soap.

The next day, before going to school, she changed the water, which was very black, poured fresh water, and let the rag soak again. At night she changed the water once more and also the next day. On Saturday night, instead of using soap for her own bath, she used it on the rag. And the next day she rinsed and rinsed until the water came all clear. When Rémi came around he did not ask any questions, but he said, "Let me rinse it dry for you." And later he said, "My room has the afternoon sun. You can put it there to dry." And Louise said, "That's a good idea. I won't put it right in the sun, but the room is warm." She did and three days later the old wool rag was dry. It looked awful, but it was pretty clean.

Then Louise started to unravel the whole thing and it took her ages because it was all in pieces and she had to tie the yarn together all the time. But finally she had four big balls of yarn. The next day when they had said good-by to Charles after school she showed the yarn to the rest of the gang. They touched it respectfully, caressed it, ran their cheeks against it, and weighed it in their cupped hands.

Louise said, "I am going to make a sweater."

"Won't be a pretty color," said Paul.

"What of it?" challenged Rémi somewhat angrily.

"Sure," said Jules. "Take it easy. But Paul is right. That ugly color will make it hard to barter."

"He *is* right," said Louise. "It should be dyed. But I have no dye," she added sadly.

That evening, as she was getting supper there was a knock at the door. It was Jules. He gave her an envelope. "Listen, here is the dye. I stood in line two hours to get matches for the woman who runs the notion store, and in exchange she gave me the dye. Dark blue. That's all she had. So long! All for the gang!" he shrieked, tumbling downstairs.

The yarn was dyed and Louise began to knit.

She was a fast knitter and it was not long before she was working on the last sleeve. It was on a Thursday afternoon and she took her work with her to show it to the others. Zézette could not get up yet so Charles would not be able to come to the garden.

The gang was very excited. Rémi was proud of his sister and they started discussing how many eggs they might get for the sweater. Jules said sharply, "No use kidding ourselves. We won't get much. The wool is too thin in too many places."

Rémi snatched the sweater and held it against the sunlight.

It was only too true. Louise did not say anything. She felt like weeping. All that work!

Rémi said, "Louise couldn't you fill these thin places? Like embroidering something?"

"With what?" asked Louise bitterly. "There won't be any yarn left."

Paul jumped to his feet, "I know!" he shouted. "Mother has a bagful of tiny pieces of yarn. All colors. She never throws anything away."

"Wonderful," said Louise brightening up. "I could embroider all the thin spots with colored yarn. Oh! Paul, do you think your mother will let you have it?"

"I am going right home," said Paul, "and work it out. See you tomorrow."

That evening Paul set the table, wiped the dishes, took the garbage downstairs, all without being asked, and to top it all he went to bed without being told twice. When his mother came to say good night she said, "What's on your mind?" And Paul threw his arms around her neck and said, "How did you know?" And he asked her about the colored pieces of yarn. His mother said, "Those pieces of yarn are very precious nowadays, Paul. You cannot have them to play with."

"I know," said Paul emphatically. "But it's for our gang, you know, the Gang-of-the-Cat-Who-Goes-Fishing. And we are making something. Something to buy a present for Zézette who is sick."

"So," said Mother smiling, "you are trying to barter setting the table, wiping the dishes, taking the garbage down, and going to bed at once, for my little pieces of colored yarn?"

"That's it," said Paul brightly. And as his mother remained silent he added thoughtfully. "Perhaps that's not enough. You do have to offer a lot to get a little. If you wish, I can do it tomorrow too, and the day after, and the rest of the week, and the whole month, and . . . and always, always. Forever."

Mother stroked Paul's hair gently. "Zézette is a nice girl, isn't she? The gang is doing a good thing. You may have the pieces, only a little at a time every day as long as needed, provided during that time you keep helping me. Is that a bargain?"

"Check," said Paul putting his hand in his mother's. Leaning back sleepily on his pillow, he yawned, "Maman, do you think it will take Louise an awfully long time to do the embroidery?"

And now it was Holy Week and the sweater was finished. It was all dotted here and there with bright colored flowers and birds. It was unique. Pretty. Beautiful. Rémi had been appointed by the gang to go to the country and barter it for eggs. Rémi was a scout and he had a bicycle. It was the afternoon of Thursday of Holy Week, and Rémi was standing by his bicycle to start and his father was saying, "Rather strange this outing. And where are you supposed to sleep tonight, Rémi?"

Rémi said mildly, "In a farm, Papa."

"Look here," said Rémi's father, "no matter if you are a scout, I don't like your riding around alone on country roads at night. You are too young."

"But Papa, don't you remember last *year?* I sneaked out alone at night to bring a message to the F. F. I."

Louise said, "Please, Papa, let him go. He will be all right. We are not like children of Before."

Rémi was riding on the road, his bike bumping continuously through holes. He had gotten out of Paris easily. There was practically no traffic at all, and now he was alone in the midst of the Montmorency forest. Trees, trees, trees. No houses. No cars except an occasional jeep. As the sun went down, Rémi felt his heart thumping more heavily. The sun disappeared before Rémi was out of the forest. He would not light up his lantern in order to save fuel. He rolled along alone in the quiet twilight. An owl hooted mournfully. A deer leaped across the road. A bat brushed past his hair. Rémi gripped his handle bars and went on. He would make it. He would. At least the forest was behind him. Rémi stopped and lit his lantern. He continued rolling along the slightly hilly road bordered with poplar trees. By ten o'clock he decided he had better try to sleep somewhere. It was still too damp to sleep in the open. Half a mile or so from the road he saw a faint light. He turned on a side lane and went toward the light. He nearly broke his lantern, bumping suddenly into a pile of rubble. The farm had been bombed. Rémi knocked at the heavy door. A man's voice asked gruffly: "Who is there?"

"I am looking for a place to sleep, please," shouted Rémi.

The door was opened a crack and a storm lantern flashed in Rémi's face.

"A kid," said the man. "Come in."

Rémi went into the room crowded with all the stuff which had been saved from the bombing. He said, "*Bonsoir, M'sieur, Dame.*"

"*Bonsoir,*" said the man. "Park your wheel there against the wall. You can sleep on the bench if you want to. There is nothing else." He made a circular motion with his arm. "We have been bombed."

"Yes, I see," said Rémi gravely. He looked at the man and the woman standing there. They were young people. They were sad.

Rémi said, "It's better if I say now that I can't pay."

"Pay for what?" asked the man.

"For sleeping here tonight."

The man answered, "My idea is that you should not be running along the roads at night alone. But, nowadays, children . . . it's not like Before . . ."

"No, it's not like Before," echoed Rémi quietly.

The woman went to the cupboard, took a piece of dark bread and a pitcher of milk and set it on the table.

"Sit down," she said, "and eat. As much as you want."

"But," said Rémi, "the money . . ."

"Eat," ordered the man. "The wife told you."

Rémi came toward the table. "My name is Rémi Renault," he said.

The man said, "Ours, it's Bonnet." They shook hands and the three of them sat down. Rémi ate and ate. He was very hungry.

He ate the whole hunk of dark bread and drank the whole pitcher of milk. The man and the woman sat looking at him. The man asked how things were in Paris. If there was enough food. "Cannot send anything to the city. No trucks. No trains. Nothing. Rich people manage to get things from the country. Some farmers are making a lot of money. I don't mean us. We have been bombed. We have just one cow left and a few chickens . . . and," he whispered, "our sorrow."

"Have you a little sister?" asked the woman abruptly of Rémi.

"No," said Rémi, "but there is Zézette. And it's because of her that I am on the road. I am not on the road for any rich people. I know how it is. But I am here for Zézette."

And he told them the whole story. Zézette's sickness. The doctor's advice. The Gang-of-the-Cat-Who-Goes-Fishing. The dust rag. The dye. The colored pieces of yarn. The sweater. The eggs.

They listened quietly with a funny little expression in their eyes, as if they were about to weep.

"Let us see the sweater," they said. Rémi showed it to them.

"Never seen anything prettier," said the woman. "And to think that it all came out of an old dirty dust rag!"

"If you go a little farther north tomorrow morning," said the man, "there they have not been bombed and you should be able to get a lot of food in exchange for this sweater."

Rémi's eyes sparkled.

"You're a good kid," said Madame Bonnet. "I dare say all of you of the Gang-of-the-Cat-Who-Goes-Fishing are good kids . . . like my little angel who is in heaven," she added softly.

"Stretch out on the bench, Rémi," interrupted the man. "*Bonsoir, mon gars.*" He snuffed out the lamp.

When Rémi awoke the next morning he saw there was milk again on the table and another piece of dark bread. The sweater was spread on the table and next to it were two dozen eggs.

"*Bonjour,*" said Madame Bonnet. "Come and eat before you go."

"Here are two dozen eggs for Zézette," said Monsieur Bonnet.

"So you do like the sweater," cried Rémi.

"*Mon petit gars,*" said Monsieur Bonnet, "the sweater is worth much more than that. We cannot afford to barter for that sweater. We have been bombed. But here are two dozen eggs for Zézette."

"But," said Rémi, "what can I give . . . I don't understand."

"The eggs, we give them to you. No money." And seeing Rémi's puzzled expression Monsieur Bonnet added, "Sort of would like to be honorary members of the Gang-of-the-Cat-Who-Goes-Fishing, see?"

"Listen, Rémi," broke in Madame Bonnet gently. "We had a Zézette, too. Only her name was Clothilde. She would be five years old now. Just like Zézette. She was killed in the air raid."

Rémi said quietly, "Ah, poor Monsieur and Madame Bonnet! It's very sad! Zézette's father died after he had been a prisoner in Germany. My mother died because she caught pneumonia when we fled before the Germans in 1940. And your little Clothilde killed in an air raid. It's very sad."

They were silent.

"I guess I had better be going," said Rémi. He arranged the eggs carefully in the wire basket on his bike wrapping them in newspapers he had brought with him. They stepped outside. The ruins of the farm looked sadder in the bright morning light.

Monsieur Bonnet said, "Turn left on the main road and go as far as the big crossroad where the calvary is. That's about twenty miles from here. Then turn right and you will see a big prosperous farm. They have not been bombed out. You can barter the sweater, and be sure you get plenty for it."

"Yes," said Madame Bonnet. "Such a lovely thing, well knitted and all those pretty birds and flowers. Now watch that you don't break the eggs. . . . It will be two or three weeks before we have another dozen, won't it?" she said turning to her husband.

Monsieur Bonnet squared his shoulders and said, "Look here, Rémi, I have not asked my wife, but I would like to let you have another two dozen in two or three weeks, for Zézette, if you can manage to come back."

"Do what my husband says, Rémi," said Madame Bonnet evenly. "He is the boss."

"I'll come back. I'll manage it!" He shook hands with them. "*Au revoir, au revoir, Monsieur, au revoir, Madame.*" He swung on his bike, turned around and shouted, "And may the Good God bless you and send you another child."

Rémi found the way just as Monsieur Bonnet had told him. And in the prosperous farm he bartered the sweater and got for it:

five pounds of new potatoes
a heap of cornfield salad
some apples
a pound of honey
two pounds of butter
a big fat chicken

Rémi had a hard time coming back to Paris. The basket was heavy and he was holding the bag of potatoes and apples in his left hand, so that he had only his right hand to direct the bike and steady himself over the bumps. He reached home after sundown on Good Friday just as his father was coming in. And then, of course, everything had to be explained. Papa looked very suspicious, then very upset, then very happy. And he said, "Come and kiss me, and you, too, Louise. Your mother would be proud of you."

"But Papa," said Louise. "It is not Rémi and I only. It's the Gang. The Gang-of-the-Cat-Who-Goes-Fishing. I made the sweater from the dust rag. Jules got the dye. Paul the colored pieces of yarn for the thin spots to embroider, and Rémi bartered the sweater."

"And what did Charles do?" asked Papa.

"He kept Zézette going," said Louise.

"Yes, he did," said Rémi. "Kept her company *every* day. That was the hardest of all."

"Well, well, well," mused Papa. "And now there is all that food . . . What about having the whole gang here to eat it on Easter Sunday, Louise?"

And they did. The whole Gang-of-the-Cat-Who-Goes-Fishing was there: Louise, Rémi, Jules, Paul, Charles, and Zézette who got up especially for it. What an Easter it was! How they ate! Just like Before. Zézette was presented with the two dozens of eggs from Monsieur and Madame Bonnet and Rémi had to say over and over again, "They said so. I can go back and get some more."

Ah, yes! It was a beautiful Easter, last year.

And now another Easter is coming. Louise, Rémi, Jules, Paul, Charles, and Zézette, who is well now thanks to the eggs of Monsieur and Madame Bonnet, they are all sitting in the Luxembourg Gardens and looking at a piece of paper, a letter which was addressed to Rémi, and says:

To
The Gang-of-the-Cat-Who-Goes-Fishing
Monsieur and Madame Bonnet
Have the Joy of announcing
the birth of their daughter
CLOTHILDE-ZEZETTE
CHARLOTTE-LOUISE-MIMI-JULIA-
PAULETTE BONNET

DANGER IN THE DEEP

by Charles Coombs

Stan Holmes was tugging the straps of his rubber swim fins on over his heels, when he saw Doug Sanders coming down the bluff that overlooked Rocky Cove. There was no mistaking Doug's familiar light-blue trunks, or the old gray sweat shirt with the big hole in the left elbow. He carried a fish spear over one shoulder. Dangling from it were his green rubber swim fins and the glass-windowed diving mask made to fit over his eyes and nose. In the other hand he carried an old inflated inner tube with a gunny sack tied to it.

"Hi, fellow," the husky, deeply tanned boy greeted, as he dumped his diving gear on the sand beside Stan. "You down here all alone today?"

"Guess it's too cold for the others," the sandy-haired swimmer said. "But I . . . well, I kind of like it this way."

"Me, too," Doug said.

Stan wondered if the other boy's reason—his real reason, that is—was the same as his own. Actually, although he really liked to skin dive, it was more of a summer sport. On a chilly September day like this, he would much rather have been home reading a good book. But the legal lobster season was nearly over. Most of the regular commercial lobster men had gathered up their pots, because of the lateness of the season and the sudden scarcity of the shellfish.

Doug stripped out of his sweat shirt, kicked off his beach sandals, and began to pull on his diving gear. "I sure hope I can find some today," he said. "Not many around, though, I guess. The fish markets in Seaview are really paying a good price for lobsters. And how I can use a little money. Have a chance to get a paper route with the Seaview *Daily Breeze*. But I've got to have a bike to do it. Bikes cost dough."

Stan didn't mention how badly he needed spending money, too. School was about ready to start again. What clothes he hadn't outworn during the summer, he had outgrown beyond all the efforts his mother had made to keep lengthening them. At the age of thirteen, he seemed to be growing faster than Iowa corn in July.

Any other year his parents would have bought school clothes for him. But since his father's accident at the factory, the family seemed just able to get by for food and rent. Stan knew that it would relieve his mother and father of a big worry if he could earn enough money to get his own school clothes this year.

Later, his father would be well and back to work. But right now things were pretty crucial in the Holmes household.

"Well, guess I'm set," Doug said. He left his fish spear stuck in the sand, but picked up his inner tube with the open gunny sack tied to it. "Shall we go out together, Stan?" he asked.

Stan knew the standing rule that a skin diver never should go out alone. A fellow never knew when something might go wrong down below, and he'd need help. But he also knew Doug's reputation as one of the best young divers at the cove. If they went down together and there were any lobsters around, Doug would probably get to them first.

"I . . . I guess not," Stan said. "I'll follow you out in a few minutes. I want to try over on the other side of the point, anyway."

He felt Doug's eyes on him. "O.K., Stan," he said. "But be careful over there. They tell me there are quite a few moray eels hanging around those rocks. They can give you a nasty bite."

"I'll be careful," Stan said, thinking of some of the teeth marks other divers had on their hands and arms. Of course, if you didn't go reaching into places where you couldn't see, you didn't have much to worry about in the way of trouble from the denizens of the deep water.

Doug waded out through the rolling surf, jumped a wave, then started swimming out into the cove. He pushed the rubber tube ahead of him. Stan watched the husky boy make a couple of dives. But both times he came back to the surface empty-handed.

"Boy, I hope I have better luck than that," he said to himself, as he strapped his sheath knife to his leg. He slipped on his face mask. Carrying his own inner tube, and waddling like a duck with the rubber swim fins on his feet, he took to the water.

He swam right out past where Doug was diving. As he surfaced, the dark-haired boy shook the water from his face. "Sure don't seem to be many down here, Stan," he said. "Saw one big granddaddy bull lobster. But he was over legal size. All of the others seem to be too small."

Legal-sized lobsters were between ten and a half and sixteen inches. Smaller or larger than that, they had to be left alone or tossed back. The west coast spiny lobster was actually a large sea crawfish. It had no dangerous pinchers like the eastern lobsters. But when a fellow was down ten or fifteen feet trying to wrestle one out of a rock crevice, he had a job on his hands. Especially since the lobster was in his own back yard and the diver had only a short period of time within which he could work before having to kick for the surface and a fresh supply of air.

"I'm going to try off the point," Stan said. But he didn't ask the other boy to go over there with him. If he found any lobsters, Stan needed them for himself.

Arriving at the chosen spot, Stan turned himself loose from the inner tube. Taking a couple of deep breaths, he jackknifed his body, drove downward with his hands, and disappeared beneath the surface.

He was immediately thrilled by the breathtaking beauty of the bluish-green underwater world. No matter how often he dove, he just never got over marveling at the sights below the surface. Schools of small, brightly colored fish swam leisurely around him. Once in a while a curious and brave finny fellow would swim up close and stare into his face mask. Opening and closing its mouth, the fish seemed to be saying, "Oh, oh, brother, brother, oh, oh!" When Stan would reach out to touch one, it would quickly dart away. It, no doubt, was wondering what strange kind of sea monster it had just come across.

The seaweed and forests of sea ferns swayed gently in the ever-present currents. As he neared the bottom, Stan's ears began to rattle, and he felt his face mask push harder into his cheeks. He swallowed to clear his ears, and blew a little air through his nose into the water tight mask to ease the pressure.

The ocean bottom was covered with giant boulders, heavily encrusted with spiny sea urchins and all kinds of barnacles and razor-sharp shells. Nothing there to bother a diver if he kept his feet off the bottom. A giant crab scurried into a crevice. To his right, a large halibut fluttered across a patch of sand.

But no lobsters.

Then, just as the breath was beginning to pound in his chest, Stan saw the dark-red form of a "bug," as the divers called the lobsters, back up the side of a rock and duck into a shallow hole. Marking its location in his mind, Stan tilted upward, fluttered his swim fins, and shot back to the surface.

A hundred feet to his right he saw Doug's flippers just disappearing beneath the surface as the other boy took another dive.

Stan refilled his lungs several times. Then he nosed under for his next dive. Driving downward, he quickly spotted the lobster which had come back out of its lair. He eased up to it, and was just about to make his grab. Suddenly, from the corner of his eye, he saw the snakelike head of a large moray eel watching him from under a ledge. He knew at once that if he made a grab for the lobster, the vicious eel would make as quick a grab for him. The rows of needlelike teeth in the eel's open mouth were anything but inviting.

"That's one lobster that I don't want," Stan decided quickly. He shifted direction, following a submarine canyon through the rocks. Having made many dives at Rocky Cove and other inlets around Seaview City, Stan was used to the pressures. But now he knew that he must be nearly twenty feet down, just about as deep as he had ever gone. Older, more experienced divers thought little of thirty- or even thirty-five-foot dives. But twenty feet was plenty deep for Stan. Plenty.

Careful to keep his hands off the rocks, he threaded his way along the underwater canyon, pushing against the current. He had just decided to start back for the surface, when a sudden flurry of motion directly ahead caught his attention. A cloud of sand fogged the water. But through it, Stan was able to make out its cause.

Lobsters! There were dozens of them. An entire colony. All sizes. The place was crawling with them.

Even through the murk, Stan saw that the ledge under which they scurried was shallow. They should be a cinch to catch. Making a quick mental note, he turned and stroked back to the surface.

He came up twenty feet from his floating inner tube. He swam to get it and tow it directly over the spot where he would start his dives.

"Any bugs?" Doug called to him from fifty yards away.

Without answering, Stan held up his empty hands. Doug could figure it out for himself, he thought.

"I'm about to give up," Doug went on. There was no mistaking the disappointment in his voice. Stan wondered just how Doug would figure to get a bike now. Newspaper routes were not easy to get around Seaview City. "Kind of hate to leave you out here alone, though," the other boy went on. "It's not a good idea. Besides, the tide's due to change before long."

"Oh, I'll be all right," Stan assured his friend, although he knew it was against all common-sense rules of the sport to be out in the water alone. "I'm only going to make a few more dives, anyway."

"Then I'll stick around a while," the other boy said. "Sure don't want anything to happen to a fellow skin diver."

"Suit yourself," Stan called back. Then, anxious to get at some of those lobsters, he started back down again. He was halfway to the bottom, when a shadow suddenly passed above him. Spinning quickly in the water, he looked up—and straight into the face of a circling shark!

For an instant his blood chilled with terror. But, knowing fear to be the diver's worst enemy, he quickly calmed himself.

The shark was a fairly small one. About four feet long. He seemed just as wary of Stan's presence as Stan was of his. Stories flashed through Stan's mind of how veteran skin divers would grab sharks bigger than this one by the tail just for the sport of it. Besides, no man-eating sharks of any size had ever been seen along that part of the coast. And especially that close to shore.

Once again in full control of his nerve, Stan flailed out wildly as though he were an underwater bogeyman. With a quick flip of its tail, the torpedo-shaped shark spurted away. He turned and watched from a safer distance.

Stan smiled confidently to himself and went on his way. Approaching the ledge from a blind angle, he reached down and grabbed a nice spiny lobster before it or the others even knew what had happened. It would probably measure about fourteen inches. A real pip.

Even as he grabbed it, Stan realized what a gold mine of sea food he had discovered. There were so many of them that getting his limit would be no problem. In fact, he could mark the spot well in his mind and come back day after day until the season ended.

He swam back to the surface with the harmless, but somewhat sharp-pointed shellfish clutched firmly in one hand. Stan felt well rewarded for his efforts in coming to the cove, when most of the other sports divers had hung up their gear for the season.

But Doug hadn't given up, either. His flippers were once again just disappearing as Stan reached the surface. Quickly, before the other boy came back up, Stan swam to his floating inner tube and dumped the lobster into the sack hanging beneath it.

He took a couple of deep breaths and went down for another. He repeated the performance several times. Each time he came back up with a hefty legal-sized lobster. And each time he managed to drop it into the floating sack while Doug wasn't looking.

"Well, Stan," Doug called over, "I think I'll call it quits. I've got two pretty good ones. But all of the others seem to have gone South for the winter or something. Let's go in. It's getting cold. Tell you what. I'll give you one of my bugs. Then neither of us will be empty-handed."

"Th . . . thanks," Stan called, "but I think I'll stick a little longer."

After all, he thought, it would be nice if Doug did go on home. If he wasn't on the beach, Stan wouldn't have to explain when he finally came in dragging his own heavy sack of choice lobsters.

Yes, it would be better if Doug did go on in.

The other boy seemed to shrug. He pushed his face mask up onto his forehead. Leaning on his inner tube and propelling himself with his rubber-flippered feet, he started easing shoreward.

It was then that a feeling which had been building up slowly in Stan—almost without his knowing it—boiled over.

Doug had always been a friend. Maybe not a close one, but maybe that had been Stan's own fault. Doug had always been such a good athlete and diver that Stan just never felt in his class.

Just like today, Stan thought. He hadn't wanted to dive with Doug, because he had been afraid that the other boy might hog all of the underwater game.

And now Doug, who needed the lobsters as much as he did, maybe more, had just offered to share his only two with Stan. While all of the time, right down beneath Stan, there were plenty of lobsters for both of them.

Stan's feeling was one of selfish guilt.

"Hey, Doug," he called suddenly, "I've found a whole nest of bugs down here. Come on."

The other boy stopped and looked back. "O.K., Stan," he said, grinning. "If you don't want to be left out here alone I'll stick around a few minutes longer. But snap it up, huh?"

It didn't help Stan's feeling of guilt much when he realized that Doug probably had been sticking around for the past fifteen or twenty minutes just to be on hand if he needed help.

"No kiddin', Doug," he called. "They're down there. Lots of 'em. Come and look in my sack." He reached down carefully, pulled one out, and held it up for the other diver to see.

A strange look passed over the other boy's face. Then, just as quickly, it was gone. "Wow!" he cried, changing his course in Stan's direction. "Where'd that come from?"

Stan told him hurriedly about his underwater discovery.

"Well, let's go down and have a look," Doug said. Then he peered closely at Stan. "You sure you want me to have some of them, Stan?"

"I . . . I wasn't sure a few minutes ago, Doug," Stan said honestly. "But . . . well, I am now. Besides, I don't own the ocean, do I?"

Doug smiled. "Come on, let's go down together."

They pulled their diving masks over their faces, filled their lungs, and started down. Swimming powerfully, Stan led the way to the lobsters. Many of them had scattered and ducked into crevices. But there were still plenty to be had for the taking. Each boy picked off a good one and took it back up with him.

"Boy, you weren't just kidding, were you?" Doug said, grinning as he dropped his bug into his nearly empty sack. "How many more do you need for your limit?"

"Just one," Stan said. "I'll get it this trip, then wait for you to finish out yours." Without waiting for the other boy to clear out some sea water that had leaked through his face mask, Stan headed back down.

A small school of scarlet garibaldi perch swam past in front of him. They glistened brightly against the pastel green of the water. Rounding a rock, Stan startled a small dozing octopus. Shooting a tiny stream of ink, it pulled its eight tentacles together and jet-propelled itself quickly out of reach. Since they never grew to any threatening size along that part of the coast, the gruesome-looking octopus was another sea beast which gave no fear to an experienced skin diver.

Arriving once more at the underwater ledge, Stan was just in time to see a big bull lobster back quickly into a grotto. Stan hadn't noticed the cave before, but he visioned that it was chuck full of the spiny shellfish.

That bull lobster would make a mighty tasty morsel for someone's table.

Not considering the carelessness of his move in following the lobster, Stan poked his head and shoulders into the cave.

Just as he did, a sudden surge of underwater current lifted him from beneath. A burst of air escaped his mouth, as he felt his shoulders suddenly wedged into the V-shaped roof of the shallow cave.

A feeling of panic surged through him, as he tried to wriggle free. Then he fought back the terror, realizing that panic was as big an enemy as the current which held him fast. He felt the coarse edge of the rocks scrape his skin. He waited, conserving his breath, hoping and praying for the unseen force of the current to ease up.

Then, numbly, he realized that there was little chance of the current changing. He had stayed out too long. The tide was coming in. It was the pressure of the tide which had his shoulders pinned so tightly to the roof of the cave!

His lungs were crying for air. Rockets were beginning to explode in his head, when he felt something suddenly grasp his ankle.

The first thought that flashed into his mind was the shark. Small as it had been, maybe if it saw something struggling futilely it would become brave enough to attack. But then Stan realized that the grip had no teeth. He knew that it was two hands—Doug's two hands.

Stan's thoughts spun wildly. He realized that there was just time for one good effort. He braced his hands against the top of the cave. As he felt Doug's downward and outward pull, he shoved with all his waning strength.

And he came free!

Immediately, he kicked upward. Numbly, he felt Doug's hefty shove from beneath, adding speed to his ascent. Up, up he went.

Moments later, Stan was clinging weakly to his inner tube, when Doug's head broke the surface at his side.

"Looked like you were in a wee bit of trouble down there, chum," the husky boy said, smiling. "Don't you know that you're not supposed to go poking into . . ."

"Yeah, yeah, I know," Stan gasped. "Doug, I . . . I was a nut.

Boy, if you hadn't . . ." A shudder passed over Stan. He couldn't help wondering what might have happened if Doug hadn't arrived down there to give him a hand.

He couldn't help realizing what might have happened if he hadn't called Doug over to share his find of lobsters!

"Well, pal," Doug said, "you look a little tired. Besides, we should get some iodine on those scratches on your shoulders. What say we call it a day?"

"I'm for it," Stan managed a weak smile. "We . . . we can come back tomorrow when there's no tide running. Doug, there are still plenty of bugs down there for your bike and my school clothes. And . . . well, maybe we could even save one for ourselves. You know, have a little feast together."

"Swell idea, Stan," Doug grinned. "Maybe we can do a lot of things together, huh?"

"Yeah," Stan said happily. "Together. Boy, have I learned a couple of real lessons today!"

And, as they started shoreward, the thoughts of Stan's recent close squeak began to give way to the much pleasanter thoughts of a really swell future for him and his friend Doug—together.

2

Of Courage and Adventure

Stories of adventure and courage are always exciting, partly because what they say is so different from what we see going on around us. Whatever happens nearer home seems dull and flat by comparison. At the same time, we always live on the very edge of danger, just around the corner from adventure.

Most of the time things just jog along. But life is a constant adventure of meeting new or unexpected circumstances. These may appear at any time, without giving notice in advance. Then the great problem is, How do we deal with the unexpected? How do we face or escape danger? How do we overcome difficulties? How do we hold out when the regular things have to be put off or set aside—like food or rest or comfort? Or how do we hold out against pain or hunger or fear?

If adventure seems to belong to faraway times or faraway people, it is because the every-day courage of those living right around you hasn't been written up in books yet. If you read newspapers, you soon learn that people are all the time meeting dangers, overcoming difficulties, enduring hardships, or solving problems. Boys and girls jump into the water to save someone's life. Or drag a person overcome by smoke into the open air. Or they travel difficult or stormy paths to carry an important message or deliver needed medicine. Or they just plug along with necessary but unexciting chores and hold out until the time comes for what they really want to happen.

THE BIG BEAR

by Charles Major

Away back in the "twenties," when Indiana was a baby state, and great forests of tall trees and tangled underbrush darkened what are now her bright plains and sunny hills, there stood upon the east bank of Big Blue River, a mile or two north of the point where that stream crosses the Michigan road, a cozy log cabin of two rooms—one front and one back.

The house faced the west, and stretching off toward the river for a distance equal to twice the width of an ordinary street, was a blue-grass lawn, upon which stood a dozen or more elm and sycamore trees, with a few honey-locusts scattered here and there. Immediately at the water's edge was a steep slope of ten or twelve feet. Back of the house, mile upon mile, stretched the deep dark forest, inhabited by deer and bears, wolves and wildcats, squirrels and birds, without number.

In the river the fish were so numerous that they seemed to entreat the boys to catch them, and to take them out of their crowded quarters. There were bass and black suckers, sunfish and catfish, to say nothing of the sweetest of all, the big-mouthed redeye.

South of the house stood a log barn, with room in it for three horses and two cows; and enclosing this barn, together with a piece of ground, five or six acres in extent, was a palisade fence, eight or ten feet high, made by driving poles into the ground close together. In this enclosure the farmer kept his stock, consisting of a few sheep and cattle, and here also the chickens, geese, and ducks were driven at nightfall to save them from "varmints," as all prowling animals were called by the settlers.

The man who had built this log hut, and who lived in it and

owned the adjoining land at the time of which I write, bore the name of Balser Brent. "Balser" is probably a corruption of Baltzer, but, however that may be, Balser was his name, and Balser was the hero of the bear story which I am about to tell you.

Mr. Brent and his young wife had moved to the Blue River settlement from North Carolina, when young Balser was a little boy five or six years of age. They had purchased the "eighty" upon which they lived, from the United States, at a sale of public land held in the town of Brookville on Whitewater, and had paid for it what was then considered a good round sum—one dollar per acre. They had received a deed for their "eighty" from no less a person than James Monroe, then President of the United States. This deed, which is called a patent, was written on sheepskin, signed by the President's own hand, and is still preserved by the descendants of Mr. Brent as one of the title-deeds to the land it conveyed. The house, as I have told you, consisted of two large rooms, or buildings, separated by a passageway six or eight feet broad which was roofed over, but open at both ends—on the north and south. The back room was the kitchen, and the front room was the parlor, bedroom, sitting room and library all in one.

At the time when my story opens Little Balser, as he was called to distinguish him from his father, was thirteen or fourteen years of age, and was the happy possessor of a younger brother, Jim, aged nine, and a little sister one year old, of whom he was very proud indeed.

On the south side of the front room was a large fireplace. The chimney was built of sticks, thickly covered with clay. The fireplace was almost as large as a small room in one of our cramped modern houses, and was broad and deep enough to take in backlogs which were so large and heavy that they could not be lifted, but were drawn in at the door and rolled over the floor to the fireplace.

The prudent father usually kept two extra backlogs, one on each side of the fireplace, ready to be rolled in as the blaze died down; and on these logs the children would sit at night, with a rough slate made from a flat stone, and do their "ciphering," as the study of arithmetic was then called. The fire usually furnished all the light they had, for candles and "dips," being expensive luxuries, were used only when company was present.

The fire, however, gave sufficient light, and its flare upon a cold night extended halfway up the chimney, sending a ruddy, cozy glow to every nook and corner of the room.

The back room was the storehouse and kitchen; and from the beams along the walls hung rich hams and juicy sidemeat, jerked venison, dried apples, onions, and other provisions for the winter. There was a glorious fireplace in this room also, and a crane upon which to hang pots and cooking utensils.

The floor of the front room was made of logs split in halves with the flat, hewn side up; but the floor of the kitchen was of clay, packed hard and smooth.

The settlers had no stoves, but did their cooking in round pots called Dutch ovens. They roasted their meats on a spit or steel bar like the ramrod of a gun. The spit was kept turning before the fire, presenting first one side of the meat and then the other, until it was thoroughly cooked. Turning the spit was the children's work.

South of the palisade enclosing the barn was the clearing—a tract of twenty or thirty acres of land, from which Mr. Brent had cut and burned the trees. On this clearing the stumps stood thick as the hair on an angry dog's back; but the hard-working farmer plowed between and around them, and each year raised upon the fertile soil enough wheat and corn to supply the wants of his family and his stock, and still had a little grain left to take to Brookville, sixty miles away, where he had bought his land, there to exchange for such necessities of life as could not be grown upon the farm or found in the forests.

The daily food of the family all came from the farm, the forests, or the creek. Their sugar was obtained from the sap of the sugar-trees; their meat was supplied in the greatest abundance by a few hogs, and by the inexhaustible game of which the forests were full. In the woods were found deer just for the shooting; and squirrels, rabbits, wild turkeys, pheasants, and quails, so numerous that a few hours' hunting would supply the table for days. The fish in the river, as I told you, fairly longed to be caught.

One day Mrs. Brent took down the dinner horn and blew upon it two strong blasts. This was the signal that Little Balser, who was helping his father down in the clearing, should come to the house. Balser was glad enough to drop his hoe and to run home. When he reached the house his mother said:

"Balser, go up to the drift and catch a mess of fish for dinner. Your father is tired of deer meat three times a day, and I know he would like a nice dish of fried redeyes at noon."

"All right, mother," said Balser. And he immediately took down his fishing-pole and line, and got the spade to dig bait. When he had collected a small gourdful of angle-worms, his mother called to him:

"You had better take a gun. You may meet a bear; your father loaded the gun this morning, and you must be careful in handling it."

Balser took the gun, which was a heavy rifle considerably longer than himself, and started up the river toward the drift, about a quarter of a mile away.

There had been rain during the night and the ground near the drift was soft.

Here, Little Balser noticed fresh bear tracks, and his breath began to come quickly. You may be sure he peered closely into every dark thicket, and looked behind all the large trees and logs, and had his eyes wide open lest perchance "Mr. Bear" should step out and surprise him with an affectionate hug, and thereby put an end to Little Balser forever.

So he walked on cautiously, and, if the truth must be told, somewhat tremblingly, until he reached the drift.

Balser was but a little fellow, yet the stern necessities of a settler's life had compelled his father to teach him the use of a gun; and, although Balser had never killed a bear, he had shot several deer, and upon one occasion had killed a wildcat, "almost as big as a cow," he said.

I have no doubt the wildcat seemed "almost as big as a cow" to Balser when he killed it, for it must have frightened him greatly, as wildcats were sometimes dangerous animals for children to encounter. Although Balser had never met a bear face to face and alone, yet he felt, and many a time had said, that there wasn't a bear in the world big enough to frighten him, if he but had his gun.

He had often imagined and minutely detailed to his parents and little brother just what he would do if he should meet a bear. He would wait calmly and quietly until his bearship should come within a few yards of him, and then he would slowly lift his gun. Bang! and Mr. Bear would be dead with a bullet in his heart.

But when he saw the fresh bear tracks, and began to realize that he would probably have an opportunity to put his theories about bear killing into practice, he began to wonder if, after all, he would become frightened and miss his aim. Then he thought of how the bear, in that case, would be calm and deliberate, and would put his theories into practice by walking very politely up to him, and making a very satisfactory dinner of a certain boy whom he could name. But as he walked on and no bear appeared, his courage grew stronger as the prospect of meeting the enemy grew less, and he again began saying to himself that no bear could frighten him, because he had his gun and he could and would kill it.

So Balser reached the drift; and having looked carefully about him, leaned his gun against a tree, unwound his fishing-line from the pole, and walked out to the end of a log which extended into the river some twenty or thirty feet.

Here he threw in his line, and soon was so busily engaged drawing out sunfish and redeyes, and now and then a bass, which was hungry enough to bite at a worm, that all thought of the bear went out of his mind.

After he had caught enough fish for a sumptuous dinner he

bethought him of going home, and as he turned toward the shore, imagine, if you can, his consternation when he saw upon the bank, quietly watching him, a huge black bear.

If the wildcat had seemed as large as a cow to Balser, of what size do you suppose that bear appeared? A cow! An elephant, surely, was small compared with the huge black fellow standing upon the bank.

It is true Balser had never seen an elephant, but his father had, and so had his friend Tom Fox, who lived down the river; and they all agreed that an elephant was "purt nigh as big as all outdoors."

The bear had a peculiar, determined expression about him that seemed to say:

"That boy can't get away; he's out on the log where the water is deep, and if he jumps into the river I can easily jump in after him and catch him before he can swim a dozen strokes. He'll have to come off the log in a short time, and then I'll proceed to devour him."

About the same train of thought had also been rapidly passing through Balser's mind. His gun was on the bank where he had left it, and in order to reach it he would have to pass the bear. He dared not jump into the water, for any attempt to escape on his part would bring the bear upon him instantly. He was very much frightened, but, after all, was a cool-headed little fellow for his age; so he concluded that he would not press matters, as the bear did not seem inclined to do so, but so long as the bear remained watching him on the bank would stay upon the log where he was, and allow the enemy to eye him to his heart's content.

There they stood, the boy and the bear, each eyeing the other as though they were the best of friends, and would like to eat each other, which, in fact, was literally true.

Time sped very slowly for one of them, you may be sure; and it seemed to Balser that he had been standing almost an age in the middle of Blue River on that wretched shaking log, when he heard his mother's dinner horn, reminding him that it was time to go home.

Balser quite agreed with his mother and gladly would he have gone, I need not tell you; but there stood the bear, patient, determined, and fierce; and Little Balser soon was convinced in his mind that his time had come to die.

He hoped that when his father would go home to dinner and find him still absent, he would come up the river in search of him, and frighten away the bear. Hardly had this hope sprung up in his mind, when it seemed that the same thought had also occurred to the bear, for he began to move down toward the shore end of the log upon which Balser was standing.

Slowly came the bear until he reached the end of the log, which for a moment he examined suspiciously, and then, to Balser's great alarm, cautiously stepped out upon it and began to walk toward him.

Balser thought of the folks at home, and, above all, of his baby sister; and when he felt that he should never see them again, and that they would in all probability never know of his fate, he began to grow heavy-hearted and was almost paralyzed with fear.

On came the bear, putting one great paw in front of the other, and watching Balser intently with his little black eyes. His tongue hung out, and his great red mouth was open to its widest, showing the sharp, long, glittering teeth that would soon be feasting on a first-class boy dinner.

When the bear got within a few feet of Balser—so close he could almost feel the animal's hot breath as it slowly approached—the boy grew desperate with fear, and struck at the bear with the only weapon he had—his string of fish.

Now, bears love fish and blackberries above all other food; so when Balser's string of fish struck the bear in the mouth, he grabbed at them, and in doing so lost his foothold on the slippery log and fell into the water with a great splash and plunge.

This was Balser's chance for life, so he flung the fish to the bear, and ran for the bank with a speed worthy of the cause.

When he reached the bank his self-confidence returned, and he remembered all the things he had said he would do if he should meet a bear.

The bear had caught the fish, and again had climbed upon the log, where he was deliberately devouring them.

This was Little Balser's chance for death—to the bear. Quickly snatching up the gun, he rested it in the fork of a small tree nearby, took deliberate aim at the bear, which was not five yards away, and shot him through the heart. The bear dropped into the water dead, and floated downstream a little way, where he lodged at a ripple a short distance below.

Balser, after he had killed the bear, became more frightened than he had been at any time during the adventure, and ran home screaming. That afternoon his father went to the scene of battle and took the bear out of the water. It was very fat and large, and weighed, so Mr. Brent said, over six hundred pounds.

Balser was firmly of the opinion that he himself was also very fat and large, and weighed at least as much as the bear. He was certainly entitled to feel "big"; for he had got himself out of an ugly scrape in a brave, manly, cool-headed manner, and had achieved a victory of which a man might have been proud.

The news of Balser's adventure soon spread among the neighbors and he became quite a hero; for the bear he had killed was one of the largest that had ever been seen in that neighborhood, and, besides the gallons of rich bear oil it yielded, there were three or four hundred pounds of bear meat; and no other food is more strengthening for winter diet.

There was also the soft, furry skin, which Balser's mother tanned, and with it made a coverlid for Balser's bed, under which he and his little brother lay many a cold night, cozy and "snug as a bug in a rug."

HIGH WATER IN ARKANSAS!

by Charles J. Finger

Perhaps you heard Tad North's voice over the radio a short time ago. The program ended suddenly, you remember. He had been presented with a medal because of the part he played in the flood. Then someone asked him to talk into the microphone and tell what happened.

"But I didn't do anything," he said. "It just all came about like it did."

No persuasion could get him to say more, to be photographed, to be interviewed, or to regard himself as a hero. There he was, a freckled, healthy, straight-limbed boy of thirteen, in faded blue overalls. He took the medal shyly, thanked the giver, said those few words into the microphone, and then withdrew. Some few knew that the affair had to do with the Arkansas River flood, but no one, not even the local newspaper, got it exactly right.

This is how it was.

Proctor K. North, Tad's father, owned the ferryboat that went back and forth between Proctor's Landing and the other side. It was not much of a craft to look at, being little more than a roughly made platform built on two flatboats, and just large enough to take a couple of Model T Fords if they were parked close, and carefully. It was propelled by a little gasoline engine on a very small flatboat lashed alongside. Except when "school kept" (and it kept for only twelve weeks a year in that district) Tad ran the engine. He took great pride in it and had run it, off and on, since he was nine. That makes four years' experience. His father, Proctor K., was captain as well as owner, steersman, fare-collector, also comforter for nervous tourists. And tourists often were nervous when they saw the steep clay bank, the ramshackle ferry, the rickety gangway, the swift river, and the road up the levee on the other side which had two hairpin turns.

"Is it safe?" some of them would ask.

"Safe as a hornet's nest," Proctor K. would assure them. "Why, it's been on the job ever since I came from the war in France, and it's like to be here when me and you isn't." Then, with his mind on business, he would say, with rough hand extended for the money, "Two bits for the car, and a dime for every passenger. Forty cents if you come back. We don't give no tickets, but we'll remember your face all right."

Proctor K. had made that speech so often, that Tad, who had seen no other ferry except that up at Cuming's Crossing (which was almost a twin), wondered if ferry-owners in places like New York, and Seattle, and Norfolk had to assure doubtful passengers.

Well, last spring it was high water in Arkansas. On the fourth day people began to call it flood stage, with more coming, and the ferry business was down to nothing. The lower branches of the willows along the river banks were burdened with floating sticks, corn stalks, and odds and ends. All the morning, snags had been drifting down; once a haystack, then a hen coop with two doubtful hens for sailors, then a dead pig, then a mile-long tangle of corn stalks. Hourly the river rose, became yellower and yellower, noisier, angrier, wider. About nine o'clock, Proctor K. said, "I guess we'll call it a day, Tad, and lay up."

"Meanin' it's dangerous?" asked Tad.

"Not what you'd call plumb dangerous, Tad, only the way I look at things is that a pocketful of caution is worth more'n a hundred sacks of take-a-chance. What isn't wisdom is danger, always."

Tad nodded, considered, then asked, "What about Sim's delivery truck, the bread and all that?"

Proctor K. looked at the racing clouds, looked down river and up river, then said, "Why, *if* he comes, and the roads can't be none too good considerin', it'll be within the next hour. Of course we'll take him over. If he doesn't come by then, why, folks'll have to bake fer themselves like they did when I was a boy. But the roads'll be like pancake batter if I know mutton from goat."

But in spite of the worst kind of roads, Sim's delivery truck was no more than twenty minutes late, and, as usual, Sim was cheerful. His Scottie, Susie, was as cheerful as her master and announced her coming with joyous barks. As soon as the truck was aboard, she capered about the deck and barked at the water in a frenzy of enthusiasm.

"Maybe I ought to tie her up for once, she's that excited," said Sim, doubtfully. "Dogs, they know when anything's out of the usual quicker'n some men. Why, she's been worked up all mornin' since we took on some groceries for Bernses what he phoned over for just a little afore the 'phone went out. Dogs, they know things."

Sim went across the gangway to lend a hand to Proctor K., who was preparing to cast off the line. Tad, testing his engine, thought it would be a pity to tie Susie, seeing how she enjoyed everything.

Then things happened. A rabbit appeared on the bank. Susie gave a sharp hunting cry, scampered across the gangway and started up the bank in chase. Tad looked up to see the dog silhouetted against the sky on the top of the levee, heard Sim say, "Dag gum it! I knew I ought to have tied her. Wait a bit! I'll be back!" Then Sim went running up the bank and Proctor K., after taking a half-hitch round the post to hold the ferryboat, followed.

That was the moment when the second thing happened. No one saw it.

Down stream, not floating nor even in sight, because it had long been water-logged, came rolling the stump of a tree. Now and then one of its roots came above water, vicious looking hooked roots they were, ready to do mischief. One of them reaching high, caught at the rope and dragged it under water at the moment when the end of the tree trunk struck the ferryboat and drove it sideways. Feeling the shock, Tad seized an oar to prevent being driven against the bank. At the same moment he saw the post dragged out of the soft earth and start riverwards.

Almost before he realized what had happened, twenty feet of

yellow water separated ferryboat from river bank. Tad saw Sim on the bank with Susie under his arm, saw Proctor K. at the water's edge, saw the willows sliding strangely northwards and Sim and Proctor K. sliding with them. Then he knew he was adrift, and panic seized him. But his panic was for a moment only. In a trice he had his engine going, but almost immediately he knew how useless it was.

"What isn't wisdom is danger," ran through his mind. So he stopped the motor. He must not waste gasoline which might come in useful, though he could not tell how or when. The ferryboat was in the grip of the current and already sweeping round Union Point and into one of the many horseshoe-shaped lakes between Proctor's Crossing and the place where the Arkansas River joined the Mississippi.

"Tad, you've got to think straight," he told himself.

He got on the ferryboat, walked to the rope which was trailing in the river, hauled it in and coiled it ready for use. He examined the chocks under the tires of the delivery truck to make sure the auto would ride well, for if that rolled or slid—! He shook his head as he thought of possibilities. Next he took his ragged coat and covered the engine. Tad felt that if he got wet it would do no harm, but the engine was another matter. Then, believing all in order, he climbed to the roof of the delivery truck to take observations.

What he saw was a world strange, yet familiar—strange when he looked at things near, familiar when he looked far off. The Arkansas River was a band of tossing water, ugly yellow, roaring, with leaping waves where the swift current broke on snags which were held fast on mud banks. If the ferryboat struck one of those—! It was like a nightmare to think of what might be, and like a pleasant dream to look at the sun shining brightly, to hear a thousand birds chattering. Then he saw the Mason place, the house now on a little island; washing hanging out to dry on another little island, only the barn roof above water.

It was then, for the first time, that he realized he was not alone on that flooded river. Ahead was a shantyboat, a sort of little Noah's ark, one of those rough-made floating houses in which people live who fish for mussels, gathering shells to sell to button factories. Tad felt happy enough to sing when he thought that there might be a man, or men on board; but the hope waned when, drawing nearer, he saw a Negro woman waving a white cloth, and three children seated on the roof.

Then Tad became breathless. Ahead, in the line the shantyboat would take, was a long and wicked looking wave which told its tale of jammed snags. Into that tangle the ark with its four passengers must certainly drift. There was no escape. Tad knew what would happen, how the shantyboat would catch broadside on, how it would tilt, how the water piling against it would pour in, how the boat would founder, how the disaster would mean a swift end for woman and children. All that came to him in a few moments. Then Tad became active.

Down he ran to his engine and started it. Back he ran to the steering oar and tugged to change the course, no matter how slightly, so that the drift of the ferryboat would be near the shantyboat. If the engine held out, if no swirl swept the ferry back into midstream, and, most important, if the woman knew what to do and did it at the right moment when he threw the rope, there might be a chance. There were many "ifs."

"Catch! Make fast!" shouted Tad as he flung the rope. He saw the woman bend forward to catch the flying rope, saw the three frightened children on the roof, heard his little engine chugging bravely, saw how the woman, used to river ways, caught the rope, took a swift turn round the bollard post, and he knew the trick was done.

Getting the ark alongside, and holding it there while the woman and children got on board, was fairly easy. Then Tad shut his engine down, and there were explanations. Also there were rejoicings when Tad, wondering if it was honest to do so, opened the door of Sim's delivery truck and took out bread and doughnuts for the children. They stuffed rather than ate, so ravenous they were.

"Lawdy! Lawdy! Two days they got never a bite," said the mother. Then she turned to Tad and asked, "Is you all alone on this rescue boat?"

So Tad had to explain. "This isn't a rescue boat," he said. "I'm adrift like you all. An accident."

"Lawdy! Lawdy! Why, it's no accident at all, mister captain." She persisted in giving him that title. "Why, don't you see it's the Lawd's work? He sent that rabbit. He sent that dog. He sent you down the river to us."

She munched some bread herself, regarding the swift moving panorama of trees and drift and distant highlands.

"He done arranged it all, captain. Two bends in the river and it's Cypress Bend where I was in the high water in '32. Good Lawd's sendin' us all there."

And what with the whirling waters, racing bayous and islands of slush, they were in sight of Cypress Island when Tad thought they were still miles away. They saw four shanties, dots that were men and women, a raging river at the cut-off and white breakers ahead. If the little engine could force the ferryboat into still water behind the island, there was hope. The next minute or two meant quick work. Tad sent Nancy to the ferry steering oar, opened the rear door of the delivery truck and bundled the children in where they would be safe, ran to his boat alongside and started the engine. Immediately they were in wild water and racing like an express train, the world full of noise.

Once the ferryboat pivoted on a hidden snag and the shantyboat tore loose and went down stream on its side. Once the engine fluttered, as if it had done its best and, wearied, could do no more. But they won. The ferryboat slid into calmer water in the lee of the island, and into the water, waist deep, ran some of the marooned islanders. They laid hands on the ferryboat and pulled it inshore, while the engine chug-chugged bravely.

"You made it," said one of the men, a tall, bronzed fellow.

"More mouths to fill and nothin' much to give 'em," said another, laughing.

"I tell you the Lawd knows His business and don't do it half way," declared Nancy, and pointed to the stores in the delivery wagon.

The marooned share-croppers were willing to believe that a little later when, with a blazing fire for comfort, all of them were feasting on Sim's bread and doughnuts, sardines and canned salmon, pork and beans, bacon, condensed milk, cheese, crackers, and much more. And when one of the share-croppers wondered who was going to repay Sim, Nancy relieved her own mind, even if she did not relieve Tad's by saying again, "The Lawd don't do things half way! It'll come out right." And as it turned out, Nancy was a good prophet.

All that was the part of the adventure which few people knew, except those on the rescue boat sent down from Helena, which arrived five days later. We, on that relief steamboat, expected to find famished people on Cypress Bend. Instead, there were fifteen high-hearted men, women and children, well fed and comfortable, a brave flag fluttering on a newly erected flagpole, and things in general wearing the air of a picnic rather than flood disaster.

When the relief supervisor and the Memphis newspaper man got Tad in a corner and said things about his good work, talking about a medal, Tad said exactly what he said a week later when they pushed him to the microphone:

"But I didn't do anything. It just all came about like it did."

KINTU

by Elizabeth Enright

Kintu was a little black boy who lived in Africa. He lived with his father and mother and his five brothers and sisters in a big mud hut with a straw roof, shaped like a beehive. The beehive in which Kintu lived was the largest of a great group of beehives in the middle of the jungle, for Kintu's father, Kitomba, was the chief of his tribe, and therefore a very important person.

Kintu was his eldest son, which meant that he, too, would one day be a chief.

He had two brothers and three sisters to play with. There was Timbo, who could throw a spear farther than Kintu could, although he was a year younger. And there were Kakopa and Kaku, who were twins and who looked so much alike that Kakopa had to wear a ring in her nose so that people could tell which was which. Then there was Wapi, who was fat, and rather bowlegged and always eating something. And last of all there was Nomba, who was the baby and who spent most of her time in a little hammock which hung from her mother's shoulders.

They were very busy children; their days were filled with lessons—most exciting ones. Kintu had more of these than anyone else, because he was the eldest son and to be a chief you must know many things.

You must know, for instance, how to throw a spear faultlessly, how to shoot an arrow perfectly; and every day Kintu practiced for hours, hurling his spear and shooting his arrows at a red circle painted on the trunk of a baobab tree.

He learned how to play the drums, and with the palms of his hands make them talk the drum language which in Africa is the way that messages are sent from village to village.

"Look out, look out," say the drums, beating deeply, "an enemy tribe is coming down the river"; or "Look out, look out, an angry storm approaches from the east!" Usually they send warning messages but sometimes they only converse together.

Kintu would sit with his drum (n'goma) before him, his hands thumping on the tightly stretched skin, and for miles around the jungle murmured with the sounds he made.

A chief's son must be able to dance to the drums as well as to play them. Kintu learned devil dances and fever dances, dances of triumph, dances to bring good hunting, or fine weather, or the rain, and all of them were different. Kintu liked the devil dances best because when he did them, he wore a magnificent headdress made of crimson feathers and telephone wire. (His father considered the telephone wire a great bargain; he had got it from a white trader who had passed that way several years before, and he had only given four leopard skins and a pair of elephant's tusks in exchange for a big coil of it. They used it for all sorts of things: Kintu's mother wove it into their headdresses, and made baskets out of it; it even held their roof together in places.)

The devil dances took longer than any of the others, and were more interesting because there was a great deal of leaping and shouting to them. The drumbeats grew louder and louder till your ears rang with the sound of them, and you kept on dancing till you fell exhausted in the dust, and had to be taken home.

Kintu learned many other things, too. He was taught how to cure the hides of wild animals, and how to make arrowheads and spearheads of metal and stone. He learned how to kindle a fire with two sticks, how to set a trap, how to climb trees almost as fast as a monkey. He learned which berries were poisonous, and which ones were the best cure for snakebite.

Timbo and Wapi had lessons much the same as his own, but Kakopa and Kaku learned other things; they made pottery and cooked and wove mats of grass and palm leaves. They had their dances, too. All the children were dressed alike in little colored skirts except for Nomba who was attired simply in a bracelet and a head necklace. All of them had brass ornaments on their ankles and around their necks and would have felt strange without the quiet jingling which accompanied their walking.

Every day the children awoke at the very first light of dawn, and rising from the hard earth which was the only bed they had, shook themselves like little dogs and walked straight out of the hut to work or play as they pleased. Kintu took up his spear and practiced throwing it. Kakopa and Kaku wove their mats; and Timbo and Wapi played leapfrog or pretended to be hunters stalking a panther in the jungle. Nomba was too fat and too young to do anything but lie in the sun, chewing a piece of sugar cane.

In the middle of the morning, their mother made a fire by rubbing two sticks together till a spark caught the leaves and kindling on the flat stone which was her fireplace. Then in a great earthenware pot she cooked their breakfast—corn and manioc root and eggs (and sometimes chicken).

When it was done she called them, and they all sat down around the big pot and dipped into it with their fingers. Wapi usually managed to get the most, and often burned himself because he never could bear to wait for things to cool.

Their only other meal was in the evening and was usually exactly the same as the first; but sometimes, as a special treat, their mother made them a delicious pudding of corn flour and palm oil and dried white caterpillars.

After supper the people of the village would gather around a fire and talk or sing. The men spoke of hunting, and the oldest ones had stories to tell of the times when lions were fiercer and elephants bigger than any found nowadays. Kintu, sitting beside his father, would shiver and try not to listen, because though nobody knew it, he was afraid of the jungle.

Now living in a jungle is very much like living next door to the zoo, except that the animals are not in cages, which makes quite a difference. Sometimes at night Kintu would lie awake and listen to the strange sounds made by wild creatures in the jungle, and be very afraid.

There was an insect which ticked all night long like a little watch, and an insect which made a loud noise, like an alarm clock. There were the excited voices of suddenly awakened monkeys, and the croaking of big frogs which sounded like old men talking together in deep hoarse voices. There were panthers and leopards whose snarls were like the sound of thick canvas being torn. And there were the grunts of hippopotami who left the river and walked on land at night. There were noises made by nightjars and cicadas, and all the other hundreds of creatures who preferred to do their talking after dark.

Kintu would lie on his hard earthen bed and shake with fright, because he knew that when he was older his father would expect him to hunt in the jungle and to know it as well as he knew his own village. It would never do for a chief's son to be afraid!

It worried Kintu badly, and finally he decided to go and see the witch doctor and ask him for a spell to make him braver.

So one morning, after breakfast, he stole away from his brothers and sisters and playmates, and all by himself walked to the witch doctor's hut.

It was set apart from the rest of the village, and on either side of the door were little idols carved of black wood. One had a very ugly, cross face, and one grinned from ear to ear showing a double row of square, ivory teeth. Kintu bowed and raised his spear to each of them, then he entered the hut and came face to face with the witch doctor.

The witch doctor was very old and very wise, and he wore a derby hat, which he had got from the same trader who brought the telephone wire. From his great height he looked down at Kintu, without smiling, and Kintu would have shaken in his shoes if he had any to shake in.

"Chief's son," said the witch doctor, "why have you come to see me?"

"Witch doctor," began Kintu bravely, "I am in great trouble. I am afraid of the jungle!" He paused, and glanced up to see if the witch doctor looked disapproving, but there was no change in the old man's expression so he continued. "Yes, I'm afraid of it. All of it. Its beasts, its noises and its huge trees. I don't even like the way it smells. How can I ever be a great chief like my father when I am such a coward?"

He hung his head for he was very much ashamed.

"This is bad!" said the witch doctor. "I must think." And he sat down on the floor, pulled his derby hat over his nose and thought. Kintu leaned against the wall and watched him almost without breathing, he was so terribly excited.

After several minutes (long ones, they seemed) the witch doctor stood up, pushing back his hat. Still without smiling he looked down at Kintu.

"Chief's son," he said, "I believe I have a cure for you."

He leaned down, took something out of a red earthenware bowl, and put it into Kintu's little black hand.

"Take this," he said, "and tomorrow, when the sun is at its highest walk three hundred paces into the jungle towards the east. After you have walked for three hundred paces, plant this charm at the foot of the first baobab tree you find; then, when you have buried it, say these words——" (But what the words were I cannot tell you for they were black magic, and a secret.)

"In the jungle? All by myself?" asked Kintu in a timid voice.

"All by yourself, chief's son," said the witch doctor firmly.

Kintu walked slowly home. Once he stopped and opened his hand to see what the charm was like; it was nothing but the dry stone of a fruit and didn't look as though it had much magic in it; but the witch doctor had said it had, and Kintu believed him.

That evening he couldn't eat his supper and his mother was worried about him.

"You have been eating between meals again," she said. "When *will* you learn to leave that monkey-bread tree alone?"

But Kintu only sighed, and said nothing. Very late that night he lay awake and listened to the jungle sounds which seemed louder and more terrifying than ever. He thought the cicadas were chanting a jeering song: "Afraid, afraid, afraid," they cried, over and over again.

"Perhaps after tomorrow you'll be singing another song," whispered Kintu into the darkness; and feeling a little more cheerful, he went to sleep.

The next day dawned bright and very hot; and Kintu went through his duties in a daze.

When, soon after their morning meal, the sun had ridden to its highest point, and everybody else had gone to sleep in the shade, Kintu picked up his spear (ekonga), and holding the charm in his other hand, tiptoed through the drowsy village and into the jungle.

It was hot and steamy under the great trees; it smelled like the inside of a greenhouse, warm and damp. Everywhere the silk cotton trees raised their great trunks; and high, high overhead a whole, separate airy world existed: parrots called in cross voices, a thousand birds sang different songs, and monkeys leapt nimbly along the boughs, chattering and scolding.

Counting all the time, and forgetting to be afraid, Kintu looked up and stubbed his toe badly on a root. By this time he had walked his first hundred paces and was beginning his second hundred. The farther he walked the wilder the jungle grew, and he had to beat back the undergrowth and tear apart the vines which hung, covered with flowers, from every tree.

Once he surprised a group of little brown monkeys who were sitting sociably on the ground in a circle, eating berries. They simply leapt up the trunk of a palm tree when they saw him, and sat high in the leaves telling him what they thought of him till long after he had passed.

Great moths flew blindly into his face; and once he came upon a hibiscus bush so beautiful, with its flaming red flowers, that he stopped and stared at it.

All this time he had forgotten about being afraid, but now as he came to the middle of his last hundred paces the shadows seemed suddenly darker, and the trees taller than before, and he found himself counting more and more rapidly.

"Two hundred and eighty," said Kintu, leaping over a log, "two hundred and eighty-one—eighty-two—eighty-three . . ." On his right something gave a squeal and plunged into the bushes.

"Eighty-four, eighty-five," shouted Kintu in a loud, bold voice (he was running now), "eighty-six, eighty-seven, eighty-eight, eighty-nine . . ."

At last the three hundred paces were behind him, and he began to look about for a baobab tree.

There were silk cotton trees, and gum trees, and pandanus trees, and borassus trees, and ebony trees, and rubber trees, and mahogany trees, and Kakula trees; but there was not a single baobab tree in sight!

Kintu sighed; his heart was beating like a tom-tom and the palms of his hands felt cold and damp; but he had come this far and he simply couldn't turn back till he had buried the magic fruit pit.

So he hunted and he hunted, and went farther and farther into the jungle, and at last he came upon an enormous baobab tree standing all by itself in a clearing.

He felt safer somehow now that he had found it, and with relief he knelt among its great roots and scooped out a hole in the ground with the head of his spear; he buried the charm and covered it with earth. After that, he said the words of black magic which the witch doctor had taught him.

Then he picked up his spear and started back.

It had taken him a long time to find the baobab tree and by now it was the middle of the afternoon; the shadows were growing longer.

A crowd of little gnats circled around his head as he walked, buzzing in high thin voices till his ears rang and he felt dizzy. He kept waving his spear at them to drive them away, but they didn't mind it in the least and came back again as soon as he stopped.

On and on stumbled Kintu, among flowers, and tendrils, and great leaves. He realized that he had lost his way, and that so far the magic had not worked, because he felt more frightened than ever.

He thought about his family all safe together in the village, and wondered when they would miss him and begin to look for him. He thought about the stories told by the old hunters of fierce lions who sometimes come into the jungle at night, of hyenas whose cry is like the laughter of a devil-god, of great elephants with tusks of ivory who can uproot small trees with their trunks. He thought about the buried fruit pit and the magic words, and they seemed small protection against the jungle and its many dangers. He wished that he had never gone to see the witch doctor at all, and that he had allowed himself to be a coward in peace.

Kintu began to cry quietly, because he was sure that he would never see his family again, and he was terribly afraid. He stopped walking and stood very still among great ferns like giant feather dusters: it seemed foolish to go on when whatever direction he took was bound to be the wrong one.

It was growing darker now, and already the tree toads had begun their evening conversation. "Wack-a-wack-a-wack," they cried in harsh voices from every tree. The gnats, fortunately, had got tired of Kintu's waving spear and had all gone off together to find some other creature to torment; so except for the remarks of the tree toads, and the occasional cry of a bird, it seemed very still.

Then, all at once, quite near, he heard a sound like that of thick canvas being torn in two. The snarl of a leopard!

It no longer seemed useless to go on; in fact, it seemed most necessary to go somewhere very quickly: and Kintu, spear in hand, began to run faster than he had ever run before.

Ahead of him, six little monkeys who had also heard the dangerous sound, went leaping and skipping along the ground at great speed. Kintu, feeling somehow that they were his friends, followed them; and when they came to a huge tree hung with creepers which the monkeys swarmed neatly up, like little sailors climbing up a rigging, he went right after them as fast as he could go.

Up and up he struggled, with his spear between his strong teeth, and his little black fingers and toes curling around the thick vine almost as cleverly as the monkeys' did. The creeper looped itself over one of the lower branches and returned to earth on the other side, so Kintu began climbing up the boughs; stretch, pull, swing! Stretch, pull, swing!—till he had nearly reached the top of the tree, and then he sat down on a huge limb with his shoulder against the broad trunk, and his spear across his knees. His heart was thumping like anything and he was out of breath, but he felt slightly safer.

The six little monkeys, who didn't seem to mind him at all, sat on a branch just above him, and said things very fast in monkey language about leopards. Kintu wished that he could understand them and join in their conversation; he wanted to ask them if leopards were any good at climbing trees. Still, even if he couldn't speak to them, it was a comfort just to have them there, and he hoped they wouldn't go away.

All about him stretched the strange leaves and branches of jungle trees, and below him he saw the great ferns and flowers through which he had beaten his way. Overhead the sky was a darker blue, with a little purple in it, and already there was a star, pale and cold, shining just over the place where the sun had set.

The air was filled with queer smells. A clump of yellow orchids bloomed in a deserted bird's nest several feet below him and gave off a perfume so strong and heavy that he grew tired of it very soon. There were big red berries on a tree nearby that had an odor rather like cough medicine; and you've been in the monkey house at the zoo, haven't you? So you know how the monkeys smelled.

It was really twilight now; and Kintu saw the bright busy lights of fireflies everywhere. Huge mosquitoes came whining out of the shadows; cicadas sang at the tops of their voices, and the tree toads almost screamed at each other. An evening wind stirred for a moment in the feathery treetops and moved the branch above Kintu where the monkeys were dozing in a row. It woke them up, and they chattered anxiously at each other for a minute. But they soon went back to sleep; and Kintu, feeling like the loneliest person on earth, continued to stare at the sparkling patterns made by fireflies against the darkness.

Presently the moon rose, huge and lopsided, above the world; each leaf glittered in its light, and the brass bracelets on Kintu's ankle looked as if they were made of purest gold.

The night was full of sounds: rustling sounds and scratchings and scamperings; squeaks and grunts in the darkness below; the singing of the night birds in the leaves above.

Then Kintu heard another sound—a new one. He heard the heavy, soft footsteps of an enormous creature stepping quietly; the snapping of shrubs and the squelching sound of wet earth under huge feet. He leaned forward and peered still more intently into the blackness below him. A tremendous shape darker than the shadows from which it came, moved gently and ponderously towards the tree where he was hidden. Bigger than a house, it looked; almost as big as a mountain, Kintu thought. Slowly, slowly the Thing approached; then paused directly below him. Suddenly there was a faint sound of scraping, and the tree began to quiver as though in an earthquake; the monkeys jabbered nervously, and Kintu knew that an elephant, the largest of all wild creatures, was scratching his back on a branch.

Then slowly, as before, the great beast went on its way; the noise of snapping twigs and heavy tread grew fainter, and it was seen no more.

Hours passed; the moon was high in the sky; and Kintu, too tired to think of fear any longer, settled himself against the tree trunk and slept with the monkeys.

He must have slept a long time, because when the shrill, excited voices of the monkeys woke him, he saw that the moon had set, and the world was as black as the inside of a pocket.

He looked down wondering what was the matter. At first he saw nothing but the roaming lights of the fireflies. And then a chill of fear ran up the calves of his legs and along his spine to the nape of his neck; for below him he saw two small lights, side by side, which did not move; two small lights which he knew were the eyes of an animal watching him.

Squealing and scolding, the monkeys bounded along the branches, dived into the boughs of another tree and were gone.

Kintu faced real danger, alone.

Once more he heard the low snarl which had so frightened him earlier in the evening. The leopard had found him, after all.

The two lights moved a little; Kintu knew that the animal was crouching, making sure of the distance before he sprang.

Then the eyes leapt forward; there was the swish of a heavy body flying through the air, the impact of it against the tree, and the sound of sharp claws tearing wood.

Determinedly, the leopard climbed the tree towards Kintu.

It was useless to be frightened now. Something would have to be done, and quickly too.

Swiftly and quietly Kintu stood up on the branch. He held on to the trunk with his left hand, and in his right he raised the spear high above his shoulder.

He could hardly see the dark shape of the animal climbing towards him, but he would have to take a chance.

"Now or never," said Kintu in a small voice, and hurled the spear.

Then there was a grunt and the thud of a soft, heavy weight falling upon the earth. After that there were no more sounds at all: and Kintu knew that the leopard would not bother him again. Not this one, anyway.

Trembling all over, but almost shouting with triumph, he climbed, feeling his way, a little higher in the tree. How glad he was, now, that his father had made him practice throwing the spear hour after hour, day after day.

"I certainly won't sleep again," said Kintu; and slept.

The next time he woke up it was morning. Long pale fingers of early sunlight slanted through the leaves. Every bird was singing as though it were necessary to sing louder than any other bird. The world was golden and fresh and drenched with dew.

Kintu stretched his stiff arms and legs, and yawned with a great noise. He looked for his spear and wondered for a moment if he had dropped it. Then he remembered about the leopard.

Quickly he climbed down the branches and slid along the creepers to the ground.

There, stretched at the foot of the tree, lay the leopard, so beautiful with its tawny dark-spotted fur that Kintu was sorry he had killed it. But when he looked closer and saw the cruel curling white teeth, and the glittering claws half hidden in the soft paws, he was sorry no longer.

"It is better to kill than to be killed," said Kintu wisely; and pulling his spear from the leopard's hide, he started off once more to find his village.

It was a beautiful morning! Wet leaves glittered in the sun like leaves of gold. Great drops of dew fell on his head; and there was a little pool in the cup of every flower.

Feeling thirsty, he tipped a big leaf down to his open mouth, and water poured into it as if from a pitcher.

He was hungry, too, and stopped for a minute to pull some purple berries from a vine. Nothing had ever tasted so delicious.

He felt like a king as he strode through the jungle, brandishing his spear and singing: "I am not afraid!"

The wild creatures, watching him, knew that this was true.

"He is not afraid," screamed the gray parrots in the treetops. "He is not afraid," sang all the birds together. "He is not afraid, he is not afraid," chattered the noisy monkeys; and great serpents, sunning themselves on branches, watched him through the leaves, and said in slow voices, "He is not afraid."

The leopards saw him, too, and the black panther with golden eyes, hidden behind a screen of flowers. "No, he is not afraid," they said, and turned away into the shadows feeling fear themselves.

Never had Kintu been so happy; he was filled with hope, and was sure that he would find his village, and that everything would be all right after all. He listened with joy to all the shrieking, babbling, singing, chattering noises of the early morning jungle. He liked its noises. He loved the way it smelled.

Then something made him stop, quite still, in his tracks. He held his breath, and listened with ears which had been trained to sharpness by the jungle, to another sound. Far, far to the right of him, there was a faint throbbing in the air. Yes! There could be no doubt about it; it was the beating of drums that he heard and this is what they were saying:

"Chief Kitomba's eldest son has disappeared. Has he been seen? Has he been seen?"

And then, still farther away, to his left, the drums of another village replied, "Chief Kitomba's son has not been seen. Chief Kitomba's son has not been seen."

Kintu's heart skipped a beat. The drums which had spoken first were the drums of his village, he knew. If he turned to the right and followed their sound he would surely find his way home.

He couldn't go fast enough! He ran; and skipped over creepers and leapt high in the air, twirling his spear, and yelling for joy. But he did not forget to stop now and then and make a scratch on the bark of a tree with his spearhead. When he got back to the village he would ask some of the men to get the leopard for him. And he wanted them to be sure and find it.

The jungle was loud with the sound of drumbeats now. All the villages for miles around were answering the message from his village, and relaying it to others still farther away.

It grew very hot; yellow mist rose from the damp ground. The gnats came after him in swarms; but he didn't care: the world was beautiful and exciting and full of adventures, and he was no longer afraid.

Then he saw the hibiscus bush with its scarlet flowers, the very same one that he had noticed the day before; and he knew that he was near his home! He broke one of the bright blossoms from its stem and stuck it behind his ear as a badge of triumph.

There was a shout behind him suddenly, and turning he saw his father running towards him between the trees.

"Father!" cried Kintu, throwing his spear to the ground and leaping into Chief Kitomba's arms.

"I was lost! I spent the night in a tree, I saw an elephant, I killed a wicked n'gwe, and I'm not afraid," said Kintu all in one breath.

"You are safe, my son; you are not hurt?" asked Chief Kitomba anxiously.

"No, but I am very, *very* hungry," answered Kintu.

His mother was so glad to see him that she cooked him the special pudding which is made of corn flour and palm oil and dried white caterpillars. Then she stood over him and watched to see that he ate it all.

His brothers and sisters sat around him in a circle, each of their mouths hanging open an inch, and listened to the story of his night in the jungle. He had to tell it three times.

"Let us play a game about it," said Wapi to Timbo; "you can be the leopard and I will be Kintu in the tree."

"No, indeed," said Timbo; "you forget that I'm the eldest. *I* will be Kintu, and *you* can be the leopard!"

All the people of the village were so glad that Kintu had returned and was unharmed, that Chief Kitomba said, "Light the bonfires; bring out the big n'gomas; we will have a jubilee, as soon as the leopard's brought back to the village."

"A jubilee!" screamed everybody in delight, and clapped their hands and ran to fetch wood for the bonfires. Half a dozen men followed Kintu's markings to the place where the slain leopard lay beneath a tall tree. Cutting a slim strong sapling with their knives they lashed the heavy animal to it and, raising the burden to their strong right shoulders, walked singing and laughing back to the village. When they had reached it they went at once to the hut of Kintu's father, and set the leopard down beside the door. Everybody came to look at it, and said what a big one it was, and what a fine coat it had, and how wicked and dangerous it must have been when it was alive.

Kintu could feel happiness and pride swelling inside of his chest like a big balloon. His ribs felt almost too narrow to hold it. He looked downwards and drew a circle in the dust with his big toe.

"Now we will celebrate," said Chief Kitomba.

Kintu went into the hut and put on his favorite headdress of crimson feathers and telephone wire, for he felt that this was a very special occasion. Then he walked to the central clearing in the village where all the tribe was gathered.

The fires had been lighted, and were burning like five great towers of flame and smoke, soaring and snapping. Half a dozen of the bravest warriors in the village stood behind the big drums, waiting to play them.

"Come here, my son," said Chief Kitomba, and Kintu went to him. Around his neck his father fastened a necklace made of leopard's teeth; and around his waist he tied a leopard's skin so that the tail hung down behind just as it should.

"Now dance," said Chief Kitomba, and Kintu for the first time in his life was allowed to do the Dance of the Victorious Hunter; for had he not killed the leopard, that creature feared and hated by all jungle dwellers, men and beast alike?

"Boom. Boom. Boom-a-diddy-boom!" sang the drums, and Kintu's feet moved swiftly through the dust, hopping and leaping. Around him all the people of the village clapped their hands and stamped in time to the music.

Kintu finished his dance with a whoop and a yell. And then everybody danced!

Drums boomed, brass anklets jingled, spears clashed together, dry gourds were shaken like rattles, people sang, monkeys screamed in the thickets. Never had there been such a loud and joyful jubilee in the history of the village!

It went on till very late at night. They brought out delicious things to drink, too, in tall black jars.

Long after it was dark the fires still burned high, and the village was filled with flickering lights and dark moving shadows.

Everyone was happy, and Kintu was the happiest of all, for his father had said to him, "I am well pleased with you, my son; you will be a good chief to our people when I am gone. Only fear can make a strong man weak, and you have conquered that."

At last, when they had all grown tired of dancing and had eaten too much, they sat down around one of the dying bonfires and asked Kintu to tell them his story.

He told them about climbing the tree after the monkeys and about the elephant who had come unsuspectingly so near to him; he told them all about the leopard. But he did not tell them why he had gone into the jungle in the first place or about the magic charm; that was a secret between the witch doctor and himself and the baobab tree.

Finally, when he was sure that he couldn't stay awake more than two minutes longer, Kintu stood up and said goodnight to all his proud, well-fed relatives and friends. But before he went to his father's hut, he tiptoed through the shadowy village to the hut which was surrounded by little black idols. The witch doctor was leaning in his doorway.

"Well, chief's son," he said, and from his great height he looked down at Kintu without smiling. But this time Kintu was not timid in the least.

"Well, witch doctor," he said, "I am very grateful to you. I did everything you told me to, and then I got lost. I spent the night in the jungle among wild creatures; I even killed a leopard. And this morning when I woke up, I knew I wasn't frightened any more!"

The witch doctor didn't look very much impressed.

Kintu waited for him to speak. At last he nodded his head slowly up and down and said "Good." That was all, but Kintu felt that it was enough.

Turning, he left the witch doctor's hut and walked slowly

through the darkness. It was quieter, now. There were occasional bursts of laughter from groups of people, but the voices were subdued, and the fires had died into heaps of glowing coals.

Kintu entered his hut and removed the headdress of crimson feathers and telephone wire. Then he lay down on the earth against the wall. Above the voices and the laughter he heard the night sounds of the jungle. He heard the tree toads, and the monkeys and the insects which tick like little watches. Far, far away he heard a sound like that of thick canvas being torn in two. Kintu knew that another leopard roamed the jungle, terrifying all creatures. He reached out and patted the handle of his spear companionably.

But above all these noises he was aware of the song of the cicadas. No longer could he make the words "Afraid, afraid, afraid" fit their chanting. There were no words for it. The thousands of voices pulsed together like the sound of a heart beating and the longer Kintu listened to them the drowsier he became. And at last with his cheek pressed against the earth and with one hand on his spear he went to sleep.

HOW HORATIUS HELD THE BRIDGE

by Henry W. Lanier

The last of the Roman Kings was Tarquin the Proud. He came to the throne by murder, and held it by tyranny. After twenty-five years of misrule, the people revolted under the leadership of Tarquin's nephew, who had only escaped his father's and brother's fate by pretending to be half-witted and meekly accepting the name of Brutus (stupid). The tyrant was driven out.

Tarquin raised an army among the Tuscans and led it against Rome, but it was defeated, though his son and Brutus killed each other in battle. Again and again the deposed King tried to regain his throne.

At last he formed an alliance with Lars Porsena of Clusium, a powerful prince to the north of Rome, who took up the fugitive's cause as his own. When the Romans refused Porsena's demands to reinstate their former ruler, he warned them when and where he meant to attack, and gathered all his forces for the effort.

Word came of his approach. The people were filled with terror, for this was one of the foremost powers of Italy which was descending upon them. Moreover, the Tuscan ranks were swelled with their bitterest enemies: deserters and exiles, and all who envied their growing power; and they knew only too well what bloody Tarquin's course would be if he succeeded in his attempts.

But the consuls, Publicola and Lucretius, as if to show their disregard of the enemy, proceeded to build the new-walled city of Sigliura, and place within it a colony of seven hundred men.

This bravado had little effect upon Porsena, at least.

He assaulted the town, drove out the garrison, and sent them flying in disorder toward Rome. Nor did he give them any chance to recover, but followed so hard upon them that a panic seized the citizens. The gates must be kept open to admit their own people; but the foe was so close upon their heels that it looked as if this meant letting him in also. The walls of Rome they felt were impregnable against anybody; a victorious enemy actually within the gates was another matter.

Great was the confusion as the press of battle swayed to and fro by the Tiber's side. The Romans fought valiantly but they were outnumbered; and in spite of their utmost efforts they were being forced back upon the wooden bridge spanning the Tiber River.

The river was the main natural defense of the city on the west; once in possession of the Sublician bridge, an enemy had a direct entrance, so that the struggle for possession became more and more desperate.

At the critical instant, the consul Publicola sallied out of the gate with a chosen band. For a time his onslaught drove the Tuscans back. But before long he fell, desperately wounded; his followers carried him back out of the fight, and the pressure at the bridge head was renewed.

The other consul, Lucretius, attacked bravely also. He too fell wounded. With both leaders gone, the Romans lost heart and retreated before the fierce onslaughts. A dash of the invaders captured the Janiculum, and from thence the Tuscan host pressed triumphantly forward.

There was clearly but one chance left. The bridge must be destroyed. If they could break it down before Porsena's army could pass, "Father Tiber" would guard his chosen town. For the river was in flood and it would be a bold man who would even venture to try to cross it in the face of a hostile force.

All this was clear as day to those in command. What was not clear at all was how the Tuscans were to be held back even for the short time required to saw and hack through the bridge timbers on the city side. To be sure, it was a narrow passage, where a few men side by side could guard the way. But where were there any who would attempt such a foolhardy feat?

It looked like certain death. Even if one were warrior stout enough to defend himself from those fierce war-wolves thronging forward so eagerly, what would happen when the bridge fell behind him?

There was a moment's silence in the hurried council of war, as the menacing facts impressed themselves on every mind.

Then up stood one, Horatius. He was nephew to Horatius the consul, and came of that line which had made the name memorable in the tremendous combat between the Horatii and Curiatii in the reign of Tullius Hostilius. He bore his own record upon his face, for he had received in the wars such a wound between the eyes that at first glance he seemed to have but one great eye in his forehead. Hence he was Cyclops, the one-eyed, which had somehow been converted by the ignorant populace into Cocles.

He bade his disheartened comrades face the grim truth: the one chance for safety lay in facing the enemy.

"Let him who thinks to escape death by deserting his post reflect that if he flies, there will soon be more of the enemy in the Palatium and Capital than now are in the Janiculum.

"Besides, death comes to all: how can a man die better than in defending his home and gods?

"Do ye break down the bridge, by sword, by fire, or by any means whatever. What one man can do to hold back the foe, that will I do."

Like a lion among a frightened flock, he strode across to the first entrance to the bridge. Breasting the current of those whose backs were toward the enemy, he reached the narrow passage; and the exulting Tuscans paused in sheer surprise at the sight.

Two Romans there were who were inspired by his example. Spurius Lartius and Herminius, patricians both and proved warriors, rushed forward and took their places, one on his right hand, the other on his left.

The road to Rome was guarded. It was three men against an army. But they were three who were concerned only to purchase with their lives the minutes necessary to destroy the bridge behind them. And already their comrades, shamed into action by their devotion, were hacking desperately at the timbers.

The Tuscan warriors were not slow to accept the challenge. Their champions sprang forward from the serried ranks into the confined space. Warily the three met the onset. Swords and spears clashed upon their ready shields. Their own weapons flashed in the sunlight, then bit deep into their assailants, cleaving through armor and flesh.

One after another of the assailants went down and were dragged away to make room for a fresh attack. Battered, and covered with blood and sweat, Horatius and his supporters glared at each fresh adversary like some wild boar surrounded by baying hounds, awaiting the instant to strike a fatal blow.

Never a word spoke they, but strained their ears backward for the sound of axe and lever which came from the rear.

Maddened by the check and the sudden obstacle to the easy victory that had lain before them, the Tuscans attacked more furiously than ever. Bitter was the chagrin of Porsena and the traitor Sextus to see their doughtiest warriors laid low, their whole vast force held back by that thin wall of human courage.

A shout from behind made even the combatants turn. "It falls! It falls!" ran the cry from those who wrought so eagerly at destruction. "Back, Horatius! Back, Lartius! Back, Herminius!"

The leader of the three looked round. Coolly he bade his comrades to retreat. They darted back, and as they sped to safety the timbers cracked beneath their feet.

In a frenzy of rage the assailants hurled a perfect cloud of spears upon the solitary defender. Skilfully protecting himself with his shield, he defied them with taunts that bit deeper than their weapons.

"Slaves are ye all," he called, "slaves of haughty tyrants. Ye have lost your own freedom, yet ye think to take away the liberty of Romans."

There was a mighty crash, above which rose the triumphant shouts of the Romans. The great bridge collapsed into a mass of wreckage, and the swift waters of the Tiber seized hold of truss and girder. Horatius was cut off between the gap and the threatening mass of the enemy.

There was a moment's pause as the realization sank into their minds. Then there rose a hoarse cry from a thousand throats, demanding vengeance on the one who had wrecked their hopes.

Horatius sprang to the edge of the shattered bridge. He raised his hand aloft.

"Holy Father Tiber," cried he, "receive these arms and this thy soldier in thy propitious stream."

With this invocation, he leaped into the flood. A silence fell upon friend and foe alike as the gallant warrior reappeared on the surface, and encumbered as he was by his heavy armor, struck out for the city shore.

Recovering themselves, many of the Tuscans hurled javelins at him as he strove against the buffeting waves and current. One of these wounded him in the thigh, but with powerful strokes he swam across the space in safety and rose dripping from the shallows among the cheering multitude of his countrymen. He had saved Rome, and Rome gave him full meed of gratitude.

Publicola, the consul, decreed that, in spite of the public scarcity, every citizen should present to him one day's provisions for his maintenance; and even the women were proud to be among the hundreds of thousands who thus honored the one-eyed, and now lamed, hero. He was granted as much land as he could encircle with a plough in a day. And a brazen statue of him was set up in the temple of Vulcan, that future generations might ever remember the son of Rome who was ready to give her all, including life itself.

HOW KARI SAVED OUR LIVES IN THE JUNGLE*

by Dhan Gopal Mukerji

When Kari grew to be five years old, he was almost as high as the ceiling. He was never trained for hunting. We never thought of killing anything except snakes and tigers, and these we killed when they came toward the village and injured men. So Kari never

* Taken from *Kari the Elephant,* by Dhan Gopal Mukerji. Published and copyrighted 1922 by E. P. Dutton & Co., New York.

had the training of a hunting elephant. Just the same, he was very alert and steady in the face of danger, so when it was a question of going into the jungle on the back of an elephant, we generally took Kari with us. During such trips we did not put a cloth of gold on his back or silver bells on his sides. These bells are made in certain parts of India where silversmiths know how to melt and mix silver so that when the clapper strikes the sides of the bell there will be a sound like rushing water. The two bells are tied by a silver chain and slung over the elephant's back, one dangling on each side of him. We never put a *howdah* on the back of Kari. Very few Hindus put *howdahs* on elephants.

Do you know what a *howdah* is? It is a box with high sides inside of which there are chairs for travelers. The *howdahs* are generally for people who are not accustomed to elephants. They need the high sides so that when the elephant walks they will not fall from his back. They stay in their seats leaning on the edge of the box and see very little, especially children who are not tall enough to see over the sides. That is why Indian children prefer riding bareback on an elephant to taking a *howdah*.

One evening when my brother and I went out, we put a mattress on Kari's back and tied it very tightly with cords so that it would not slip, for it is not pleasant to slip and fall under an elephant's belly and be stepped on. But Kari was trained so that he would not have stepped on us even if we had slipped under him. We tightened the cords to the mattress, however, and lay down for the night. Though we had bells, we lifted them up and silenced the clappers, so that in walking through the jungle road they would not ring and frighten the animals, for the forest is the dwelling place of silence, and silence being the voice of God, no man dares to disturb it. We lay on the back of Kari and looked up at the stars. In India, the stars are so close that you can almost pluck them with your hands and the velvet blue of the sky is like a river of stillness running between banks of silver.

As we lay there, unable to go to sleep right away, we heard jungle sounds. The heavy tread of the elephant was like clouds brushing the crests of the forest. Once in a while you could see a tiger come out of the jungle, cross a road and disappear in the distance, but Kari was so brave he never condescended to notice the comings and goings of tigers. Once we heard the bark of a fox very near us and then he came out of the jungle. Kari stopped and the fox passed across the road, then we moved on again. In the moonlight which made the road before us look like a river of silver we saw squirrels leaping from branch to branch.

You know, perhaps, that elephants can sleep as they walk. Presently Kari's walk slackened into a slow pace, and we felt quite sure that he was dozing. Then we remembered nothing, for we too fell asleep. I cannot tell how much time passed before we were startled out of our sleep by a terrible roar, a ghastly trumpeting of the elephant and a terrible lunge of his body. We had to hold on to his back very tightly to avoid being thrown off. In a few seconds both of us had turned over—I do not know how—and were lying on our faces, holding on to the cords that held the mattress to Kari's back, while he broke into a run.

Trees bent and broke, branches fell, and we could hear the monkeys stampeding from tree to tree, and flocks of birds, startled out of their sleep, falling upon us, their wings beating our faces. We shouted to Kari to be calm, but he went on as if he were mad. We heard boars snorting, and running away, and strange-looking horned creatures leaping and bounding off in all directions. Then a tree in front of us fell, and the jungle throbbed for a moment. It seemed as though a shiver ran through Kari's body, and he stopped stock still. It was very difficult to tell exactly what had happened until we got off Kari's back. I spoke to him and he shook his head, then I spoke again and urged him to put up his head. He obeyed and I climbed down by his trunk. I felt it was very wet, however, and he shook me off with pain.

My brother spoke to me from above and said when I told him how the trunk felt, "Now I know. You see, this is autumn when bears eat Mohula in the moonlight under the thick shade of the trees. As you know, Mohula intoxicates bears and makes them sleepy. Some bear had fallen asleep under the trees and Kari, who was also asleep and consequently did not even smell him with his trunk, must have come upon him without suspecting his presence. Although all bears are brought up to respect elephants, this one, no doubt, was so sleepy that he did not know who was upon him and so I am sure he must have sprung up in his surprise and scratched Kari's trunk."

If Kari had been wide awake he would have killed the bear, but being sleepy, the shock and the surprise of the attack and the pain in his trunk frightened him so that he ran out into the jungle mad with terror.

I put my hand on the trunk again. Yes, it was bleeding; I could see in the moonlight that it was not perspiration because my hand was dark red. I spoke to Kari again; this time he did not shake his head so furiously. He was rather willing to listen and I told him I was very sorry about his trunk but could do nothing here. I also told him to go back to the road. He shook his head—that meant "No." Do you know why he did not want to go back to that road? You shall learn at the end of this story.

I got upon his back again. "Since he won't go back to the road," said my brother, "we must give him the master call so that he can make a road through the jungle" and we gave him the master call.

At this Kari lifted his bleeding trunk and smote down the first tree, and then he struck down the next tree. He came upon a third which his trunk could not pull down, so he turned around and walked away from it. After taking a few steps he stopped and slowly walked backwards and with one push of his back, knocked this tree down.

At this we could hear the flocks of birds flying in the air and feel the stamping feet below as herds of animals ran in every direction. We heard the vibrant jabber of monkeys from tree-tops, and each time a new tree fell there was more jabbering and more leaping away from tree to tree.

We clung to the elephant's back with our nails and teeth.

Soon we found ourselves on the road, three miles ahead of where Kari had been frightened by the bear.

Do you know why he did not go back to the same spot? Because no animal ever likes to return to the place where he lost his pride. For to be frightened is to lose one's pride.

WAUKEWA'S EAGLE

by James Buckham

One day, when the Indian boy Waukewa was hunting along the mountainside, he found a young eagle with a broken wing, lying at the base of a cliff. The bird had fallen from a ledge, and being too young to fly, had fluttered down the cliff and hurt itself so severely that it was likely to die. When Waukewa saw it he was about to drive one of his sharp arrows through its body, for the passion of the hunter was strong in him, and the eagle plunders many a fine fish from the Indian's drying frame. But a gentler impulse came to him as he saw the young bird quivering with pain and fright at his feet, and he slowly stooped over the panting eaglet. For fully a minute the wild eyes of the wounded bird and the eyes of the Indian boy, growing gentler and softer as he gazed, looked into one another. Then the struggling and panting of the young eagle ceased; the wild frightened look passed out of its eyes, and it suffered Waukewa to pass his hand gently over its ruffled and draggled feathers. The fierce instinct to fight, to defend its threatened life, yielded to the charm of the tenderness and pity expressed in the boy's eyes; and from that moment Waukewa and the eagle were friends.

Waukewa went slowly home to his father's lodge, bearing the

wounded eaglet in his arms. He carried it so gently that the broken wing gave no twinge of pain, and the bird lay perfectly still, never offering to strike with its sharp beak the hands of the boy.

Warming some water over the fire at the lodge, Waukewa bathed the broken wing of the eagle, and bound it up with soft strips of skin. Then he made a nest of ferns and grass inside the lodge, and laid the bird in it. The boy's mother looked on with shining eyes. Her heart was very tender. From girlhood she had loved all the creatures of the woods, and it pleased her to see some of her own gentle spirit waking in the boy.

When Waukewa's father returned from hunting, he would have caught up the young eagle and wrung its neck. But the boy pleaded with him so eagerly, stooping over the captive and defending it with his small hands, that the stern warrior laughed and called him his "little squawheart." "Keep it, then," he said, "and nurse it until it is well. But then you must let it go, for we will not raise up a thief in the lodges." So Waukewa promised that when the eagle's wing was healed and grown so that it could fly, he would carry it forth and give it its freedom.

It was a month—or, as the Indians say, a moon—before the young eagle's wing had fully mended and the bird was old enough and strong enough to fly. And in the meantime Waukewa cared for it and fed it daily, and the friendship between the boy and the bird grew very strong.

But at last the time came when the willing captive must be freed. So Waukewa carried it far away from the Indian lodges, where none of the young braves might see it hovering over and be tempted to shoot their arrows at it, and there he let it go. The young eagle rose toward the sky in great circles, rejoicing in its freedom and its strange new power of flight. But when Waukewa began to move away from the spot, it came swooping down again; and all day long it followed him through the woods as he hunted. At dusk, when Waukewa shaped his course for the Indian lodges, the eagle would have accompanied him. But the boy suddenly slipped into a hollow tree and hid, and after a long time the eagle stopped sweeping about in search of him and flew slowly and sadly away.

Summer passed, and then winter; and spring came again, with its flowers and birds and swarming fish in the lakes and streams. Then it was that all the Indians, old and young, braves and squaws, pushed their light canoes out from shore and with spear and hook waged pleasant war against the salmon and the red spotted trout. After winter's long imprisonment, it was such joy to toss in the sunshine and the warm wind and catch savory fish to take the place of dried meats and corn!

Above the great falls the salmon sported in the cool, swinging current, darting under the lee of the rocks and leaping full length in the clear spring air. Nowhere else were such salmon to be speared as those which lay at the head of the rapids. But only the most daring braves ventured to seek them there, for the current was strong, and should a light canoe once pass the danger point and get caught in the rush of the rapids, nothing could save it from going over the roaring falls.

Very early in the morning of a clear April day, just as the sun was rising splendidly over the mountains, Waukewa launched his canoe a half mile above the rapids and floated downward, spear in hand, among the salmon. He was the only one of the Indian lads who dared to fish above the falls. But he had been there often, and never yet had his watchful eye and his strong paddle suffered the current to carry his canoe beyond the danger point. This morning he was alone on the river, having risen long before daylight to be first at the sport.

The riffles were full of salmon, big, lusty fellows, who glided about the canoe on every side in an endless silver stream. Waukewa plunged his spear right and left, and tossed one glittering victim after another into the bark canoe. So absorbed in the sport was he that for once he did not notice when the canoe began to glide more swiftly among the rocks. But suddenly he looked up, caught his paddle, and dipped it wildly in the swirling water. The canoe swung sidewise, shivered, held its own against the torrent, and then slowly inch by inch began to creep upstream toward the shore. But suddenly there was a loud, cruel snap, and the paddle parted in the boy's hands, broken just above the blade! Waukewa gave a cry of despairing agony. Then he bent to the gunwale of his canoe and with shattered blade fought desperately against the current. But it was useless. The racing torrent swept him downward; the hungry falls roared tauntingly in his ears.

Then the Indian boy knelt calmly upright in the canoe, facing the mist of the falls, and folded his arms. His young face was stern and lofty. He had lived like a brave hitherto—now he would die like one.

Faster and faster sped the doomed canoe toward the great cataract. The black rocks glided away on either side like phantoms. The roar of the terrible waters became like thunder in the boy's ears. But still he gazed calmly and sternly ahead, facing his fate as a brave Indian should. At last he began to chant the death-song, which he had learned from the older braves. In a few minutes all would be over. But he would come before the Great Spirit with a fearless hymn upon his lips.

Suddenly a shadow fell across the canoe. Waukewa lifted his eyes and saw a great eagle hovering over, with dangling legs, and a spread of wings that blotted out the sun. Once more the eyes of the Indian boy and his old friend the eagle met; but now it was the eagle who was master!

With a glad cry the Indian boy stood up in his canoe, and the eagle hovered lower. Now the canoe tossed up on that great swelling wave that climbs to the cataract's edge, and the boy lifted his hands and caught the legs of the eagle. The next moment he looked down into the awful gulf of waters. The canoe was snatched from beneath him and plunged down the black wall of the cataract; but he and the struggling eagle were floating outward and downwards through the cloud of mist. The cataract roared terribly, like a wild beast robbed of its prey. The spray beat and blinded, the air rushed upward as they fell. But the eagle struggled on with his burden. He fought his way out of the mist and the flying spray. His great wings threshed the air with a whistling sound. Down, down, they sank, the boy and the eagle, but ever farther from the precipice of water and the boiling whirlpool below.

At length, with a fluttering plunge, the eagle dropped on a sand bar below the whirlpool, and he and the Indian boy lay there a minute, breathless and exhausted. Then the eagle slowly lifted himself, took the air under his free wings, and soared away, while the Indian boy knelt on the sand, and watched with shining eyes the great bird until he faded into the gray of the cliffs.

STORM FLIGHT

by Rutherford G. Montgomery

The Napier lurched and bounced as her low wings cracked the rough air that backwashed from Mount Kirby. Tommy wiped the usual smile from his lips and glanced at the flight bubble. Ahead lay trouble! It was written all over the spruce-choked side of the mountain. Gray-black clouds piled high in the notch toward which the Napier was heading. And there was no other crossing for a hundred miles along the divide, aside from the narrow pass. Heavily loaded, the Napier did not have ceiling enough to top the naked ridges towering above the storm.

Barrows, who sat beside Tommy, leaned over and shouted. His voice sounded like a whisper as it cut through the scream of the hurtling winds.

"Do you want to turn back?"

Tommy shook his head and gave the Napier all she had. Her big, radial motor shook the sills inside her fuselage as it responded.

Had the ship been loaded within her weight limit, the Napier would have taken clearance, and Tommy could have zoomed above the onrushing wall of storm that was rolling up out of the valley beyond the pass.

"People are starving across the hump! We must get this food through to them! We've got to!" shouted Barrows.

Tommy's eyes shifted to the gray mass that swirled down upon them. Barrows' face was expressionless. If Tommy cracked up the Napier, it would mean a loss of seven thousand dollars for Barrows, to say nothing of the danger to their lives. Barrows had picked Tommy to fly the load of rescue food into Happy Valley where a mountain community was stormlocked and starving.

Barrows was not a flier, himself. He had come along because he would not ask anyone to fly into a danger he would not face. He had picked Tommy from a recruit line because he was certain that the slender, steel-muscled boy with the curly hair and cold, blue eyes would not turn back.

The Napier shoved her slicing propeller into a swirling mass of powder-dry snow. The particles hurtled against the glass panes of the cabin. The Napier shifted suddenly, and one wing lifted with a sickening lurch. Tommy fought to keep her level and to hold his altitude.

Barrows settled back in his bucket seat and stared out of the little window at his side. Like a flash the walls of the mountain were wiped out by the swirling mass of snow. No landmark showed the way to the pass. On both sides granite walls lurked in the white mists. Tommy would have to feel the Napier through the notch or crack up. Barrows looked across at his pilot and caught Tommy's eyes. He grinned and wrinkled his nose at the storm.

Tommy leveled off and the Napier bore into the storm. Suddenly the white wall ahead scattered like the mass of a jig-saw puzzle that has been roughly shaken. A wall of granite, studded with scrub growth, came hurtling at them through the storm! Tommy laid the Napier over sharply and she lifted high into the air. The upward lift shot them into the storm again and blotted out all vision. Desperately Tommy put her nose down again. He must see where he was going! Again the clouds cleared and this time no walls of granite loomed ahead. Tommy sent the big ship roaring over the tops of the tall spruce toward the pass.

Flying close to the tops of tall spruce in a raging storm is a tough job, and Tommy felt a strange coldness in the region of his belt. Then he remembered the starving folks in Happy Valley and his lips set tight. Beside him Barrows was unmoved.

Tommy sucked in a breath of cold air. He could see the notch ahead, a low-lying valley that curved down from high ranges on either side. The Napier was bouncing and jerking as she hit the pass and roared through with less than five hundred feet of ceiling. Barrows reached over and slapped Tommy on the back. He bent close and roared into Tommy's ear.

"You get a regular job from now on!"

"Thanks!" Tommy shouted back. A regular job with Barrows meant flying into places that were considered as impossible, but Barrows paid top wages and had the best planes.

The Napier was almost clear of the mountain side when the updraft of the storm hit her. A howling demon of lashing air clutched at the ship, hurling it high into the air, turning it over on its side and crashing Barrows against the little window at his side.

The Napier came out of the clutches of the storm with sickening suddenness. Her tail swept up and she spiraled dizzily, then she plunged downward and buried her nose in the white wall of storm that was sweeping up through the pass. Tommy fought to level off, but the wind was too powerful and he could not right the ship. For two or three sickening seconds they hurtled downward, then a rending crash shook them and a jarring impact jerked them sharply. Black lights flickered before Tommy's eyes.

When Tommy opened his eyes, he was numb with cold and icy particles were pelting his face. He sat up dizzily. A sharp pain shot through his left side. He shouted loudly:

"Barrows! Barrows!"

Only the howling of the wind answered him. He staggered to his feet and looked around. Little could be seen through the driving storm. The Napier lay twisted and battered, her nose buried in a deep drift and her tail elevated. Tommy realized that he had been thrown through the window and side plates. He thanked his padded suit for being alive as he plowed to the ship and bent to look inside.

Barrows lay sprawled over the controls. Much of the packed food had piled upon him. Tommy fought back the numbing pain in his side and began pulling Barrows free of the plane. Barrows groaned and opened his eyes as Tommy laid him in the snow beside the wrecked Napier. A wavering smile came to his lips.

"Have to have a fire. Feet cold—cold——" Barrows slumped back and his eyes closed.

Tommy found plenty of logs in the snow. Hurriedly he swept clear a space and built a fire. He dug a heavy blanket from the wreck and fixed a shelter. Tommy guessed that Barrows was internally injured, but he had no way of knowing how seriously. Tommy watched and hoped that his boss would recover consciousness. But Barrows did not come to. His lips moved but he did not speak.

Tommy faced the danger coolly. He knew they could not be rescued for perhaps a week. The dwellers of Happy Valley did not know they were coming, so there was no hope of help from them, though the plane must be close to the settlement.

Tommy stood up. Night was beginning to darken the swirling storm. Grimly Tommy fixed the shelter over his boss. He knew what Barrows would order if he were conscious, and he meant to follow that course. Hesitating only a moment, he plunged into the storm heading down the mountain. Their objective was still ahead, and Barrows would expect him to carry on.

Through the first drift he wallowed, always going downhill. His side pained and weakened him, and he began to think he had acted the fool in braving the storm and leaving Barrows uncon-

scious, possibly dying beside the fire. The storm rag
shutting out the world and piling drifts in the ope

But fate cares for those who dare greatly, and wh
is mercy bound they are oftentimes lucky. Tomm
drift. He raised himself wearily and wiped the snow from his face. Then he saw a light glimmering ahead. Eagerly he staggered forward and threw himself against the plank door of a snow-covered cabin.

Rough mountain men met him at the door. They were gaunt from hunger but they dragged him inside and placed him on a bunk. He had found the outmost cabin of the settlement. Tommy refused to rest until they back tracked to the Napier. They were wildly joyous when they learned that the ship was loaded with food.

In a very short time Tommy and the men of Happy Valley had rescued Barrows, unloaded the welcome supplies, and returned to the waiting community. All of Happy Valley was rounded up to share the food they so badly needed.

Late that night Barrows and Tommy sat beside a roaring fire and sipped tinned soup that was simmering hot. Barrows was bandaged and at rest. Tommy's side had ceased to pain.

"You have what it takes to fly for me," Barrows said.

"Thanks!" Tommy said, and went on sipping his soup.

JOURNEY INTO SPACE

by Katherine B. Shippen

This is the story of a journey. But it is not a journey in a railroad train, with the cars sliding safely along their steel tracks. Nor is it a journey in an automobile between one town and another along a well-marked highway. Nor even a journey by airplane from one airport to another on motor-driven wings. This is a journey into uncharted space, leaving the earth behind, flying outward toward the sun.

Near the gas works of the town of Wolverhampton, England, on a September day in 1862, a great balloon, which looked like a mass of wrinkled taffeta, was slowly filled with gas. As it gradually puffed and swelled, Mr. Henry Coxwell the balloonist examined again the ropes by which its anchor held it to the ground.

"I shouldn't want it to go off without us," he said.

Some idlers who had been drinking in the public house left the bar when they saw the balloon taking shape, and wandered over to see what was going on. A little group of members and their wives, from the British Association for the Advancement of Science, looked on with an air of ownership, for they had paid for the balloon and the gas that filled it. A black-and-white dog, watching the unfamiliar globe, put his head down on his front paws and barked, then ran away to the edge of the field to watch.

At last when the balloon was nearly ready a closed carriage drove up to the gas works. Out of it stepped Professor James Glaisher, a bearded man wearing a large fur coat. He walked carefully over to the balloon carrying a large thermometer, and behind him an assistant brought various tubes, bottles, dials, and a large telescope.

"We're all ready, Dr. Glaisher," Coxwell called out to him. Then both men took their places in the big wicker basket, the anchor was freed, and the balloon floated upward as if some child at a circus had let go the string.

"Good luck! Good luck!" the members of the British Association called to them, watching their investment float upward.

"Nutty, I calls it," said one of the patrons of the pub, as the idlers turned back to their bar.

To the watchers on the ground, the balloon soon appeared not much bigger than an orange, and then it was not much bigger than a good-sized speck in the sky. And then a summer cloud blew across the sky and it disappeared altogether.

In the wicker basket which hung below the balloon, Mr. Coxwell busied himself pulling in the rope from which the anchor hung, and checking the valve which controlled the balloon's inflation. But Dr. Glaisher took a large telescope and looked down through the transparent air to the land which he was leaving. He could see the members of the British Association in their stovepipe hats. He could see the big gas tank and the fields, and the roofs of the town of Wolverhampton. The wind blew in from the ocean to the west of them and rocked the basket, as if it was hanging from the bough of a tree, he thought. Then the soft white cloud blew across their way. England disappeared, and they were rushing upward through the mist.

Soon the cloud was beneath them, dazzling bright in the sun, and England was a green patch set in a silver sea.

"It's getting cold," Dr. Glaisher said, pulling his fur cap down over his ears, and fastening his muffler carefully about his neck.

"Yes," Coxwell replied, "we're going up about a thousand feet a minute." He was examining the dial of an indicator which recorded the speed of their ascent.

From far away, very thin and faint, they heard a dog's bark—the black-and-white dog that had watched them at the gas works probably. Was it to be the last sound that they would ever hear from the familiar earth?

The rocking of the basket had stopped now, and there were no more clouds. The air about them was clear and still as they rushed upward. Coxwell looked across the basket at Dr. Glaisher. The scientist was busy filling little bottles with air, recording the pull of a magnet, putting down information about electricity, gravity, and air pressure. He was so busy that he did not notice, as Coxwell did, that both their faces had turned a kind of bronze color, nor did he notice that his breath was coming in short, quick gasps. He was happy, since his recording and reckonings seemed to show that conditions at these altitudes were what he had expected they would be—and there is no greater happiness for a scientist than that.

The atmosphere about them now was very still. There was no breath of wind, but only the steady rush of air as the balloon shot upward. The sky had been blue and sunny when they started. Now it changed gradually to a deeper color, a kind of purple gray, a kind of twilight, like the light that is on the earth in a very heavy storm. It grew colder and colder. It was so cold that their feet and hands were numb and stiff. Dr. Glaisher was troubled by the stiffness of his fingers, for it made him feel clumsy in writing his neat records.

At last he looked up from his work with annoyance.

"What's that beating?" he asked.

Coxwell had noticed the beating, too, and although he was no scientist, he knew what it was. In the stillness around them the throbbing of their hearts sounded so loud that it seemed almost to shake their bodies.

"Knock. Knock. Knock. Knock." Their hearts beat against their ribs.

"It's twenty-nine thousand feet," Coxwell said. "That's almost five and a half miles. Perhaps we ought to go down."

But Dr. Glaisher bent over his instruments.

"It's exactly as I had anticipated," he was saying. "It would be a pity not to continue the ascent. I don't know when I shall be here again—and I think I know now what to expect at thirty-five thousand."

Coxwell said nothing, but he was thinking, "It'll be a fine record. The fellows at the gas works would never have believed me if I had told them we were going up this high."

Up and up the balloon shot, through the cold, through the half dark.

"I'd better be sure the valve ropes are in good order," Coxwell said. He was surprised to find how much effort it was to climb up to the balloon ring.

"I might as well stay here," he thought, sitting still and feeling that any movement was a tremendous effort.

Up and up they soared, through the dark, through the stillness and the cold.

"Thirty-one thousand feet," Coxwell observed, and he looked down into the basket at Dr. Glaisher. Even as he looked, Dr. Glaisher slumped over, his bearded head among his bottles, his limp arm hanging over the basket's rim.

With a tremendous effort, Coxwell moved himself toward the rope that controlled the balloon's gas valves. Then, to his horror, he found that both his hands were frozen. He could not move so much as one finger to clutch the rope that would open the valve and bring them to the earth again.

He clung to the balloon's ring and felt the air rushing past him. Below him, his companion lay among his scientific instruments. Around him, the emptiness was filled with the noisy beating of his own heart. And somewhere, far away, was the world he knew with houses and people, and beds and suppers, and children and little black-and-white dogs. With a tremendous effort Coxwell raised himself and, with his teeth, he tore the valve open. Then he too fainted. The balloon continued its ascent until the dial registered 37,000 feet. Then for a moment, with its senseless passengers, it paused at the edge of the stratosphere, hanging in space while all the worlds moved round it. When sufficient gas had escaped through the valve, it started to fall back to earth, as Dr. Glaisher would have anticipated.

So through the twilight, through the stillness and the cold, the balloon plunged downward. Down to the clear sunlight, to the winds and the clouds, down where the noises of the earth, men calling, dogs barking, came up to meet their senseless ears. It hung at last on the branches of an oak tree at the edge of a farmer's field. The farmer, turning at the end of a long furrow, looked back and saw it. He let go the handle of his plough and ran back across the newly turned field. The balloon was tangled in the oak tree's branches, its basket hanging free just above the earth.

"Are ye alive? Are ye alive?" cried the farmer, peering into the basket. They stirred, and he looked at them as if they were spirits returned from another world. And, indeed, this was more truly the case than he knew.

NO LAND IN SIGHT

by Thor Heyerdahl

This sample is from *Kon-Tiki,* the story of a remarkable journey taken by four Norwegians across the Pacific Ocean in a raft with a sail. They went to test an idea about the possible connection between ancient peoples living in Peru and the inhabitants of Easter Island.

On the forty-fifth day at sea we had advanced from the 78th degree of longitude to the 108th and were exactly halfway to the first islands ahead. There were over 2,000 sea miles between us and South America to the east, and it was the same distance on to Polynesia in the west. The nearest land in any direction was the Galapagos Islands to east-northeast and Easter Island due south, both more than 500 sea miles away on the boundless ocean. We had not seen a ship, and we never did see one, because we were off the routes of all ordinary shipping traffic in the Pacific.

But we did not really feel these enormous distances, for the horizon glided along with us unnoticed as we moved and our own floating world remained always the same—a circle flung up to the vault of the sky with the raft itself as center, while the same stars rolled on over us night after night.

We no longer had the same respect for waves and sea. We knew them and their relationship to us on the raft. Even the shark had become a part of the everyday picture; we knew it and its usual reactions. We no longer thought of the hand harpoon, and we did not even move away from the side of the raft, if a shark came up alongside. On the contrary, we were more likely to try and grasp its back fin as it glided unperturbed along the logs. This finally developed into a quite new form of sport—tug of war with shark without a line.

We began quite modestly. We caught all too easily more dolphins than we could eat. To keep a popular form of amusement going without wasting food, we hit on comic fishing without a hook for the mutual entertainment of the dolphins and ourselves. We fastened unused flying fish to a string and drew them over the surface of the water. The dolphins shot up to the surface and seized the fish, and then we tugged, each in our own direction, and had a fine circus performance, for if one dolphin let go another came in its place. We had fun, and the dolphins got the fish in the end.

Then we started the same game with the sharks. We had either a bit of fish on the end of a rope or often a bag with scraps from dinner, which we let out on a line. Instead of turning on its back, the shark pushed its snout above the water and swam forward with jaws wide to swallow the morsel. We could not help pulling on the rope just as the shark was going to close its jaws again, and the cheated animal swam on with an unspeakably foolish, patient expression and opened its jaws again for the offal, which jumped out of its mouth every time it tried to swallow it. It ended by the shark's coming right up to the logs and jumping up like a begging dog for the food which hung dangling in a bag above its nose. It was just like feeding a gaping hippopotamus in a zoological garden, and one day at the end of July, after three months on board the raft, the following entry was made in the diary:
—*We made friends with the shark which followed us today. At dinner we fed it with scraps which we poured right down into its open jaws. It has the effect of a half fierce, half good-natured and*

friendly dog when it swims alongside us. It cannot be denied that sharks can seem quite pleasant so long as we do not get into their jaws ourselves. At least we find it amusing to have them about us, except when we are bathing.

One day a bamboo stick, with a bag of sharks' food tied to a string, was lying ready for use on the edge of the raft when a sea came and washed it overboard. The bamboo stick was already lying afloat a couple of hundred yards astern of the raft, when it suddenly rose upright in the water and came rushing after the raft by itself, as if it intended to put itself nicely back in its place again. When the fishing rod came swaying nearer us, we saw a ten-foot shark swimming right under it, while the bamboo stick stuck up out of the waves like a periscope. The shark had swallowed the food bag without biting off the line. The fishing rod soon overtook us, passed us quite quietly, and vanished ahead.

But, even if we gradually came to look upon the shark with quite other eyes, our respect for the five or six rows of razor-sharp teeth which lay in ambush in the huge jaws never disappeared.

One day Knut had an involuntary swim in company with a shark. No one was ever allowed to swim away from the raft, both on account of the raft's drift and because of sharks. But one day it was extra quiet and we had just pulled on board such sharks as had been following us, so permission was given for a quick dip in the sea. Knut plunged in and had gone quite a long way before he came up to the surface to crawl back. At that moment we saw from the mast a shadow bigger than himself coming up behind him, deeper down. We shouted warnings as quietly as we could so as not to create a panic, and Knut heaved himself toward the side of the raft. But the shadow below belonged to a still better swimmer, which shot up from the depths and gained on Knut. They reached the raft at the same time. While Knut was clambering on board, a six-foot shark glided past right under his stomach and stopped beside the raft. We gave it a dainty dolphin's head to thank it for not having snapped.

Generally it is smell more than sight which excites the sharks' voracity. We have sat with our legs in the water to test them, and they have swum toward us till they were two or three feet away, only quietly to turn their tails toward us again. But, if the water was in the least bloodstained, as it was when we had been cleaning fish, the sharks' fins came to life and they would suddenly collect like bluebottles from a long way off. If we flung out shark's guts, they simply went mad and dashed about in a blind frenzy. They savagely devoured the liver of their own kind and then, if we put a foot into the sea, they came for it like rockets and even dug their teeth into the logs where the foot had been. The mood of a shark may vary immensely, the animal being completely at the mercy of its own emotions.

The last stage in our encounter with sharks was that we began to pull their tails. Pulling animals' tails is held to be an inferior form of sport, but that may be because no one has tried it on a shark. For it was, in truth, a lively form of sport.

To get hold of a shark by the tail we first had to give it a real tidbit. It was ready to stick its head high out of the water to get it. Usually it had its food served dangling in a bag. For, if one has fed a shark directly by hand once, it is no longer amusing. If one feeds dogs or tame bears by hand, they set their teeth into the meat and tear and worry it till they get a bit off or until they get the whole piece for themselves. But, if one holds out a large dolphin at a safe distance from the shark's head, the shark comes up and smacks his jaws together, and, without one's having felt the slightest tug, half the dolphin is suddenly gone and one is left sitting with a tail in one's hand. We had found it a hard job to cut the dolphin in two with knives, but in a fraction of a second the shark, moving its triangular saw teeth quickly sideways, had chopped off the backbone and everything else like a sausage machine.

When the shark turned quietly to go under again, its tail flickered up above the surface and was easy to grasp. The shark's skin was just like sandpaper to hold on to, and inside the upper point of its tail there was an indentation which might have been made solely to allow of a good grip. If we once got a firm grasp there, there was no chance of our grip's not holding. Then we had to give a jerk, before the shark could collect itself, and get as much as possible of the tail pulled in tight over the logs. For a second or two the shark realized nothing, but then it began to wriggle and struggle in a spiritless manner with the fore part of its body, for without the help of its tail a shark cannot get up any speed. The other fins are only apparatus for balancing and steering. After a few desperate jerks, during which we had to keep a tight hold of the tail, the surprised shark became quite crestfallen and apathetic, and, as the loose stomach began to sink down toward the head, the shark at last became completely paralyzed.

When the shark had become quiet and, as it were, hung stiff awaiting developments, it was time for us to haul in with all our might. We seldom got more than half the heavy fish up out of the water; then the shark too woke up and did the rest itself. With violent jerks it swung its head round and up on to the logs, and then we had to tug with all our might and jump well out of the way, and that pretty quickly, if we wanted to save our legs. For now the shark was in no kindly mood. Jerking itself round in great leaps, it thrashed at the bamboo wall, using its tail as a sledge hammer. Now it no longer spared its iron muscles. The huge jaws were opened wide, and the rows of teeth bit and snapped in the air for anything they could reach. It might happen that the war dance ended in the shark's more or less involuntarily tumbling overboard and disappearing for good after its shameful humiliation, but most often the shark flung itself about at random on the logs aft, till we got a running noose round the root of its tail or till it had ceased to gnash its devilish teeth forever.

The parrot was quite thrilled when we had a shark on deck. It came scurrying out of the bamboo cabin and climbed up the wall at frantic speed till it found itself a good, safe lookout post on the palm-leaf roof, and there it sat shaking its head or fluttered to and fro along the ridge, shrieking with excitement. It had at an early date become an excellent sailor and was always bubbling over with humor and laughter. We reckoned ourselves as seven on board—six of us and the green parrot. The crab Johannes had, after all, to reconcile itself to being regarded as a cold-blooded appendage. At night the parrot crept into its cage under the roof of the bamboo cabin, but in the daytime it strutted about the deck or hung on to guy ropes and stays and did the most fascinating acrobatic exercises.

At the start of the voyage we had turnbuckles on the stays of the mast but they wore the ropes, so we replaced them by ordinary running knots. When the stays stretched and grew slack from sun and wind, all hands had to turn to and brace up the mast, so that its mangrove wood, as heavy as iron, should not bump against and cut into the ropes till they fell down. While we were hauling and pulling, at the most critical moment the parrot began to call out with its cracked voice: "Haul! Haul! Ho, ho, ho, ho, ha ha ha!" And if it made us laugh, it laughed till it shook at its own cleverness and swung round and round on the stays.

At first the parrot was the bane of our radio operators. They might be sitting happily absorbed in the radio corner with their magic earphones on and perhaps in contact with a radio "ham" in Oklahoma. Then their earphones would suddenly go dead, and they could not get a sound however much they coaxed the wires and turned the knobs. The parrot had been busy and bitten off the wire of the aerial. This was specially tempting in the early days, when the wire was sent up with a little balloon. But one day the parrot became seriously ill. It sat in its cage and moped and touched no food for two days, while its droppings glittered with golden scraps of aerial. Then the radio operators repented of their angry words and the parrot of its misdeeds, and from that day Torstein and Knut were its chosen friends and the parrot would never sleep anywhere but in the radio corner. The parrot's mother tongue was Spanish when it first came on board; Bengt declared it took to talking Spanish with a Norwegian accent long before it began to imitate Torstein's favorite ejaculations in full-blooded Norwegian.

We enjoyed the parrot's humor and brilliant colors for two months, till a big sea came on board from astern while it was on its way down the stay from the masthead. When we discovered that the parrot had gone overboard, it was too late. We did not see it. And the *Kon-Tiki* could not be turned or stopped; if anything went overboard from the raft, we had no chance of turning back for it—numerous experiences had shown that.

The loss of the parrot had a depressing effect on our spirits the first evening; we knew that exactly the same thing would happen to ourselves if we fell overboard on a solitary night watch. We tightened up on all the safety regulations, brought into use new life lines for the night watch, and frightened one another out of believing that we were safe because things had gone well in the first two months. One careless step, one thoughtless movement, could send us where the green parrot had gone, even in broad daylight.

We had several times observed the large white shells of cuttlefish eggs, lying floating like ostrich eggs or white skulls on the blue swell. On one solitary occasion we saw a squid lying wriggling underneath. We observed the snow-white balls floating on a level with ourselves and thought at first that it would be an easy matter to row out in the dinghy and get them. We thought the same that time when the rope of the plankton net broke so that the cloth net was left behind alone, floating in our wake. Each time we launched the dinghy, with a rope attached, to row back and pick up the floating object. But we saw to our surprise that the wind and sea held the dinghy off and that the line from the *Kon-Tiki* had so violent a braking effect in the water that we could never row right back to a point we had already left. We might get within a few yards of what we wanted to pick up, but then the whole line was out and the *Kon-Tiki* was pulling us away westward. "Once overboard always overboard" was a lesson that was gradually branded into our consciousness on board. If we wanted to go with the rest, we must hang on till the *Kon-Tiki* ran her bow against land on the other side.

The parrot left a blank in the radio corner, but, when the tropical sun shone out over the Pacific next day, we soon became reconciled to his loss. We hauled in many sharks the next few days, and we constantly found black curved parrots' beaks, or so we thought, among tunnies' heads and other curiosities in the shark's belly. But on closer examination the black beaks always proved to belong to assimilated cuttlefish.

The two radio operators had had a tough job in their corner since the first day they came on board. The very first day, in the Humboldt Current, sea water trickled even from the battery cases so that they had to cover the sensitive radio corner with canvas to save what could be saved in the high seas. And then they had the problem of fitting a long enough aerial on the little raft. They tried to send the aerial up with a kite, but in a gust of wind the kite simply plunged down into a wave crest and disappeared. Then they tried to send it up with a balloon, but the tropical sun burned holes in the balloon so that it collapsed and sank into the sea. And then they had the trouble with the parrot. In addition to all this, we were a fortnight in the Humboldt Current before we came out of a dead zone of the Andes in which the short wave was as dumb and lifeless as the air in an empty soapbox.

But then one night the short wave suddenly broke through, and Torstein's call signal was heard by a chance radio amateur in Los Angeles who was sitting fiddling with his transmitter to establish contact with another amateur in Sweden. The man asked what kind of set we had and, when he got a satisfactory answer to his question, he asked Torstein who he was and where he lived. When he heard that Torstein's abode was a bamboo cabin on a raft in the Pacific, there were several peculiar clickings until Torstein supplied more details. When the man on the air had pulled himself together, he told us that his name was Hal and his wife's name Anna and that she was Swedish by birth and would let our families know we were alive and well.

It was a strange thought for us that evening that a total stranger called Hal, a chance moving-picture operator far away among the swarming population of Los Angeles, was the only person in the world but ourselves who knew where we were and that we were well. From that night onward Hal, alias Harold Kempel, and his friend Frank Cuevas took it in turns to sit up every night and listen for signals from the raft, and Herman received grateful telegrams from the head of the U.S. Weather Bureau for his two daily code reports from an area for which there were extremely few reports and no statistics. Later Knut and Torstein established contact with other radio amateurs almost every night, and these passed on greetings to Norway through a radio "ham" named Egil Berg at Notodden.

When we were just a few days out in mid-ocean, there was too much salt water for the radio corner, and the station stopped working altogether. The operators stood on their heads day and night with screws and soldering irons, and all our distant radio fans thought the raft's days were ended. But then one night the signals LI 2 B burst out into the ether, and in a moment the radio corner was buzzing like a wasp's nest as several hundred American operators seized their keys simultaneously and replied to the call.

Indeed one always felt as if one were sitting down on a wasp's nest if one strayed into the radio operators' domain. It was damp with sea water, which forced its way up along the woodwork everywhere, and, even if there was a piece of raw rubber on the balsa log where the operator sat, one got electric shocks both in the hinder parts and in the finger tips if one touched the Morse key. And, if one of us outsiders tried to steal a pencil from the well-equipped corner, either his hair stood straight up on his head or he drew long sparks from the stump of the pencil. Only Torstein and Knut and the parrot could wriggle their way about in that corner unscathed, and we put up a sheet of cardboard to mark the danger zone for the rest of us.

Late one night Knut was sitting tinkering by lamplight in the radio corner when he suddenly shook me by the leg and said he had been talking to a fellow who lived just outside Oslo and was called Christian Amundsen. This was a bit of an amateur record, for the little short-wave transmitter on board the raft with its 13,990 kilocycles per second did not send out more than 6 watts, about the same strength as a small electric torch. This was August 2, and we had sailed more than sixty degrees round the earth, so that Oslo was at the opposite end of the globe. King Haakon was seventy-five years old the day after, and we sent him a message of congratulations direct from the raft; the day after that Christian was again audible and sent us a reply from the King, wishing us continued good luck and success on our voyage.

Another episode we remember as an unusual contrast to the rest of the life on the raft. We had two cameras on board, and Erik had with him a parcel of materials for developing photographs on the voyage, so that we could take duplicate snapshots of things that had not come out well. After the whale shark's visit he could contain himself no longer, and one evening he mixed the chemicals and water carefully in exact accordance with the instructions and developed two films. The negatives looked like long-distance photographs—nothing but obscure spots and wrinkles. The film was ruined. We telegraphed to our contacts for advice, but our message was picked up by a radio amateur near Hollywood. He telephoned a laboratory and soon afterward he broke in and told us that our developer was too warm; we must not use water above 60° or the negative would be wrinkled.

We thanked him for his advice and ascertained that the very lowest temperature in our surroundings was that of the ocean current itself, which was nearly 80°. Now Herman was a refrigerating engineer, and I told him by way of a joke to get the temperature of the water down to 60°. He asked to have the use of the little bottle of carbonic acid belonging to the already inflated rubber dinghy, and after some hocus-pocus in a kettle covered with a sleeping bag and a woolen vest suddenly there was snow on Herman's stubbly beard, and he came in with a big lump of white ice in the kettle.

Erik developed afresh with splendid results.

Even though the ghost words carried through the air by short wave were an unknown luxury in Kon-Tiki's early days, the long ocean waves beneath us were the same as of old and they carried the balsa raft steadily westward as they did then, fifteen hundred years ago.

The weather became a little more unsettled, with scattered rain squalls, after we had entered the area nearer the South Sea islands and the trade wind had changed its direction. It had blown steadily and surely from the southeast until we were a good way over in the Equatorial Current; then it had veered round more and more toward due east. We reached our most northerly position on June 10 with latitude 6° 19′ south. We were then so close up to the Equator that it looked as if we should sail above even the most northerly islands of the Marquesas group and disappear completely in the sea without finding land. But then the trade wind swung round farther, from east to northeast, and drove us in a curve down toward the latitude of the world of islands.

It often happened that wind and sea remained unchanged for days on end, and then we clean forgot whose steering watch it was except at night, when the watch was alone on deck. For, if sea and wind were steady, the steering oar was lashed fast and the *Kon-Tiki* sail remained filled without our attending to it. Then the night watch could sit quietly in the cabin door and look at the stars. If the constellations changed their position in the sky, it was time for him to go out and see whether it was the steering oar or the wind that had shifted.

It was incredible how easy it was to steer by the stars when we had seen them marching across the vault of the sky for weeks on end. Indeed, there was not much else to look at at night. We knew where we could expect to see the different constellations night after night, and, when we came up toward the Equator, the Great Bear rose so clear of the horizon in the north that we were anxious lest we should catch a glimpse of the Pole Star, which appears when one comes from southward and crosses the Equator. But as the north-easterly trade wind set in, the Great Bear sank again.

The old Polynesians were great navigators. They took bearings by the sun by day and the stars by night. Their knowledge of the heavenly bodies was astonishing. They knew that the earth was round, and they had names for such abstruse conceptions as the Equator and the northern and southern tropics. In Hawaii they cut charts of the ocean on the shells of round bottle gourds, and on certain other islands they made detailed maps of plaited boughs to which shells were attached to mark the islands, while the twigs marked particular currents. The Polynesians knew five planets, which they called wandering stars, and distinguished them from the fixed stars, for which they had nearly two hundred different names. A good navigator in old Polynesia knew well in what part of the sky the different stars would rise and where they would be at different times of the night and at different times of the year. They knew which stars culminated over the different islands, and there were cases in which an island was named after a star which culminated over it night after night and year after year.

Apart from the fact that the starry sky lay like a glittering giant compass revolving from east to west, they understood that the different stars right over their heads always showed them how far north or south they were. When the Polynesians had explored and brought under their sway their present domain, which is the whole of the sea nearest to America, they maintained traffic between some of the islands for many generations to come. Historical traditions relate that, when the chiefs from Tahiti visited Hawaii, which lay more than 2,000 sea miles farther north and several degrees farther west, the helmsman steered first due north by sun and stars, till the stars right above their heads told them that they were on the latitude of Hawaii. Then they turned at a right angle and steered due west till they came so near that birds and clouds told them where the group of islands lay.

Whence had the Polynesians obtained their vast astronomical

knowledge and their calendar, which was calculated with astonishing thoroughness? Certainly not from Melanesian or Malayan peoples to the westward. But the same old vanished civilized race, the "white and bearded men," who had taught Aztecs, Mayas, and Incas their amazing culture in America, had evolved a curiously similar calendar and a similar astronomical knowledge which Europe in those times could not match. In Polynesia, as in Peru, the calendar year had been so arranged as to begin on the particular day of the year when the constellation of the Pleiades first appeared above the horizon, and in both areas this constellation was considered the patron of agriculture.

In Peru, where the continent slopes down toward the Pacific, there stand to this day in the desert sand the ruins of an astronomical observatory of great antiquity, a relic of the same mysterious civilized people which carved stone collossi, erected pyramids, cultivated sweet potatoes and bottle gourds, and began their year with the rising of the Pleiades. Kon-Tiki knew the movement of the stars when he set sail upon the Pacific Ocean.

ROCKET RIDER

by Charles Coombs

A ghostly morning haze clings to the beige Mojave Desert sand as Captain Tom Benton leaves the pre-flight briefing at Edwards Air Force Base. He strides stiff-legged across the concrete apron toward the X-15, a fifty foot sharp shiny black sliver of tough metal alloy called Inconel-X.

Tom hopes the technicians with him will attribute his stiff walk to the tightness of the MC-2 full pressure space suit he is wearing.

He hopes they don't sense the other reason, the one Tom has been trying to hide, even from himself.

"Looks like they've got the 'beast' about ready to go," one of the men says, indicating the waiting rocket craft. "How about you, captain?"

Tom glances at the man, trying to figure if there is more to the casual query than meets the ear. "If I'm not ready," he says with forced lightness, "I should have stayed in bed."

The rocket is shackled to the end of a pylon hanging below the right wing of the B-52 mother ship, a giant eight-jet intercontinental bomber converted to the task of carrying the X-15 to high altitude before cutting the sleek craft loose for the space jaunt.

Even now men in protective, white-hooded plastic suits are pumping liquid oxygen into the X-15's oxidizer tanks. The super-cold "lox" paints a coat of white frost on the outside of the rocket craft's fuselage.

"She's ready when you're ready, captain," someone says.

Tom Benton doesn't answer right away. He looks up at the 15-ton space probing monster. Her wings seem scarcely bigger than a couple of lopsided card tables sticking out from each side of the massive fuselage—way back where wings are not normally located. Directly behind them the vertical rudders—upper and lower—protrude like great blunt-ended meat cleavers. They are so built in order to withstand the enormous pressures and the fierce friction heat generated during high-speed flight. Somewhere inside is the XLR-99 rocket engine capable of producing some 50,000 pounds of thrust—a lot of push in a small package.

Tom has lived with this beast for more than six years—ever since she was a blueprint on a designer's table. He has grown up with her; knows every welded seam, every hinge, every wire nerve, and every vein of tubing. Yet, he still stands in awe and amazement every time he looks at her.

"All set, captain?"

Tom climbs the ladder and, with the help of a couple technicians, lowers himself beneath the raised canopy with its two narrow, tempered-glass viewing slots.

"Soft landing, Tom," someone says, after plugging in his oxygen hose, his radio connections, and electronic circuits.

Then the canopy clicks down over his head, and Tom snaps the safety clamps.

He gets busy then, running through his lengthy checklist, calling off each item to the ground controllers, as well as the technicians located inside the instrumented mother ship. He is barely aware of the B-52's eight jets whining to life.

A slow dull ache begins to creep into Tom's legs. It quickly spreads toward his stomach. A knotty fist pummels his insides. He bites his lip and crowds the thought of fire from his mind. This is no new feeling. He has had it off and on for the past two years—ever since the bail-out from that flaming Super Sabre. It was a hairy experience. It had left its scars, not scars in the flesh but in the mind. This was no time for the latter . . . not here . . . not now!

With an effort Tom jerks his mind away from the memories. "Roll when you're ready," he says over the radio.

The mother ship trundles down the packed clay of Rogers Dry Lake, sixty-five square miles of smooth landing field provided by nature free of charge. Tom continues working through his checklist.

Then the B-52 turns into the wind. After getting clearance from the tower, the pilot pours the juice to the turbojets. Tom huddles in the cockpit, listening to the shriek of the jets. The mother ship lumbers slowly forward, picks up speed, sprints, then lifts gently into the air. Banking eastward, she starts climbing, determined to carry Tom and his rocket charger as high as possible before the X-15's weight and the thinning air level her off.

Tom makes more predrop checks. Even when he thinks he is finished, the ground controllers and the technicians inside the B-52 ask him for certain repeats. Despite the cool air circulating through his pressure suit, he is sweating.

But his checks are completed by the time they are over Wendover, Utah, the area of the "drop," some 480 miles east of Edwards AFB.

"We're at angels thirty-eight, captain," the B-52 pilot says. "This is about as high as we can haul you. Say when you're ready to start the countdown."

Thirty-eight thousand feet. Good. A little better than was expected, considering the heavy load.

Tom Benton's eyes sweep over the instruments. Subconsciously his gaze lingers on the fire warning lights, as he continues to crowd back old fears. The lights are dark. They should be. What did he expect? He bites his lip. Forget it!

Glancing out the right hand window slot, he sees an F-100 Super Sabre chase plane some fifty yards off and to the rear. Super Sabre! Always some reminder of his near-tragic fire. He pulls his attention back inside the cockpit, and tests the controls.

What a deal, those controls. There's the normal center stick between his knees. But there are also two other sticks—small sticks —located on the left and right hand instrument consoles. They are positioned right where his hands will be once his arms are clamped firmly to the armrests. The right hand stick moves the normal aerodynamic controls during flight through the atmosphere. The left hand stick operates the "space controls." These are small peroxide-activated rockets located around the nose and in the wingtips. Moving the left stick triggers the correct ones to steer the rocket craft up where there is no longer any air for rudders or elevators to bite into.

"Ready for the countdown," Tom says.

"Ten minutes before drop!"

More checks. More last-minute instructions from the ground. More terse queries.

"Everything in-the-green," Tom says.

At the five-minute mark the X-15's tanks are topped off with propellants from the storage tanks in the B-52. The mother ship banks gently back into a western heading.

"One minute, Tom!"

He starts the recording tapes, sets the automatic cameras, checks the telemetering switches, and makes other last-minute adjustments. This done, he clamps his arms firmly into the restrainers, and fingers the small auxiliary control sticks. He makes a mental dry-run of the operation of several strategically positioned buttons and switches within easy fingertip reach.

The final seconds of the countdown come over the intercom. ". . . five . . . four . . . three . . . two . . . one . . . DROP!"

With a metallic click the shackles release their grip upon the X-15. She hangs suspended for a moment, then drops like a rock. Tom makes no immediate move. Somewhere behind him the chase pilot is giving him a quick visual going-over for fuel leaks, vibrating parts—anything.

"Looks fine, Tom. Fine! Blast off!"

Tom thumbs the firing button. The rocket engine ignites with a cannon-like boom that rattles Tom's teeth. The giant fist of thrust smashes him into his backrest as the heavy force of acceleration doubles his weight—triples it. Luckily the clamps keep his hand in proper position on the small right control stick. He eases it gently back. The X-15 spears skyward, trailing its flaming tail.

Quickly the B-52 and the F-100 are left behind and far below. Climbing steeply the X-15 hits Mach 2—twice the speed of sound. Tom stares in awe as visible ghostly shock waves shimmer along the needle nose and flow rearward. Still accelerating, he reaches Mach 3. Friction heat scorches the outside of the plane, but internal refrigeration keeps Tom from parboiling inside the tight cockpit.

Then the air thins, the heat drops away, and he is soon slicing into the stratosphere. As speed continues to increase, over 4-G's of gravity weight sit on Tom like an overfed elephant. Only the constrictions of his pressure suit prevent him from blacking out.

He passes through Mach 5, well over 3,000 miles per hour, and still climbing. The sky darkens to a deep purple as he streaks on out of the stratosphere at 20 miles altitude—and into the chemosphere.

Ninety-nine per cent of the earth's atmospheric cloak is beneath him already. It is impossible for him to know all that is happening around him. Luckily much of his flight is being automatically controlled from the ground. He can no longer rely on his instruments. At this speed, nearly a mile-a-second, what the instruments say now happened nearly two miles ago.

At an altitude of about forty miles, higher than man ever before has gone, the X-15 begins to buffet badly. This is the "controllability barrier." Just enough thin atmosphere remains to cause trouble during a hypersonic passage. Tom fingers the controls with all the practiced skill of a concert violinist coaxing a tune from a Stradivarius.

Then, thankfully, he is through the barrier, and into the ionosphere—50 miles up—for all practical purposes, in SPACE!

And all this within ninety seconds after drop! Suddenly the fuel is gone. The rocket engine coughs dead. Yet, the tremendous build-up of speed hurls the rocket craft on upward.

A great change has taken place. As propulsion ceases, the oppressive G-forces drop away. Coasting through space in the absence of any force causes a strange sensation to sweep over Tom. He is weightless.

During the first moments of this weightlessness he feels as though he is in a high-speed elevator heading for the ground floor. Yet, as this sensation eases off he begins to feel indescribably free. Like floating in a dream.

"Weightlessness!!" he says to himself. "What a deal! Don't knock it until you've tried it!!"

He feels like laughing. But the tendency freezes in his throat as, suddenly, a red warning light begins flashing urgently on the instrument panel.

Fire! His most dreaded foe!

But where? An overheated fuel pump? A propellant leak during acceleration? A hidden pool, suddenly ignited? What difference does it make? A fire's a fire. At any time the X-15 might become a flaming torch, or simply explode into myriad pieces of space chaff!

"Hit the trigger!!" his mind shouts. "Eject. Eject!"

But to eject up here in space spells sure doom. Even his pressure suit is not designed for such a high bail-out. The fantastic sub-zero cold would freeze him solid long before he reached the ground. His limited emergency oxygen supply would never sustain him during the long fall.

But to burn! Memory floods over him. Anything is better than that! Call Mayday! Ridiculous! Who can help you up here? No one!

Tom is about to release his arms from their clamps and reach for the ejection seat trigger when a sudden thought presses into his mind and alters his decision.

"Stick with it, boy!" he tells himself. Even though his eyes keep sweeping fearfully over the flashing fire warning light, his mind tells him that it must be lying.

Just don't hit that panic button!

The sky overhead is a velvet black now, dusted with unblinking stars. Below is a hazy earth, washed by the early morning sun.

Then, at an altitude of well over 100 miles, the X-15 arches slowly over the top of its coasting trajectory and starts back down. Tom is still weightless, hanging in his seat belt and shoulder harness, coasting through the lower fringes of space.

He starts bracing himself for the big problem which will soon be upon him—a plunging meteor-like re-entry into the earth's atmosphere.

His attention to this is suddenly diverted when his instruments tell him that he is starting to spin. He quickly manipulates the small left-hand control stick. Tiny jets of peroxide steam spurt from the wingtips. The force of their reaction stops the spin, and the wings level up once again.

Then, as the X-15 plunges back into the upper fringes of the atmosphere, the firm rough hand of friction grabs Tom once again. His weightlessness ceases abruptly, and the G-forces of deceleration slam him forward against his harness.

He notices now that, for some unknown reason, the fire warning light has stopped flashing. He mentally sighs, but his contentment is short-lived.

The scorching friction heat is back again, building up an extra thousand degrees or more of temperature on the plane. The nose and leading edges of the wings turn a cherry red. If this keeps up he will be roasted like a leg of lamb, and—

But the heat doesn't last. The atmosphere, taking an ever-firmer grip upon the X-15, slows the plane down, backing it gradually out of the dangerous thermal thicket.

Then, with welcome relief, Tom sees the dry lake adjacent to Edwards Air Force Base stretching out ahead and far below. He calculates quickly that he has covered nearly 500 ground miles and goodness knows how many space miles in something like twenty minutes.

"Hey, buddy," a new voice comes into his earphones. "This is your welcome-home chase plane. I've got you spotted. Come on down and I'll lead you in. I'm at ten o'clock low."

Tom breathes easily. He releases his arms now and takes over the normal central control stick. Once again, as wings and tail surfaces take firm hold of the air, he feels as though he is riding an airplane, not a rocket beast.

The chase plane, an F-104 Starfighter this time, paces him down. Tom lowers his dual nose wheels, jettisons the lower vertical rudder to get it out of the way, and lets down the main landing skids. The dry lake bed rushes toward him.

He comes in deadstick, touching down on the hard packed clay at about 240 knots, as hot a deadstick landing as anyone ever has managed.

"You're home again, buddy!" the chase pilot calls, then peels off, his pacing chore finished.

After the long coasting skid to a standstill, Tom leans back and takes a deep breath of relief. He waits patiently for the dust-trailing caravan of vehicles racing across the dry lake toward him.

Soon eager hands help him out.

"Let's just rest here a minute," Tom suggests, once the feel of firm ground is beneath him. He sits down within the sparse shadow of the X-15.

The men smile. They understand. "Tell us about the flight," one of them asks. Then they listen, and their eyes fill with pride.

"But when you saw that fire warning light, Tom, you must have—well, after being through one bad fire—"

"You're right," Tom admits. "I just about bailed out right then and there."

"You had no way of knowing that the light was just defective—that it didn't mean a thing?"

"I sure didn't," Tom says. "But then I remembered just where I was and I nearly laughed out loud."

"How come?"

"I was in space at the time the light began flashing. And in space—where there is no oxygen to support combustion—there can be no fire."

"Tom—of course! That's right!"

Tom grins. "Let's go, now," he says and climbs into a waiting jeep. He glances up into the desert sky.

"Mind telling me what it's like up there, captain?" the jeep driver asks.

"Sure," Tom says, "you see it's . . . well . . . there's the . . ." His words trail off.

The driver looks at him, puzzled. Tom shrugs, and smiles.

After all, how can you talk about space to an earthman?

3

Folk Tales: Animals Around the World

People everywhere have been telling stories about animals—true stories, amusing stories, make-believe stories, exciting stories. These stories, naturally, are about the animals that people in any particular region know best or think most about—alligators, bears, camels, dogs, elephants, or anything else in the alphabet all the way to yaks and zebras and zebus.

Everybody is interested in animal stories because everybody is interested in animals. But these stories are interesting in a special way. For in these stories the animals are made to think and to act like the storytellers themselves. They have their own particular animal qualities; but in addition they have certain human qualities, too. One curious result is that these stories tell us a great deal about people. *They tell us about what kinds of people there are in different parts of the world, and what people in all parts of the world think about life and death, about gods and spirits, about good and evil. And they tell us also what ideas people have about what's funny.*

If you do not happen to be interested in animals, you might find these stories interesting because they do tell us, in their own way, about human beings.

FROM THE U.S.A.

BROTHER RABBIT AND THE MOSQUITOES

by Joel Chandler Harris

ADAPTED BY MARGARET WISE BROWN

One time when everything and everybody was running along just like they had wagon grease on them, Brer Rabbit and Brer Wolf they had another set-to.

Brer Wolf, he lived down in the swamp, and more than that, he had a mighty likely gal. It looked like the other creatures were all after her too. They would go down to Brer Wolf's house, they would, and they'd sit up and court the gal and enjoy themselves.

It went on this way until after a while the mosquitoes began to get monstrous bad. Brer Fox he went flying around Miss Wolf, and he sat there, he did, and ran on with her, and fought the mosquitoes just as big as life and twice as natural. At last Brer Wolf he took and caught Brer Fox slapping and fighting at his skeeters. With that he took Brer Fox by the off ear and led him out to the gate, and when he got there he allowed, he did, that no man what can't put up with mosquitoes ain't gwine to come a-courtin' his gal.

Then Brer Coon, he comes flying round the gal, but he ain't been there no time scarcely 'fore he began to knock at the mosquitoes; and no sooner had he done this than Brer Wolf shows him the door. Brer Mink, he comes and tries his hand, yet he is pleased to fight the mosquitoes and Brer Wolf asks him out.

It went on this a-way till by-and-by all the creatures been flying round Brer Wolf's gal except old Brer Rabbit, and when Brer Rabbit hears what kind of treatment the other creatures have been catching he allows to himself that he believes in his soul he must go down to Brer Wolf's house and sit the gal out one, what if it's the last act.

No sooner say, no sooner do. Off he put, and it wasn't long 'fore he finds himself knocking at Brer Wolf's front door. Old Sis Wolf, she put up her knitting and she up and allows, she did:

"Who dat?"

The gal she was standing before the looking glass sort of primping, and she chokes back a giggle, she did, and allows:

"Sh-h-h! My goodness, mammy! Dat's Mr. Rabbit. I hear de gals say he's a mighty proper en particular gentermun, en I just hope you ain't gwine ter set dar en run on like you mos' allers does w'en I got comp'ny, 'bout how much soap grease you done save up en how many kittens de ole cat got."

Old Sis Wolf she sat there, she did, and settled her cap on her head, and sort of snickers, and looks at the gal like she is monstrous proud. The gal, she took and shook herself before the looking glass a time or two, and then she tips to the door and opens it a little ways and peeps out just like she is scared someone is going to hit her a clip in the side of the head. There stood old Brer Rabbit looking just as sleek as a race horse. The gal she took and laughed, she did, and hollers:

"W'y law, maw! It's Mr. Rabbit, en here we bin 'fraid it 'uz some'un w'at ain't got no business roun' here!"

Old Sis Wolf she looks over her specs and snickers, and then she up and allows:

"Well, don't keep 'im standin' out dar all night. Ask 'im in, fer goodness' sake."

Then the gal she took and dropped her handkerchief, and Brer Rabbit, he dipped down and grabbed it and passed it to her with a bow, and the gal says she is much obliged because that is more than Mr. Fox would have ever done, and then she asks Brer Rabbit how he comes on, and Brer Rabbit allows he's right pert, and then he asks her whereabouts is her daddy, and old Sis Wolf allows she'll go find him.

It wasn't long before Brer Rabbit heard Brer Wolf stomping the mud off his foots on the back porch, and then by-and-by in he comes. They shook hands, they did, and Brer Rabbit says that when he goes calling on his acquaintance he doesn't feel natural excepting that the man of the house is sitting around somewheres.

"Ef he don't talk none," sez Brer Rabbit, sezee, "he kin just set up ag'in de chimbly-jam en keep time by noddin'."

But old Brer Wolf, he is one of these here kind of men what got the whimsies, and he up and allows that he don't let himself get to noddin' in front of company. They run on this a-way till by-and-by Brer Rabbit hears the skeeters come zoonin' round and claimin' kin with him.

They come sailing round and singing out, "*Cousin! Cousin!*" Of course they claimed kin with him. They claim kin with anyone, let alone Brer Rabbit. And you can know the skeeters are mighty close kin to you when they get to be your cousin.

Brer Rabbit he hears them zoonin' and he knows he has got to do some mighty nice talking, so he up and asks for a drink of water. The gal she took and fetched it.

"Mighty nice water, Brer Wolf." (*The skeeters they zoon.*)

"Some say it too full er wiggletails, Brer Rabbit." (*The skeeters they zoon and they zoon.*)

"Mighty nice place you got, Brer Wolf." (*Skeeters they zoon.*)

"Some say it too low in de swamp, Brer Rabbit." (*Skeeters they zoon and they zoon.*)

They zoon so bad that Brer Rabbit began to get scared, and when that creature gets scared, his mind works like one of these here flutter mills. By-and-by he allows:

"Went to town today, en dar I seed a sight w'at I never 'spected to see."

"W'at dat, Brer Rabbit?"

"Spotted hoss, Brer Wolf."

"*No*, Brer Rabbit!"

"I mos' sho'ly seed 'im, Brer Wolf."

Brer Wolf, he scratched his head, and the gal she held up her hands and made great admiration about the spotted horse. (*The skeeters they zoon and they keep on zoonin'.*) Brer Rabbit he talked on, he did:

" 'Twa'n't just one spotted hoss, Brer Wolf, 'twuz a whole team er spotted hosses en dey went gallopin'-up just like de other hosses," sezee. "Let 'lone dat, Brer Wolf, my grandaddy wuz spotted," sez Brer Rabbit, sezee.

Gal, she squeals and hollers out:

"W'y, Brer Rabbit! Ain't you 'shame' yo'se'f fer to be talkin' dat a-way, en 'bout yo' own-lone blood kin too."

"It's de naked trufe I'm a-givin' you," sez Brer Rabbit, sezee. (*Skeeter zoon en come closer.*)

Brer Wolf allows, "Well—well—well!" Old Sis Wolf she allows, "Tooby sho'ly, tooby sho'ly!" (*Skeeter zoon en come nigher en nigher.*) Brer Rabbit allows:

"Yasser! Just ez sho' ez you'er settin' dar, my grandaddy wuz spotted. Spotted all over. (*Skeeter come zoonin' up and lights on Brer Rabbit's jaw.*) He wuz dat. He had er great big spot right here!"

Here Brer Rabbit raised his foot and struck himself a resounding slap on the side of his face where the mosquito was, and no sooner did he do this than another mosquito comes zoonin' around and lights on Brer Rabbit's leg. Brer Rabbit, he talks and he talks:

"Po' ole grandaddy! I boun' he make you laff, he look so funny wid all dem spots en speckles. He had spot on der side er de head, whar I done show you, en den he had n'er spot right here on de leg," sezee. *Blip! Brer Rabbit slaps his leg.*

Mosquito zoons and lights between Brer Rabbit's shoulder blades. Then he talks:

"B'leeve me er not—b'leeve me ef you min' to, but my grandaddy had a big black spot up here on his back w'ich look like saddle mark."

Blip! Brer Rabbit tuck hisself a slap on the back!

It kept on this way till by-and-by old Brer Wolf and old Sis

Wolf they listen to Brer Rabbit till they began to nod, and then Brer Rabbit and the gal they sot up there and killed skeeters right along.

FROM INDIA

THE BANYAN DEER*

by Ellen C. Babbitt

There was once a Deer the color of gold. His eyes were like round jewels, his horns were white as silver, his mouth was red like a flower, his hoofs were bright and hard. He had a large body and a fine tail.

He lived in a forest and was king of a herd of five Banyan Deer. Near by lived another herd of Deer, called the Monkey Deer. They, too, had a king.

The king of that country was fond of hunting the Deer and eating deer meat. He did not like to go alone so he called the people of his town to go with him, day after day.

The townspeople did not like this for while they were gone no one did their work. So they decided to make a park and drive the Deer into it. Then the king could go into the park and hunt and they could go on with their daily work.

They made a park, planted grass in it and provided water for the Deer, built a fence all around it and drove the Deer into it.

Then they shut the gate and went to the king to tell him that in the park near by he could find all the Deer he wanted.

The king went at once to look at the Deer. First he saw there the two Deer kings, and granted them their lives. Then he looked at their great herds.

Some days the king would go to hunt the Deer, sometimes his cook would go. As soon as any of the Deer saw them they would shake with fear and run. But when they had been hit once or twice they would drop down dead.

The King of the Banyan Deer sent for the King of the Monkey Deer and said, "Friend, many of the Deer are being killed. Many are wounded besides those who are killed. After this suppose one from my herd goes up to be killed one day, and the next day let one from your herd go up. Fewer Deer will be lost this way."

The Monkey Deer agreed. Each day the Deer whose turn it was would go and lie down, placing its head on the block. The cook would come and carry off the one he found lying there.

One day the lot fell to a mother Deer who had a young baby. She went to her king and said, "O King of the Monkey Deer, let the turn pass me by until my baby is old enough to get along without me. Then I will go and put my head on the block."

But the king did not help her. He told her that if the lot had fallen to her she must die.

Then she went to the King of the Banyan Deer and asked him to save her.

"Go back to your herd. I will go in your place," said he.

The next day the cook found the King of the Banyan Deer lying with his head on the block. The cook went to the king, who came himself to find out about this.

"King of the Banyan Deer! did I not grant you your life? Why are you lying here?"

"O great King!" said the King of the Banyan Deer, "a mother came with her young baby and told me that the lot had fallen to her. I could not ask any one else to take her place, so I came myself."

"King of the Banyan Deer! I never saw such kindness and

mercy. Rise up. I grant your life and hers. Nor will I hunt any more the Deer in either park or forest."

FROM CHINA

HOW THE CAMEL GOT HIS PROUD LOOK*

by Berta Metzger

When the Lord of Heaven created the camel he looked very much like other animals. One day he started to walk out upon the desert and found that his feet sank into the sand, and he made little progress. So he returned to the Lord of Heaven and complained, "I long to live upon the beautiful desert, but my four small feet sink down into the sand like sticks. I pray you, make them so they will carry me over the desert."

So the Lord of Heaven reshaped the camel's feet and made them large and flat. Then the camel returned to the desert and *plop-plopped* over the sand with the greatest ease. He walked proudly, for he was much pleased with himself. He had not gone far, however, when he was overcome with hunger and thirst. He turned round, and *plop-plopped* back again. He went to the Lord of Heaven a second time and said:

"My feet carry me over the desert with the greatest ease. But I can go only a short distance when I am overcome with hunger and thirst. I pray you, change my body so I can carry enough food and drink for many days."

* Reprinted by permission of the publisher from *Picture Tales From the Chinese,* by Berta Metzger. Copyright, 1934, J. B. Lippincott Company.

The Lord of Heaven laughed good-naturedly. Then he reshaped the camel again, and back he went to the desert. He found that he could carry food and drink for many days. But whenever he met other animals they stood about and laughed and laughed, and cried out:

"See his humps and his lumps, and his pancake feet!"

This hurt the pride of the camel. He hastened back to the Lord of Heaven a third time, and complained:

"Wherever I go the other animals stand about and laugh and cry, 'See his humps, and his lumps, and his pancake feet!' I pray you, change me back to the form I had at first."

The Lord of Heaven replied, "That, even I, cannot do."

Then the camel went away, and thought and thought. At last he returned for the fourth time to the Lord of Heaven, and said, "I ask but one thing more. Give me a superior look. Then I shall gaze down upon the other animals of your creation and make them believe they are inferior to me."

The Lord of Heaven laughed heartily. He gave the camel's chin an upward shove. Then he pushed the nose back a trifle so that the camel looked as if he smelled something most unpleasant. Then off into the desert the camel *plop-plopped* on his large pancake feet. He carried his humps and his lumps proudly.

Soon he met other animals. He sniffed and looked down his nose at them with large and glassy eyes. And to this day, all animals, including men, shrink before the disdainful look of the camel.

FROM ALASKA

MR. CROW TAKES A WIFE

by Charles E. Gillham

Once upon a time there lived an old crow. He really was not a bad fellow, but he was rather proud and puffed up about himself and he thought he was very wise. Mr. Crow was as black as coal and in those days he had a long tail about which he was rather vain. He was unhappy, though, for he did not have a wife. Several of the birds he asked to marry him had refused.

"We know you are quite wise, Mr. Crow, but you are such a greedy bird. We like grass and tender roots to eat. You hunt old dead things along the beach and you seldom eat the nice food we do. No, Mr. Crow," the birds replied, "we do not want to marry you."

So Mr. Crow was sad as fall came on and he saw the birds leaving to go south. He could see long strings of geese and other birds as they headed south, driving their bird sleds through the sky. He looked up, and coming right over him were Mr. White-fronted Goose and his family. The old gander was in front, pulling, in the harness and, behind, his wife held the handle bars of the sled. The children were riding.

"Hello there, Mr. White-front," the old crow called. "Have you any daughters who would like to marry? I am looking for a wife and I would like to go south for the winter."

Mr. Goose looked down at Mr. Crow, but he kept on pulling away at his sky sled. "No, Mr. Crow," he replied, "my daughters are rather young to marry. Besides, you do not eat the things we do and you would always be away, hunting along the seashore. That is a lovely boat you are building, but our girls do not need a boat; they can all swim."

So the white-fronted geese went on their way.

Mr. Crow continued to work on his boat. He had an adz, a queer tool that all the Eskimo people use. They can take a round log and chop along it and make it up into boards. So the old crow worked on as another flock of geese came by. They were emperor geese, and Mr. Crow looked up at them. The old gander was pulling the sled and he leaned into the harness, for he was very strong. In the sled his one child, a girl goose, was riding. His wife was riding on the runners and holding the handle bars. They were really a beautiful family, with their pretty pearl-gray backs and their white heads flashing in the sun.

"Hello, Mr. Emperor Goose," the old crow called to the family. "That is a beautiful daughter you have. Do you think she would care to marry me? I would like to go with you to the birdland for the winter."

Mr. Emperor Goose looked down at Mr. Crow, and the girl goose blushed. "I do not know, Mr. Crow. Maybe it will be all right if our daughter is willing. That is a fine kayak you are building; but she really needs none, for she can swim very well." The old gander stopped near the igloo to talk it over. He took off the harness he wore while pulling the sky sled, and sat down on the grass. "What do you think about it, Mamma?" he asked Mrs. Emperor Goose.

"I suppose it is all right," she said, looking at Mr. Crow and his long tail. "He really is making a lovely kayak and he would not be such a bad-looking son-in-law. I am afraid, though, he would have trouble keeping up with us as we go to the birdland for the winter. We go very fast, for our sky sled is not heavily loaded. What if he should fall off as we cross the big wide ocean?"

"Oh, I am quite strong," Mr. Crow bragged, and he arched his long tail as he saw that Mrs. Goose had noticed it. "I can pull the sky sled, myself, and I will not get tired when we cross the big wide ocean. Just wait until I put on my parka and my water boots and close the igloo door. I am all ready to leave."

Mr. Crow was so excited that he worked quickly. "What a

lovely goose girl the young Emperor woman is," he thought. How he would show off before them when he took his turn pulling the sky sled! Soon Mr. Crow was all ready.

"You had better ride behind on the runners and hold the handle bars," Mr. Emperor Goose told the old crow. "It is really quite hard work and I do not think you are strong enough to do it."

"Nonsense," said Mr. Crow, putting on the harness. "I will pull the sled through the sky, and you ride on the runner, Mr. Goose, and hold to the handle bars."

Mr. Crow set off as fast as he could go. He wanted to show the goose girl how strong he was, and he pulled as hard as he could.

"Mercy," said Mrs. Emperor Goose, "we certainly are going fast! We should be to the big wide ocean tonight if we go this swiftly. Mr. Crow is really quite strong."

So the old crow pulled all the harder. The goose girl and her mother rode on the sky sled, and Mr. Emperor Goose held the handle bars and rode on the runner. They passed several families of other birds who were not pulling their sleds so fast. All of them were surprised to see Mr. Crow doing all the work.

After quite a distance the old crow grew tired. He had never been so fagged out in all his life. He was sorry, now, that he had not let Mr. Emperor Goose pull, in the harness, and his wings hurt so that he could hardly go another foot.

"Here, Mr. Crow," the Emperor Goose said, "let me pull the sky sled."

"Oh, I can pull it, Mr. Goose," and the old crow spurted up a bit. "I really am very strong. I think I can pull the sled clear to the land where the birds live." He pulled all the harder, but he was getting very weak.

At last the old gander went up and took the harness from Mr. Crow. "You ride behind and hold the handle bars," he told him. "I will pull the sky sled for a while."

Poor Mr. Crow was so tired he was almost dead. His lovely tail, which had streamed out behind, now drooped down. He hung on to the handle bars, and Mr. Emperor Goose went like the wind. Soon they came to the big wide ocean and started right across. When they were halfway, Mr. Crow was still gasping for breath. Suddenly they hit a rough cloud of air and the sky sled gave a terrible bounce. The poor old crow fell right off behind. He was so tired that he could not even say a word, and on went Mr. Goose with the sled. Mrs. Emperor Goose and the daughter were looking ahead, enjoying the ride. They did not know that Mr. Crow had fallen off right over the big wide ocean.

The old crow flapped as hard as he could to keep from falling into the big wide ocean. His beautiful tail was drooping and he was very weary. "Goodness," he said, "the goose people do not know that I have fallen off the sled and they are going on without me. I do not think I can ever fly the rest of the way across the big wide ocean."

Mr. Crow flapped his tired wings as strongly as he could, but he kept getting lower and lower in the sky. Soon he was only a few feet above the waves and he knew that soon he would fall right in if he did not flap his wings harder.

"Oh, I am going to drown," he thought, "and I was just going to marry the beautiful goose girl. Why did I ever act so foolish and try to pull the sky sled so fast?"

As he got closer down to the water, Mr. Crow looked ahead. He could still see Mr. Emperor Goose pulling his sled, and right beneath him he could see the shore of the big wide ocean. If he could only fly a little farther! Mr. Crow flapped and flapped, but he just could not make it. At last a big wave touched his wing; then another touched his tail and—kerplop!—the old crow fell right into the water. The shore was only a few feet away.

How Mr. Crow did wish that he had learned to swim like the geese! He went clear under and down to the bottom. Giving a kick with his feet, up he came again. The salty water from the big wide ocean got into Mr. Crow's nose and went down his throat. He choked terribly. Down he went and up he came again. He had salty water in his eyes and he was gasping. Surely, now, he would drown. Just then a big wave larger than the others washed Mr. Crow right out onto the sand. Hastily he dragged his long wet tail up away from the edge of the water.

For a long time Mr. Crow lay on the sand and gasped for breath; the water in his mouth tasted very bad and he had a stomach-ache. At last he sat up, took off his parka, and wrung the water out of it. Then he shook the water from his long tail and felt better. He rested again, then jumped into the air and followed along in the tracks that the sled had made in the sky. He must catch up with Mr. Goose and his lovely daughter.

After some time Mr. Crow saw the emperor geese. They had stopped their sled down near a lot of other birds. He saw the white-fronted geese, the snow geese, and the black brants. Even the little sandpipers were there with a tiny sled, and Mr. King Eider Duck had a very fancy one made of walrus ivory.

"We were worried about you, Mr. Crow," Mr. Emperor Goose said. "What happened to you? I could not turn my sky sled around, for we were over the big wide ocean. I knew that one so strong as you could get here all right by himself."

The old crow did not tell Mr. Emperor Goose what had happened, for he was rather ashamed of the way he had acted. Instead he asked, "What are all of these birds waiting here for? Why don't we go ahead to the south?"

"It is the Canadian geese and the curlews," Mrs. Emperor Goose answered him. "They are always late, and each year we have had to wait for them here. You see, we all try to meet here and fly through the Clapping Mountains together."

Poor Mr. Crow, he was so tired! And when Mrs. Emperor Goose spoke of the Clapping Mountains, he felt worse. Heavens, he thought, I forgot all about the Clapping Mountains. They are likely to catch me this time, because I am so tired I cannot fly very fast.

At last Mr. Emperor Goose grew impatient. "I think I will go ahead," he told his wife. "I am tired of having to wait every year for the Canadian geese and the curlews." So Mr. Goose put on his pulling harness and Mrs. Goose and the goose girl got into the sled. "We must fly very hard," Mr. Emperor Goose said. "You, Mr. Crow, hold the handle bars, but do not ride on the runner. You had better flap your wings and help me make more speed."

Away they went like the very wind.

Mr. Crow did the very best he could, but he could only flap feebly along. "Hurry faster, Mr. Crow," the Emperor Goose called back. "We will be sure to be caught in the Clapping Mountains."

The big gander pulled very hard and Mr. Crow, hanging on to the handle bars, could not even fly hard enough to keep up. His long tail streamed out behind, and he was badly frightened. Just as Mr. Emperor Goose got through the mountains, they began to tremble; in a second they clapped together as hard as they could. Mr. Crow gave a terrible squawk, for his long tail was caught between the straight walls. They cut his long feathers off short, so that he did not have any more tail than a chicken.

How foolish Mr. Crow felt with his beautiful tail gone! The goose girl even laughed, and that made him feel more silly than ever.

"If you ask me," said Mr. Emperor Goose, "I think it helps your looks decidedly not to have that silly tail waving out behind. What good is it anyway? It is only in the way and you could never swim with it on."

So the old crow felt a little better and he found that it was easier to fly too. Mrs. Emperor Goose even started asking him about Hooper Bay, and the goose girl smiled at him.

When they reached the Aleutian Islands, Mr. Emperor Goose said that this was the place they would spend the winter. As soon as Mr. Crow had an igloo built, a great feast was held and Mr. Crow and the goose girl were married. Mr. Crow, by this time, had almost forgotten all about his nice long tail that he had lost up in the Clapping Mountains, and the other birds didn't seem to notice it at all. Ever since that time, the crows have had short tails.

It is good for one always to try to pull his share of the load, but he should not be so silly as to think he can do it all.

FROM JAPAN

THE TWO FROGS

by Andrew Lang

Once upon a time in the country of Japan there lived two frogs, one of whom made his home in a ditch near the town of Osaka, on the sea coast, while the other dwelt in a clear little stream which ran through the city of Kioto. At such a great distance apart, they had never even heard of each other; but, oddly enough, the idea came into both their heads at once that they should like to see a little of the world, and the frog who lived at Kioto wanted to visit Osaka, and the frog who lived at Osaka wished to go to Kioto where the great mikado had his palace.

So one fine morning in the spring they both set out along the road that led from Kioto to Osaka, one from Osaka and the other from Kioto. The journey was more tiring than they expected, for they did not know much about traveling and that halfway between the two towns there rose a mountain which had to be climbed. It took them a long time and a great many hops to reach the top, but there they were at last, and what was the surprise of each to see another frog before him!

They looked at each other for a moment without speaking and then fell into conversation, explaining the cause of their meeting so far from their homes. It was delightful to find that they both felt the same wish—to learn a little more of their native country—and as there was no sort of hurry, they stretched themselves out in a cool, damp place and agreed that they would have a good rest before they parted to go their ways.

"What a pity we are not bigger," said the Osaka frog, "for then we could see both towns from here and tell if it is worth our while going on."

"Oh, that is easily managed," returned the Kioto frog. "We have only to stand up on our hind legs and hold on to each other, and then we can each look at the town he is traveling to."

This idea pleased the Osaka frog so much that he at once jumped up and put his front feet on the shoulders of his friend who had risen also. There they both stood, stretching themselves as high as they could, and holding each other tightly that they might not fall down. The Kioto frog turned his nose toward Osaka, and the Osaka frog turned his nose toward Kioto. But the foolish things forgot that when they stood up their great eyes lay in the backs of their heads, and that, though their noses might point to the places to which they wanted to go, their eyes beheld the places from which they had come.

"Dear me," cried the Osaka frog, "Kioto is exactly like Osaka! It is certainly not worth such a long journey. I shall go home!"

"If I'd had any idea that Osaka was only a copy of Kioto I should never have traveled all this way!" exclaimed the frog from Kioto. And as he spoke he took his hands from his friend's shoulders and they both fell down on the grass.

Then they took a polite farewell of each other and set off for home again, and to the end of their lives they believed that Osaka and Kioto, which are as different to look at as two towns can be, were as like as two peas.

FROM SOUTH AFRICA

WINDBIRD AND THE SUN*

by Josef Marais

Once the Queen of the Fountains had a beautiful daughter. Her name was Thashira and the Queen was very proud of her and gave her all that she wished. But nothing made Thashira really happy except bright colors. Gaily-colored flowers, or blankets of yellow, green and blue, or necklaces made of gaudy stones —all these gave Thashira pleasure. Nothing else interested her— in fact the Queen's daughter for most of the time was sad and unpleasant to her friends. She would not help grind corn, or fashion clay pots, as the other girls of the kraal did. She would not take part in the dance ceremonies when harvest time came. All day Thashira sat and stared at the blue of the sky. Flowers seldom bloomed in the dry country and the thorntrees and bushes were mostly bare without any color to delight her eyes. The Queen herself was busy travelling up the mountains to see the fountains, and she was very worried knowing that her daughter was so sad.

The young men of the kraal left Thashira alone. "Who wants such a dull, unpleasant girl for a wife?" they said.

Sometimes Thashira went to a nearby vlei (when there was some water there) and plucked water lilies for a wreath to put on her head. Sometimes she gathered wild berries and decorated her body with the red juice. During these times she was happy and everyone said, "Thashira has found another color," and everyone would smile at her and nod and say, "How pretty you look!" Then she tried mixing the juice of plants with the brown or red clay near the vlei and with that she painted pictures on the rocks. But

* From *Koos the Hottentot* by Josef Marais, by permission of Alfred A. Knopf, Inc. Copyright, 1945, by Alfred A. Knopf, Inc.

Thashira tired of all this and spent most of the days lying in the shade of a baobab tree and staring at the bright blue of the sky.

The Sun saw her there one day and said to her, "Beautiful Thashira, I know you love the blue color of the sky. That makes me happy because it is I who give the sky its color." She came out from under the branch of the baobab tree and looked up for a moment at the brilliant Sun and said, "Thank you, you are kind." Then she went back under the shade. She did not even smile.

The Sun sympathized with her, for he too liked colors. Every day he tried placing new and finer colors in the sky when the day was ending and he was ready to sink beyond the koppies to the west. This pleased Thashira and she made a habit of climbing the highest koppie to admire the Sun while he showed her his new glowing colors. So they became very fond of each other, the maiden and the Sun.

But Windbird fell in love with Thashira. As she lay half asleep under the baobab tree he caressed her hair and cooled her brow. It was not often that Windbird was so gentle. In the dry country he is always in a violent hurry. Most of the time Windbird is very busy journeying back and forth from the seacoast to the great lands in the interior of Africa. Above the ocean he chooses a large cloud and flies with it inland. If the mountains are very high he has to trail the cloud so high that he sometimes loses most of it on the way. Then the people are angry at him for bringing no clouds or rain. Windbird has a quick temper, and if he finds the people are angry and blaming him he gets angry too. Then he blows the dust over the Veld. And people hate him still more.

But when Windbird fell in love with the daughter of the Queen of the Fountains, he blew very gently for weeks. He brought clouds from as far as Cape Agulhas where the Indian and the Atlantic oceans meet. He tore off pieces of clouds while he flew them over the big mountains near the coast, for fear they were too big and might cause hailstones. Thus, just enough rain fell, and the flowers bloomed and the plants sprouted and there were lots of colors for the maiden to enjoy.

"That's all very well," growled Windbird to himself, "but Thashira doesn't know it is I who bring her this pleasure."

So one day while the girl was romping among the chinkerinchees, plucking bunches of the tiny white flowers with their green dotted petals, he approached her and said, "Thashira, I love you. That is why I have brought the clouds to water the ground and give you these fine flowers. I am great and strong. I am Windbird." He thought the maiden would be grateful and impressed by his prowess. But she glanced at him coolly and said, "Thank you, you are kind." Then she continued picking chinkerinchees. Windbird flew into a temper. He blew great blasts of air across the Veld so that the newly-grown grasses and plants swayed until their roots broke. The flowers were torn off their stems. The bushes were uprooted.

"Now you can see my strength," Windbird boasted, and the air currents whistled wildly across Veld and vlei. Thashira was heartbroken. All the brightly-colored plants and blossoms had disappeared. Once more the land was dusty and bare. Again she took to lying in the shade of her baobab tree and gazing at the only color that was left—the blue of the sky. When Windbird came to call on her she scornfully told him to go away.

The Queen of the Fountains returned and found her daughter sadder than ever. Thashira's only companion now was a little dove whose neck was decorated with gaily-colored feathers. When the Sun shone on the little dove her feathers reflected all the colors of the Sun's rays. The Queen saw that Thashira spent her days beneath the baobab tree. She watched Thashira whisper messages to the dove who then flew far away into the blue sky.

"Thashira, my daughter, you are so sad. True, life in this dry land is dreary. What can I do to make you happy?"

"Mother, I love the Sun for he makes the sky blue, and his warmth helps the colorful flowers to bloom."

"Is it to the Sun that you are sending your little dove with messages?" asked the Queen, and Thashira shyly nodded.

"Good—then I will order that a great ladder be built so that you may go up into the blue sky you love so much and stay forever with the Sun," cried the Queen.

The elephants and the hippos and the rhinos and the monkeys rushed to obey the Queen of the Fountains for they knew how much their lives depended on pleasing her. In the distant forests they pulled down the trees. Against all the rules of nature the Queen ordered the rivers to flood over the dry land even for a brief period so that they might bring the great logs to Thashira's home. The people built hundreds and hundreds of ladders and placed them one on top of the other. When they reached so high into the sky that the top ladder could not be seen Thashira sent her little dove with a final message to the Sun, and then while the crowds of people anxiously watched, she placed her foot on the first rung.

Suddenly from the distance came the horrible wail of the wind. Windbird was furious that the Sun had won Thashira. Now his moment for revenge had come.

"So!" Windbird roared in his anger. "You scorned the power of Windbird! Now you shall see who is stronger—the Sun or the Wind." And the dust and bushes flew across the Veld, the loose stones whipped the bodies of the multitude of people. With a tremendous crack the great ladders came tumbling down to earth. The cries of the people mingled with the cruel whistling of Windbird.

The Queen of the Fountains wept for her daughter, Thashira. She wept and wept with sorrow and her tears floated upwards in a great, grey mist. Then the little dove returned from above with one of her wings almost broken from the strong winds; but the colors of her neck feathers were brighter than ever. She alighted on the shoulder of beautiful Thashira. The next moment Thashira with the little dove was floating upward, and the misty vapor from the Queen's tears, enveloped them. The Sun burst out in all his brilliance. The whistling of the Windbird died down to a whisper . . . then there was dead stillness. The people looked upward and across the sky shone a glorious rainbow of all the colors that anyone could wish.

Thashira is the rainbow and when the Sun shines on her, she glows with happiness. Though Windbird tries and tries he cannot blow her away. From time to time Windbird breaks into one of his violent fits of temper, but Thashira remains steadfast in the sky proudly showing the Sun and the world her gorgeous colors. May Windbird never succeed in blowing Thashira, the rainbow, away!

FROM KOREA

WHY THE DOG AND THE CAT ARE NOT FRIENDS

by Frances Carpenter

Why do dogs and cats fight so, Halmoni?" the little girl asked, looking up from her tray of pine seeds.

"My grandmother used to tell me a story about that," Halmoni said, "and I'll tell it to you."

And this is the story:

The dog and the cat in my tale lived in a small wine-shop on the bank of a broad river beside a ferry, my children. Old Koo, the shopkeeper, had neither wife nor child. In his little hut he lived by himself except for this dog and this cat. The tame beasts never left his side. While he sold wine in the shop, the dog kept guard at the door and the cat caught mice in the storeroom. When he walked on the river bank, they trotted by his side. When he lay down to sleep upon the warm floor, they crept close to his back. They were good enough friends then, the dog and the cat, but that was before the disaster occurred and the cat behaved so badly.

Old Koo was poor, but he was honest and kind. His shop was not like those where travelers are persuaded to drink wine until they become drunk and roll on the ground. Only one kind of wine was sold, but it was a good wine. Once they had tasted it, Koo's customers came back again and again to fill their long-necked wine bottles.

"Where does Old Koo get so much wine?" the neighbors used to ask one another. "No new jars are ever delivered by bull carts at his door. He makes no wine himself, yet his black jug is never without wine to pour for his customers."

No one knew the answer to the riddle save Old Koo himself, and he told it to no one except his dog and his cat. Years before he opened his wine-shop, Koo had worked on the ferry. One cold rainy night when the last ferry had returned, a strange traveler came to the gate of his hut.

"Honorable Sir," he begged Koo, "give me a drop of good wine to drive out the damp chill."

"My wine jug is almost empty," Koo told the traveler. "I have only a little for my evening drink, but no doubt you need the wine far more than I. I'll share it with you." And he filled up a bowl for this strange, thirsty guest.

The stranger on leaving put into the ferryman's hand a bit of bright golden amber. "Keep this in your wine jug," he said, "and it will always be full."

Now, as Old Koo told his dog and his cat, that traveler must have been a spirit from Heaven, for when Koo lifted the black jug, it was heavy with wine. When he filled his bowl from it, he thought he had never tasted a drink so sweet and so rich. No matter how much he poured, the wine in the jug never grew less.

Here was a treasure indeed. With a jug that never ran dry, he could open a wine-shop. He would no longer have to go back and forth, back and forth, in the ferryboat over the river in all kinds of weather.

All went well until one day when he was serving a traveler, Koo found to his horror that his black jug was empty. He shook it and shook it, but no answering tinkle came from the hard amber charm that should have been inside.

"*Ai-go! Ai-go!*" Koo wailed. "I must unknowingly have poured the amber out into the bottle of one of my customers. *Ai-go!* What shall I do?"

The dog and the cat shared their master's sadness. The dog howled at the moon, and the cat prowled around the shop, sniffing and sniffing under the rice jars and even high up on the rafters. These animals knew the secret of the magic wine jug, for the old man had often talked to them about the stranger's amber charm.

"I am sure I could find the charm," the cat said to the dog, "if I only could catch its amber smell."

"We shall search for it together," the dog suggested. "We shall go through every house in the neighborhood. When you sniff it out, I will run home with it."

So they began their quest. They asked all the cats and dogs they met for news of the lost amber. They prowled about all the houses, but not a trace could they find of their master's magic charm.

"We must try the other side of the river," the dog said at last. "They will not let us ride across on the ferryboat. But when the winter cold comes and the river's stomach is solid, we can safely creep over the ice, like everyone else."

Thus it was that one winter morning the dog and the cat crossed the river to the opposite side. As soon as the owners were not looking, they crept into the houses. The dog sniffed around the courtyards, and the cat even climbed up on the beams under the sloping grass roofs. Day after day, week after week, month after month, they searched and they searched, but with no success.

Spring was at hand. The joyful fish in the river were bumping their backs against the soft ice. At last, one day, high up on the top of a great brassbound chest, the cat smelled the amber. But, *ai*, the welcome perfume came from inside a tightly closed box. What could they do? If they pushed the box off the chest and let it break on the floor, the Master of the House would surely be warned and chase them away.

"We must get help from the rats," the clever dog cried. "They can gnaw a hole in the box for us and get the amber out. In return, we can promise to let them live in peace for ten years." This plan was all against the nature of a cat, but this one loved its master and it consented.

The rats consented, too. It seemed to them almost too good to be true that both the cats and the dogs might leave them alone for ten whole peaceful years. It took the rats many days to gnaw a hole in that box, but at last it was done. The cat tried to get at the amber with its soft paw, but the hole was too small. Finally a young mouse had to be sent in through the wee hole. It succeeded in pulling the amber out with its teeth.

"How pleased our master will be! Now good luck will live again under his roof," the cat and the dog said to each other. In their joy at finding the lost amber charm, they ran around and around as if they were having fits.

"But how shall we get the amber back to the other side of the river?" the cat cried in dismay. "You know I cannot swim."

"You shall hold the amber safely inside your mouth, Cat," the dog replied wisely. "You shall climb on my back, and I'll swim you over the river."

And so it happened. Clawing the thick shaggy hair of the dog's back, the cat kept its balance until they had almost reached their own bank of the stream. But there, playing along the shore, were a number of children, who burst into laughter when they saw the strange ferryman and his curious passenger. "A cat riding on the back of a dog! Ho! Ho! Ho!" they laughed. "Ha! Ha! Ha! Ho! Ho! Ho! Just look at that." They called to their parents, and they came to laugh, too.

Now the faithful dog paid no attention to their foolish mirth, but the cat could not help joining them in the fun. It, too, began to laugh, and from its open mouth Old Koo's precious amber charm dropped down upon the river bottom.

The dog shook the cat off his back, he was so angry, and it was a miracle that the creature at last got safely to the shore. In a rage the dog chased the cat, which finally took refuge in the crotch of a tree. There the cat shook the moisture out of its fur. By spitting and spitting, it got rid of the water it had swallowed while in the river. The cat dared not come down out of the tree until the angry dog had gone away.

That, so my grandmother said, is why the dog and the cat are never friends, my dear ones. That is why, too, a cat always spits when a strange dog comes too near. That is why a cat does not like to get its feet wet.

"But what about the amber charm and poor Old Koo?" the little girl asked anxiously.

"It was that dog who finally saved the fortunes of the old wine-shop keeper," Halmoni explained. "First he tried swimming out into the stream to look for the amber. But it was too deep for him to see the bottom. Then he sat beside the river fishermen, wishing he had a line or a net like theirs that would bring up the golden prize he sought. Suddenly from a fish that had just been pulled out of the water, the dog sniffed amber perfume. Grabbing that fish up in his mouth before the fisherman could stop him, he galloped off home."

"Well done, Dog," said Old Koo. "There is only a little food left under our roof. This fish will make a good meal for you and me." The old man cut open the fish and, to his surprise and delight, the bit of amber rolled out.

"Now I can put my magic charm back into the jug," Koo said to himself. "But there must be at least a little wine in it to start the jug flowing again. While I go out to buy some, I'll just lock the amber up inside my clothes chest."

When Koo came back with the wine and opened the chest, he found that instead of the one suit he had stored in it, there were now two. Where his last string of cash had been, there were two strings. And he guessed that the secret of this amber charm was that it would double whatever it touched.

With this knowledge Koo became rich beyond telling. And in the gate of his fine new house he cut a doghole for his faithful friend, who had saved him from starving. There, day and night, like our own four-footed gate guard, the fat dog lay watching in peace and well-fed contentment. But all through his life he never again killed a mouse nor made a friend of a cat.

FROM WEST AFRICA

HUNGRY SPIDER AND THE TURTLE

by Harold Courlander and George Herzog

Spider was a hungry one, he always wanted to eat. Everybody in Ashanti knew about his appetite. He was greedy, too, and always wanted more than his share of things. So people steered clear of Spider.

But one day a stranger came to Spider's habitation out in the back country. His name was Turtle. Turtle was a long way from his home. He had been walking all day in the hot sun, and he was tired and hungry. So Spider had to invite Turtle into his house and offer him something to eat. He hated to do it, but if he didn't extend hospitality to a tired traveler it would get around the countryside and people would soon be talking about Spider behind his back.

So he said to Turtle:

"There is water at the spring for you to wash your feet in. Follow the trail and you'll get there. I'll get the dinner ready."

Turtle turned and waddled down to the spring with a gourd bowl as fast as he could. He dipped some water from the spring and carefully washed his feet in it. Then he waddled back up the trail to the house. But the trail was dusty. By the time Turtle got back to the house his feet were covered with dirt again.

Spider had the food all set out. It was steaming, and the smell of it made Turtle's mouth water. He hadn't eaten since sunrise. Spider looked disapprovingly at Turtle's feet.

"Your feet are awfully dirty," he said. "Don't you think you ought to wash them before you start to eat?"

Turtle looked at his feet. He was ashamed, they were so dirty. So he turned around and waddled as fast as he could down to the spring again. He dipped some water out of the spring with the gourd bowl and carefully washed himself. Then he scurried as fast as he could back to the house. But it takes a turtle a while to get anywhere. When he came into the house Spider was already eating.

"Excellent meal, isn't it?" Spider said. He looked at Turtle's feet with disapproval. "Hm, aren't you going to wash yourself?"

Turtle looked down at his feet. In his hurry to get back he had stirred up a lot of dust, and his feet were covered with it again.

"I washed them," he said. "I washed them twice. It's your dusty trail that does it."

"Oh," Spider said, "so you are abusing my house now!" He took a big mouthful of food and chewed it up, looking very hurt.

"No," Turtle said, sniffing the food, "I was just explaining."

"Well, run along and wash up so we can get on with the eating," Spider said.

Turtle looked. The food was already half gone and Spider was eating as fast as he could. Turtle spun around and hurried down to the spring. He dipped up some water in the gourd bowl and splashed it over his feet. Then he scrambled back to the house. This time he didn't go on the trail, though, but on the grass and through the bushes. It took him a little longer, but he didn't get dust all over his feet. When he got to the house he found Spider licking his lips.

"Ah, what a fine meal we had!" Spider said.

Turtle looked in the dish. Everything was gone. Even the smell was gone. Turtle was very hungry. But he said nothing. He smiled.

"Yes, it was very good," he said. "You are certainly good to travelers in your village. If you are ever in my country you may be assured of a welcome."

"It's nothing," Spider said. "Nothing at all."

Turtle went away. He didn't tell other people about the affair at Spider's house. He was very quiet about his experience there.

But one day many months later Spider was a long distance from home and he found himself in Turtle's country. He found Turtle on the shore of the lake getting a sunbath.

"Ah, friend Spider, you are far from your village," Turtle said. "Will you have something to eat with me?"

"Yes, that is the way it is when a person is far from home—generosity merits generosity," Spider said hungrily.

"Wait here on the shore and I'll go below and prepare the food," Turtle said. He slipped into the water and went down to the bottom of the lake. When he got there he set out the food to eat. Then he came to the top of the water and said to Spider, who was sitting impatiently on the shore, "All right, everything is ready. Let's go down and eat." He put his head under water and swam down.

Spider was famished. He jumped into the water to follow Turtle. But Spider was very light. He floated. He splashed and splashed, kicked and kicked, but he stayed right there on top of the water. For a long time he tried to get down where Turtle was eating, but nothing happened.

After a while Turtle came up, licking his lips.

"What's the matter, aren't you hungry?" he said. "The food is very good. Better hurry." And he went down again.

Spider made one more desperate try, but he just floated. Then he had an idea. He went back to the shore, picked up pebbles and put them in the pockets of his jacket. He put so many pebbles in his pockets that he became very heavy. He was so heavy he could hardly walk. Then he jumped into the water again, and this time he sank to the bottom, where Turtle was eating. The food was half gone. Spider was very hungry. He was just reaching for the food when Turtle said politely:

"Excuse me, my friend. In my country we never eat with our jackets on. Take off your jacket so that we can get down to business."

Turtle took a great mouthful of food and started chewing. In a few minutes there wouldn't be anything left. Spider was aching all over with hunger. Turtle took another mouthful. So Spider wriggled out of his coat and grabbed at the food. But without the pebbles he was so light again that he popped right up to the top of the water.

People always say that one good meal deserves another.

FROM BRAZIL

HOW THE SPECKLED HEN GOT HER SPECKLES

by Elsie Spicer Eells

Once upon a time, ages and ages ago, there was a little white hen. One day she was busily engaged in scratching the soil to find worms and insects for her breakfast. As she worked she sang over and over again her little crooning song, "Quirrichi, quirrichi, quirrichi." Suddenly she noticed a tiny piece of paper lying on the ground. "Quirrichi, quirrichi, what luck!" she said to herself. "This must be a letter. One time when the king, the great ruler of our country, held his court in the meadow close by, many people brought him letters and laid them at his feet. Now I, too, even I, the little white hen, have a letter. I am going to carry my letter to the king."

The next morning the little white hen started bravely out on her long journey. She carried the letter very carefully in her little brown basket. It was a long distance to the royal palace where the king lived. The little white hen had never been so far from home in all her life.

After a while she met a friendly fox. Foxes and little white hens are not usually very good friends, you know, but this fox was a friend of the little white hen. Once upon a time she had helped the fox to escape from a trap and the fox had never forgotten her kindness to him.

"O, little white hen, where are you going?" asked the fox.

"Quirrichi, quirrichi," replied the little white hen, "I am going to the royal palace to carry a letter to the king."

"Indeed, little white hen," said the fox, "I should like to go with you. Give me your permission to accompany you on your journey."

"I shall be glad to have you go with me," said the little white hen. "It is a very long journey to the royal palace where the king lives. Wouldn't you like me to carry you in my little brown basket?"

The fox climbed into the little brown basket. After the little white hen had gone on for some distance farther she met a river. Once upon a time the little white hen had done the river a kindness. He had, with great difficulty, thrown some ugly worms upon the bank and he was afraid they would crawl back in again. The little white hen had eaten them for him. Always after that the river had been her friend.

"O, little white hen, where are you going?" the river called out as soon as he saw her.

"Quirrichi, quirrichi, I am going to the royal palace to carry a letter to the king," replied the little white hen.

"O, little white hen, may I go with you?" asked the river.

The little white hen told the river that he might go with her and asked him to ride in the little brown basket. So the river climbed into the little brown basket.

After the little white hen had journeyed along for a time she came to a fire. Once upon a time, when the fire had been dying the little white hen had brought some dried grass. The grass had given the fire new life and always after that he had been the friend of the little white hen.

"O, little white hen, where are you going?" the fire asked.

"Quirrichi, quirrichi, I am going to the royal palace to carry a letter to the king," replied the little white hen.

"O, little white hen, may I go with you?" asked the fire. "I have never been to a royal palace and I have never had even a peep at the king."

The little white hen told the fire that he might go with her and asked him to climb into the little brown basket. By this time the little brown basket was so full, that, try as they might, they couldn't make room for the fire. At last they thought of a plan. The fire changed himself into ashes and then there was room for him to get into the basket.

The little white hen journeyed on and on, and finally she arrived at the royal palace.

"Who are you and what are you carrying in your little brown basket?" asked the royal doorkeeper when he opened the door.

"I am the little white hen and I am carrying a letter to the king," replied the little white hen. She didn't say a word about the fox and the river and the fire which she had in her little brown basket. She was so frightened before the great royal doorkeeper of the palace that she could hardly find her voice at all.

The royal doorkeeper invited the little white hen to enter the palace and he led her to the royal throne where the king was sitting. The little white hen bowed very low before the king—so low, in fact, that it mussed up all her feathers.

"Who are you and what is your business?" asked the king in his big, deep, kingly voice.

"Quirrichi, quirrichi, I am the little white hen," replied the little white hen in her low, frightened, little voice. "I have come to bring my letter to your royal majesty." She handed the king the piece of paper which had remained all this time at the bottom of the little brown basket. There were marks of dirt upon it where the friendly fox's feet had rested. It was damp where the river had lain. It had tiny holes in it where the fire had sat after he had turned himself into hot ashes.

"What do you mean by bringing me this dirty piece of paper?" shouted the king in his biggest, deepest, gruffest voice. "I am highly offended. I always knew that hens were stupid little creatures but you are quite the stupidest little hen I ever saw in my life.

"Here," and he turned to one of the attendants standing by the throne, "take this stupid, little white hen and throw her out into the royal poultry yard. I think we will have her for dinner tomorrow."

The little white hen was roughly seized by the tallest royal attendant and carried down the back stairs, through the back gate, out into the royal poultry yard. She still clung to the little brown basket which she had brought with her on her long journey to the royal palace and through all the sad experiences she had met there.

When the little white hen reached the royal poultry yard all the royal fowls flew at her. Some plucked at her rumpled white feathers. Others tried to pick out her eyes. One pulled off the cover of the little brown basket.

Out sprang the fox from the little brown basket and in the twinkling of an eye he fell upon the fowls of the royal poultry yard. Not a single fowl was left alive.

There was such a great commotion that the king, the queen, the royal attendants and all the royal servants of the palace came rushing out to see what was the matter. The fox had already taken to his heels and the little white hen lost no time in running away too. She did not, however, forget to take her little brown basket with her.

The royal household all ran after her in swift pursuit. They had almost caught her when the river suddenly sprang out of the little brown basket and flowed between the little white hen and her royal pursuers. They couldn't get across without canoes.

While they were getting the canoes and climbing into them the little white hen had time to run a long way. She had almost reached a thick forest where she could easily hide herself when the royal pursuers again drew near. Then the fire which had changed itself into hot ashes jumped out of the little brown basket. It immediately became dark, so dark that the royal household could not even see each other's faces and, of course, they could not see in which direction the little white hen was running. There was nothing for them to do but to return to the royal palace and live on beef and mutton.

The fire which had turned itself into ashes sprang out of the little brown basket so suddenly that it scattered ashes all over the little white hen. From that day she was always speckled where the ashes fell upon her. The chickens of the little white hen (who was now a little speckled hen) were all speckled too. So were their chickens and their chickens and their chickens' chickens, even down to this very day. Whenever you see a speckled hen you may know that she is descended from the little white hen who carried a letter to the king, and who, in her adventures, became the first speckled hen.

FROM RUSSIA

THE CAT WHO BECAME HEAD-FORESTER

by Arthur Ransome

If you drop Vladimir by mistake, you know he always falls on his feet. And if Vladimir tumbles off the roof of the hut, he always falls on his feet. Cats always fall on their feet, on their four paws, and never hurt themselves. And as in tumbling, so it is in life. No cat is ever unfortunate for very long. The worse things look for a cat, the better they are going to be.

Well, once upon a time, not so very long ago, an old peasant had a cat and did not like him. He was a tom-cat, always fighting; and he had lost one ear, and was not very pretty to look at. The peasant thought he would get rid of his old cat, and buy a new one from a neighbour. He did not care what became of the old tom-cat with one ear, so long as he never saw him again. It was no use thinking of killing him, for it is a life's work to kill a cat, and it's likely enough that the cat would come alive at the end.

So the old peasant he took a sack, and he bundled the tomcat into the sack, and he sewed up the sack and slung it over his back, and walked off into the forest. Off he went, trudging along in the summer sunshine, deep into the forest. And when he had gone very many versts into the forest, he took the sack with the cat in it and threw it away among the trees.

"You stay there," says he, "and if you do get out in this desolate place, much good may it do you, old quarrelsome bundle of bones and fur!"

And with that he turned round and trudged home again, and bought a nice-looking, quiet cat from a neighbour in exchange for a little tobacco, and settled down comfortably at home with the new cat in front of the stove; and there he may be to this day, so far as I know. My story does not bother with him, but only with the old tom-cat tied up in the sack away out there in the forest.

The bag flew through the air, and plumped down through a bush to the ground. And the old tom-cat landed on his feet inside it, very much frightened but not hurt. Thinks he, this bag, this flight through the air, this bump, mean that my life is going to change. Very well; there is nothing like something new now and again.

And presently he began tearing at the bag with his sharp claws. Soon there was a hole he could put a paw through. He went on, tearing and scratching, and there was a hole he could put two paws through. He went on with his work, and soon he could put his head through, all the easier because he had only one ear. A minute or two after that he had wriggled out of the bag, and stood up on his four paws and stretched himself in the forest.

"The world seems to be larger than the village," he said. "I will walk on and see what there is in it."

He washed himself all over, curled his tail proudly up in the air, cocked the only ear he had left, and set off walking under the forest trees.

"I was the head-cat in the village," says he to himself. "If all goes well, I shall be head here too." And he walked along as if he were the Tzar himself.

Well, he walked on and on, and he came to an old hut that had belonged to a forester. There was nobody there, nor had been for many years, and the old tom-cat made himself quite at home. He climbed up into the loft under the roof, and found a little rotten hay.

"A very good bed," says he, and curls up and falls asleep.

When he woke he felt hungry, so he climbed down and went off into the forest to catch little birds and mice. There were plenty of them in the forest, and when he had eaten enough he came back to the hut, climbed into the loft, and spent the night there very comfortably.

You would have thought he would be content. Not he. He was a cat. He said, "This is a good enough lodging. But I have to catch all my own food. In the village they fed me every day, and I only caught mice for fun. I ought to be able to live like that here. A person of my dignity ought not to have to do all the work for himself."

Next day he went walking in the forest. And as he was walking he met a fox, a vixen, a very pretty young thing, gay and giddy like all girls. And the fox saw the cat, and was very much astonished.

"All these years," she said—for though she was young she thought she had lived a long time—"all these years," she said, "I've lived in the forest, but I've never seen a wild beast like that before. What a strange-looking animal! And with only one ear. How handsome!"

And she came up and made her bows to the cat, and said,—

"Tell me, great lord, who you are. What fortunate chance has brought you to this forest? And by what name am I to call your Excellency?"

Oh! The fox was very polite. It is not every day that you meet a handsome stranger walking in the forest.

The cat arched his back, and set all his fur on end, and said, very slowly and quietly,—

"I have been sent from the far forests of Siberia to be Head-forester over you. And my name is Cat Ivanovitch."

"O Cat Ivanovitch!" says the pretty young fox, and she makes more bows. "I did not know. I beg your Excellency's pardon. Will your Excellency honour my humble house by visiting it as a guest?"

"I will," says the cat. "And what do they call you?"

"My name, your Excellency, is Lisabeta Ivanovna."

"I will come with you, Lisabeta," says the cat.

And they went together to the fox's earth. Very snug, very neat it was inside; and the cat curled himself up in the best place, while Lisabeta Ivanovna, the pretty young fox, made ready a tasty dish of game. And while she was making the meal ready, and dusting the furniture with her tail, she looked at the cat. At last she said, shyly,—

"Tell me, Cat Ivanovitch, are you married or single?"

"Single," says the cat.

"And I too am unmarried," says the pretty young fox, and goes busily on with her dusting and cooking.

Presently she looks at the cat again.

"What if we were to marry, Cat Ivanovitch? I will try to be a good wife to you."

"Very well, Lisabeta," says the cat; "I will marry you."

The fox went to her store and took out all the dainties that she had, and made a wedding feast to celebrate her marriage to the great Cat Ivanovitch, who had only one ear, and had come from the far Siberian forests to be Head-forester.

They ate up everything there was in the place.

Next morning the pretty young fox went off busily into the forest to get food for her grand husband. But the old tom-cat stayed at home, and cleaned his whiskers and slept. He was a lazy one, was that cat, and proud.

The fox was running through the forest, looking for game, when she met an old friend, the handsome young wolf, and he began making polite speeches to her.

"What had become of you, gossip?" says he. "I've been to all the best earths and not found you at all."

"Let be, fool," says the fox very shortly. "Don't talk to me like that. What are you jesting about? Formerly I was a young, unmarried fox; now I am a wedded wife."

"Whom have you married, Lisabeta Ivanovna?"

"What!" says the fox, "you have not heard that the great Cat Ivanovitch, who has only one ear, has been sent from the far Siberian forests to be Head-forester over all of us? Well, I am now the Head-forester's wife."

"No, I had not heard, Lisabeta Ivanovna. And when can I pay my respects to his Excellency?"

"Not now, not now," says the fox. "Cat Ivanovitch will be raging angry with me if I let any one come near him. Presently he will be taking his food. Look you. Get a sheep, and make it ready, and bring it as a greeting to him, to show him that he is welcome and that you know how to treat him with respect. Leave the sheep near by, and hide yourself so that he shall not see you; for, if he did, things might be awkward."

"Thank you, thank you, Lisabeta Ivanovna," says the wolf, and off he goes to look for a sheep.

The pretty young fox went idly on, taking the air, for she knew that the wolf would save her the trouble of looking for food.

Presently she met the bear.

"Good-day to you, Lisabeta Ivanovna," said the bear; "as pretty as ever, I see you are."

"Bandy-legged one," says the fox; "fool, don't come worrying me. Formerly I was a young, unmarried fox; now I am a wedded wife."

"I beg your pardon," says the bear, "whom have you married, Lisabeta Ivanovna?"

"The great Cat Ivanovitch has been sent from the far Siberian forests to be Head-forester over us all. And Cat Ivanovitch is now my husband," says the fox.

"Is it forbidden to have a look at his Excellency?"

"It is forbidden," says the fox. "Cat Ivanovitch will be raging angry with me if I let any one come near him. Presently he will be taking his food. Get along with you quickly; make ready an ox, and bring it by way of welcome to him. The wolf is bringing a sheep. And look you. Leave the ox near by, and hide yourself so that the great Cat Ivanovitch shall not see you; or else, brother, things may be awkward."

The bear shambled off as fast as he could go to get an ox.

The pretty young fox, enjoying the fresh air of the forest, went slowly home to her earth, and crept in very quietly, so as not to awake the great Head-forester, Cat Ivanovitch, who had only one ear and was sleeping in the best place.

Presently the wolf came through the forest, dragging a sheep he had killed. He did not dare to go too near the fox's earth, because of Cat Ivanovitch, the new Head-forester. So he stopped, well out of sight, and stripped off the skin of the sheep, and arranged the sheep so as to seem a nice tasty morsel. Then he stood still, thinking what to do next. He heard a noise, and looked up. There was the bear, struggling along with a dead ox.

"Good-day, brother Michael Ivanovitch," says the wolf.

"Good-day, brother Levon Ivanovitch," says the bear. "Have you seen the fox, Lisabeta Ivanovna, with her husband, the Head-forester?"

"No, brother," says the wolf. "For a long time I have been waiting to see them."

"Go on and call out to them," says the bear.

"No, Michael Ivanovitch," says the wolf. "I will not go. Do you go; you are bigger and bolder than I."

"No, no, Levon Ivanovitch, I will not go. There is no use in risking one's life without need."

Suddenly, as they were talking, a little hare came running by. The bear saw him first, and roared out,—

"Hi, Squinteye! trot along here."

The hare came up, slowly, two steps at a time, trembling with fright.

"Now then, you squinting rascal," says the bear, "do you know where the fox lives, over there?"

"I know, Michael Ivanovitch."

"Get along there quickly, and tell her that Michael Ivanovitch the bear and his brother Levon Ivanovitch the wolf have been ready for a long time, and have brought presents of a sheep and an ox, as greetings to his Excellency . . ."

"His Excellency, mind," says the wolf; "don't forget."

The hare ran off as hard as he could go, glad to have escaped so easily. Meanwhile the wolf and the bear looked about for good places in which to hide.

"It will be best to climb trees," says the bear. "I shall go up to the top of this fir."

"But what am I to do?" says the wolf. "I can't climb a tree for the life of me. Brother Michael, Brother Michael, hide me somewhere or other before you climb up. I beg you, hide me, or I shall certainly be killed."

"Crouch down under these bushes," says the bear, "and I will cover you with the dead leaves."

"May you be rewarded," says the wolf; and he crouched down under the bushes, and the bear covered him up with dead leaves, so that only the tip of his nose could be seen.

Then the bear climbed slowly up into the fir tree, into the very top, and looked out to see if the fox and Cat Ivanovitch were coming.

The hare ran up and knocked on the door, and said to the fox,—

"Michael Ivanovitch the bear and his brother Levon Ivanovitch the wolf have been ready for a long time, and have brought presents of a sheep and an ox as greetings to his Excellency."

"Get along, Squinteye," says the fox; "we are just coming."

And so the fox and the cat set out together.

They were coming; oh yes, they were coming!

The bear, up in the top of the tree, saw them, and called down to the wolf,—

"They are coming, Brother Levon; they are coming, the fox and her husband. But what a little one he is, to be sure!"

"Quiet, quiet," whispers the wolf. "He'll hear you and then we are done for."

The cat came up, and arched his back and set all his furs on end, and threw himself on the ox, and began tearing the meat with his teeth and claws. And as he tore he purred. And the bear listened, and heard the purring of the cat, and it seemed to him that the cat was angrily muttering, "Small, small, small . . ."

And the bear whispers: "He's no giant, but what a glutton! Why, we couldn't get through a quarter of that, and he finds it not enough. Heaven help us if he comes after us!"

The wolf tried to see, but could not, because his head, all but his nose, was covered with the dry leaves. Little by little he moved his head, so as to clear the leaves away from in front of his eyes. Try as he would to be quiet, the leaves rustled, so little, ever so little, but enough to be heard by the one ear of the cat.

The cat stopped tearing the meat and listened.

"I haven't caught a mouse today," he thought.

Once more the leaves rustled.

The cat leaped through the air and dropped with all four paws, and his claws out, on the nose of the wolf. How the wolf yelped! The leaves flew like dust, and the wolf leapt up and ran off as fast as his legs would carry him.

Well, the wolf was frightened, I can tell you, but he was not so frightened as the cat.

When the great wolf leapt up out of the leaves, the cat screamed and ran up the nearest tree, and that was the tree where Michael Ivanovitch the bear was hiding in the topmost branches.

"Oh, he has seen me. Cat Ivanovitch has seen me," thought the bear. He had no time to climb down, and the cat was coming up in long leaps.

The bear trusted to Providence, and jumped from the top of the tree. Many were the branches he broke as he fell; many were the bones he broke when he crashed to the ground. He picked himself up and stumbled off, groaning.

The pretty young fox sat still, and cried out, "Run, run, Brother Levon! . . . Quicker on your pins, Brother Michael! His Excellency is behind you; his Excellency is close behind!"

Ever since then all the wild beasts have been afraid of the cat, and the cat and the fox live merrily together, and eat fresh meat all the year round, which the other animals kill for them and leave a little way off.

And that is what happened to the old tom-cat with one ear, who was sewn up in a bag and thrown away in the forest.

"Just think what would happen to our handsome Vladimir if we were to throw him away!" said Vanya.

FROM ENGLAND

THE HARE AND THE HEDGEHOG

by Walter de la Mare

Early one Sunday morning, when the cowslips or paigles were showing their first honey-sweet buds in the meadows and the broom was in bloom, a hedgehog came to his little door to have a look at the weather. He stood with arms akimbo, whistling a tune to himself—a tune no better and no worse than the tunes hedgehogs usually whistle to themselves on fine Sunday mornings. And as he whistled, the notion came into his head that, before turning in, and while his wife was washing and tidying up the children, he might take a little walk into the fields and see how the young nettles were getting on. For there was a tasty beetle that lived among the nettles; and no nettles—no beetles.

Off he went, following his own little private path into the fields. And as he came stepping along around a bush of blackthorn, its blossoming now over and its leaves showing green, he met a hare; and the hare by the same chance had come out early to have a look at his spring cabbages.

The hedgehog bowed and bade him a polite "Goodmorning." But the hare, who felt himself a particularly fine sleek gentleman in this Sunday sunshine, merely sneered at his greeting.

"And how comes it," he said, "that *you* happen to be out so early? I always supposed you were one of these night-creepers."

"I am taking a walk, sir," said the hedgehog.

"A walk!" sniffed the hare. "I should have thought you would use those bandy little legs of yours to far better purpose."

This angered the hedgehog, for as his legs were crooked not by choice but by nature, he couldn't bear to have bad made worse by any talk about them.

"You seem to suppose, sir," he said, bristling all over, "that you can do more with your legs than I can with mine. We both have four."

"Well, perhaps," said the hare, airily.

"See here, then," said the hedgehog, his beady eyes fixed on the hare, "I say you *can't*. Start fair, and I'd beat you in any race—nought to ninepence. Ay, every time."

"A race, my dear Master Hedgehog!" said the hare, laying back his whiskers. "You must be beside yourself. It's crack-brained. It's *childish*. But still, what will you wager?"

"I'll lay a Golden Guinea to a Bottle of Brandy," said the hedgehog.

"Done!" said the hare. "Shake hands on it, and we'll start at once."

"Ay, but not quite so fast," said the hedgehog. "I have had no breakfast yet. But if you will be here in half an hour's time, so will I."

The hare agreed, and at once indulged in a little frisky practice along the dewy green border of the field, while the hedgehog went shuffling home.

"He thinks a mighty deal of himself," thought the hedgehog on his way. "But we shall see what *she* shall see." When he reached home he bustled in and, casting a solemn look at his wife, said:

"My dear, I have need of you. In all haste. Leave everything and follow me at once into the fields."

"Why, what's going on?" says she.

"Well," said her husband, "I have bet the hare a Golden Guinea to a Bottle of Brandy that I'll beat him in a race, and you must come and see it."

"Heavens, husband!" Mrs. Hedgehog cried. "Are you daft? Are you gone crazy? You! Run a race with a hare! And where's the guinea coming from?"

"Hold your tongue, woman," said the hedgehog. "There are things simple brains cannot understand. Leave all this fussing and titivating. The children can dry themselves; and you come along at once with me." So away they went together.

"Now," said the hedgehog, when they had reached the plough-land beyond the field which was sprouting with young green wheat, "listen to me, my dear. This is where the race is going to be. The hare is over there at the other end of the field. I am going to arrange that he shall start in that deep furrow, and that I shall start up there beside him in this one. But as soon as I have scrambled along a yard or two and he can't see me, I shall turn back. And what you, my dear, must do is this: When he comes out of his furrow *there*, you must be sitting puffing like a porpoise *here*. And when you see him you say, 'Ahah! so you've come at last?' Do you follow me, my dear?"

At first Mrs. Hedgehog was a little dense because she was so nervous, but she was amused at her husband's cunning, and gladly agreed at last to do what he said.

The hedgehog then went back to where he had promised to meet the hare, and he said, "Here I am, you see; and very much the better, sir, for a good breakfast."

"Indeed," simpered the hare scornfully. "How shall we run? Down or over; sideways, longways; two, three or four legs? It's all one to me."

"Well, to be quite candid with you," said the hedgehog, "let me say this. I have now and then watched you taking a gambol and disporting yourself with your friends in the evening, and a very dainty and pretty runner you are. But you never keep *straight*. You all go round and round, and round and round, scampering now this way, now that and chasing each other's scuts as if you were crazy. And as often as not you run uphill! But you can't run *races* like that. You must keep straight, you must begin in one place, go steadily on, and end in another."

"I could have told you that," said the hare angrily.

"Very well, then," said the hedgehog. "You shall keep to that furrow, and I'll keep to this."

And the hare, being a good deal quicker on his feet than he was in his wits, agreed.

"*One! Two! Three!—and* AWAY!" he shouted, and off he went like a little whirlwind up the field. But the hedgehog, after scuffling along a few yards, turned back and stayed quietly where he was.

When the hare came out of his furrow at the upper end of the field, the hedgehog's wife sat panting there as if she would never be able to recover her breath, and at sight of him she sighed out, "Ahah! sir, so you've come at last?"

The hare was shocked by her words. His ears trembled. His eyes bulged out of his head. "You've run it? You've *run* it!" he cried in astonishment. For she being so exactly like her husband, he never for a moment doubted that her husband she actually was.

"Ay," said she, "but I began to be afraid you must have gone lame."

"Lame!" said the hare, "lame! But there, what's *one* furrow? 'Every time,' was what you said. We'll try again."

Away once more he went, and he had never run faster. Yet when he came out of his furrow at the top of the field, there was the hedgehog! And the hedgehog laughed, and said: "Ahah! So here you are again! At last!" At this the hare could hardly contain himself for rage.

"Not enough! not enough!" he said. "Three for luck! Again, again!"

"As often as you please, my dear friend," said the hedgehog. "It's the long run that really counts."

Again, and again, and yet again the hare raced up and down the long furrow of the field, and every time he reached the top, and every time he reached the bottom, there was the hedgehog, as he thought, with his mocking, "Ahah! So here you are again! At last!"

But at length the hare could run no more. He lay panting and speechless; he was dead beat. Stretched out there, limp on the grass, his fur bedraggled, his eyes dim, his legs quaking, it looked as if he might fetch his last breath at any moment.

So Mrs. Hedgehog went off to the hare's house to fetch the Bottle of Brandy; and if it had not been the best brandy, the hare might never have run again.

News of the contest spread far and wide. From that day to this, never has there been a race to compare with it. And lucky it was for the hedgehog that he had the good sense to marry a wife like himself, and not a weasel, or a wombat, or a whale!

FROM THE NORTH AMERICAN INDIANS

THE GHOST OF THE GREAT WHITE STAG

by Arthur C. Parker

There is a mighty mountain of the northlands. It rises from the placid waters of a beautiful lake and its summit catches the glint of the sun. On all sides but one are other towering peaks, but none rivals the mighty mountain, for here dwells the great white stag whom no hunter can kill.

In the valley of the lake there is another glimmering lakelet and beyond a wooded slope where the forest-folk have their council grounds. It is a far-off retreat, but a safe one, and here all the fur-folk meet as friends.

In those dim days, Turtle was chief, and it was he who called the fur-folk and the feather-folk together. Turtle was chief because his shell was thick and he could draw in his head. A leader should be like that, oh, nephew. A thick skin, ears that do not hear and a mouth that is shut in a shell are things that every chief needs. But Wolf was envious, and *he* would be chief. So now comes the story, —jah-goh!

The call had gone forth, and from far and wide the animals came to the council. Something had happened. What could it be?

All through the woodland there was motion—the deer were coming. All through the brushland there was a swaying—the mink and the beaver, the muskrats and the raccoons were coming. All through the swampland there was a rustling—the beaver and the otter were coming. All through the waterways there was a splashing—the turtles and the lizards were coming. Above in the air were countless birds and above them, urging them on, was Sah-dah-gey-ah, the Great Blue Eagle, chief of all the feather-folk. All creatures had answered the call of Turtle.

Through the tangles slunk Timber Wolf, the envious one. Very sly was he, for he had a reason for keeping out of sight. His plan was a deep one, and if he could but succeed, he would be chief.

It is known to all, oh, nephew, that in the beginning of things, every animal and every bird had a magic pouch in which to keep its magical charms that gave power. This pouch every creature wore on its neck. While it possessed this it had power over other beasts and could not be injured. Now it was the custom for the animals in coming to the council to place their magic pouches in a great bark dish which Turtle kept by the council-fire. This meant that they had come for a council of peace and sat as equals.

Timber Wolf knew all this, and it was his plan to steal the basket of power and run with it to a secret cave where it might be hidden. This would weaken all the animals and they would have to look to him for favor. Oh, how they would beg to get even a little of that power back! Timber Wolf licked his chops at the thought of how he would make his brother beasts obey. The cowering things—more than one would slide down his throat before he got through!

Then Timber Wolf grew eager, and when night fell in the forest, he slunk about looking for sleepers that he might begin to steal their secret power even before the council was called.

He skulked around until he found an Old Bear. Here was luck, indeed, for Old Bear was on his back, his paws over his eyes, and his pouch of secret power bulging from his neck. It took but a snap of Timber Wolf's sharp teeth to sever the thong that bound the pouch to the Bear,—just a snap. Timber Wolf gave a slight growl of satisfaction and bounded away to hide the magic in his own pouch. Bear was now in his power! The beginning was good.

Morning came and all the animals and birds started on their journey again,—all save Old Bear who slept too long and arose weak and dazed. He did not know what had happened to him, but he knew that he felt sick. He shook himself and tried to amble along, but reeled from side to side. Still he made up his mind to keep on and never turn back, for Turtle had called a council and Turtle was chief. This being so, Bear would obey!

At length the great day came and Turtle saw around him a great host of tribesmen. Each sought his own group, its own corner or its own side of the fire. Turtle stood upon a stump and looked over the throng.

"Are all here?" he shouted.

A great shout went up, "We're here!"

"I do not hear the voice of Bear," called out Turtle. "Who has seen Bear? Perhaps, like White Stag, some traitor has slain him."

No one answered, but all remembered the tragedy of White Stag.

"Those who fail shall be without the new power," said Turtle. "Oh, all ye who are friends, place your magic power pouches in the great basket of friendship. Sit here as equals."

One by one the beasts and birds put their pouches into the basket. Even Timber Wolf put in a pouch, but kept one slyly hidden. It was his own, so that he could betray Turtle when the moment came.

Turtle surveyed the basket and spoke again. "I see the pouch of Bear but not of Timber Wolf," said Turtle. "Nevertheless, I see Timber Wolf here and do not see Bear. It appears that mischief has come upon us." You see, Turtle was very wise.

"How do you know that Bear's pouch is there and that mine is missing?" growled Timber Wolf, edging closely to the basket.

"Because Turtle is chief, and Turtle is wise," came the answer.

Wolf gave a snarl and sprang at Turtle, tipping him over and throwing him upon his back on the ground. All the animals leaped toward Wolf, who turned round and round, showing his fangs. Not a fur-folk or a feather-folk could touch Timber Wolf, for all power to fight was in the basket of friendship.

"Stand back," growled Timber Wolf. "Behold your chief sprawling on his back, overthrown by a swish of my paw! A fine chief is he. His dignity is to be admired! Oh, able leader of all the wood-folk, how neatly you spin upon your shiny shell! How yellow your breastplate, how beautifully marked! How your stubby hands and feet clutch at the air, appealing to the clouds to turn you over. Ho-hoh, ho-hoh!"

Timber Wolf now sprang to the stump and began to address the wood-folk. "Obey me," he shouted, "and I shall lead you forth to make war!"

There was a sudden sound behind him, and Timber Wolf gave one swift glance over his shoulder. He saw Turtle extend his head, dig his nose in the earth, give a twist of his neck and turn over with a flop. Timber Wolf's mouth opened and his tongue hung out, for Turtle now leaped into the air and came down upon the basket of friendship with a splash. As he landed, all the pouches of power popped out like seeds from a snap-dragon pod, and flew back where they belonged, and one flew far, far into the forest, and struck the neck of poor Old Bear, limping along so slowly.

Immediately all the animals growled and rushed upon Timber Wolf, holding him prisoner in a circle of extended claws and sharp teeth. Timber Wolf was now in for it, and knew his time had come.

Turtle Chief now mounted the stump. "Hold the prisoner

while I give you the great news," said he. "I have called this council to tell you that the *Ongwe* are coming, the mighty *Ongwe Oweh*, who are wiser than all the wood-folk."

"Who are the *Ongwe* that we should consider their coming?" snapped Timber Wolf from the circle.

There was a rustle and a snort. Into the council square leaped Old Bear. "Oh, chief," shouted he, "I have been greatly wronged and by trickery delayed. My power was stolen, but by magic came back to me. Still, my delay has shown me a great thing. The *Ongwe* are coming."

"The *Ongwe!*" shouted all the animals. "Who are the *Ongwe?*"

"I was about to tell you," shouted Turtle. "The *Ongwe* are *men-beings* and they are going to hunt, and there is one whom they shall hunt because they will hate him. He is Timber Wolf."

Timber Wolf snarled and with a sudden spring leaped high over the heads of the beasts around him, and dashed for the mighty mountain, swimming the lake, skulking the brush land and then scaling the peak. Here he found refuge in a dark cave, —it was a den to his liking, for he could look down upon the council and lay his schemes against it.

"What shall we do now?" asked Turtle, when the excitement had died down.

"Let us hunt Timber Wolf and force him to run the gauntlet," cried many voices.

"Let us catch him and leave none among us for the *Ongwe* to hate," cried others, planning to rend him limb from limb.

And so it was that all the birds and animals scattered in the forest, looking for Timber Wolf, but when night had come not one had seen him, though Timber Wolf had seen them all.

Wolf now crept into his dark cave, but drew back with a sharp cry. Before him in the darkness were two glowing eyes of evil. Some one was spying on him! He turned and fled to the mountain side, where he cowered behind a great rock, but here was a rustle, a constant rustle. Who could be here? Spies were everywhere!

Wolf now slunk along with greater caution to an open space where the moonlight fell. Here he could see his foes if any appeared. But what was that? A great black shadow waved over the ground. Wolf's hair rose in a shaggy crest from his neck to his tail. The black shadow beckoned and swayed. Then there came a creak and a groan, "Djis-gaah, djis-gaah!" So came the sound, and it was a word meaning *ghost!* Timber Wolf now looked up at the moon and gave a long despairing howl. His whole body trembled.

"Oh, to escape this awful place!" So thought Wolf, as he crept away from the open and sought refuge behind a great pine. Here he heard a rattle and, looking down in the dim light, saw the bones of the great elk which he had stalked in the snow and slain only the winter before when the council had gathered.

The bones glinted a ghastly white in the dim light that filtered in through the branches. Timber Wolf felt a chill gripping his very marrow, and with mincing steps he crawled out from the bone pile. Again he sought the open, but no sooner had he reached the clearing than he saw a great patch of white, like a cloud, slowly moving through the open spaces. It seemed to grow large and then small, and a portion waved up and down. Timber Wolf grew cold with terror and stood as if frozen to the ground. The ghostly white thing came nearer and nearer.

Wolf could not move now and his jaws grew hard. The ghost was upon him. There was a crash. He felt himself lifted high and borne away, nor could he even struggle now, for a great spear was thrust through his lower jaw and another through his hind leg. Only a faint whimper escaped from his throat as he felt himself carried on and on and on.

Down in the council circle a great fire blazed and all about it were the faithful fur-folk discussing the coming of the *Ongwe.* Suddenly Turtle Chief raised his hand.

"Some one is coming," said he. "Be still."

There was a crackling of sticks and the dashing of swift feet.

Then into the glare of the light leaped the great White Stag, Timber Wolf pinned in his antlers.

"I have come," began White Stag. "I have come with the culprit who disobeyed the laws of friendship and who sought power by theft."

"Deliver him to us," shouted all the fur-folk.

"I give him to you," answered the White Stag. "Let him forever be despised and hunted. Know you that last year, when winter came, and we gathered in council, Timber Wolf took me as I slept and killed me. I am the ghost of him whom you once called the Great White Stag. I am now the spirit of this mountain and watch over it. When the moon shines over the peak you will see me leaping through the clouds and now and again leaping down the mountain side into the water."

"Oh, Great White Stag," said Turtle, "you have done a good deed. Your slayer shall be punished. When the *Ongwe* come we shall suffer, perhaps, but Timber Wolf shall suffer more, for we shall call out to the *Ongwe* when Wolf prowls 'round."

"Begone, Timber Wolf," called out Turtle. "Know that you are hated and despised."

"I go," snarled Timber Wolf, "and I go hating all of you."

"Farewell," called out the Great White Stag, leaping into the air and up to the clouds.

The fur-folk and the feather-folk looked in amazement as their friend sped away, and as they watched, they saw him descend from the clouds and drop down upon the mountain he loved.

"He was the Great White Stag," said Turtle Chief, "but henceforth we shall call him by a new name; it shall be White Face, for it is the law of the forest that, once gone to the spirit world, the earth-name may not be used."

And so, forever after, all the forest-folk looked up to the mountain, and called out to their friend White Face, who dwelt there.

When the *Ongwe Oweh* (Indians) came, they often saw White Face leaping from crag to crag, up in the air and down in the lake. Well did they know that their arrows never could reach him, for White Face was a ghost.

In the days when wisdom came and Ha-yo-wen-tha brought the truth, the story of White Face came to men, and then all who were *Ongwe Oweh* went out to hunt Timber Wolves and to kill them.

The wolves have gone from the great forest and not one ever visits the mighty mountain now, but the spirit of the Great White Stag may still be seen, for it is he who guards the mountain, the lake and the valley and brings sweet peace.

Look on a starry night when the sky is bright and the moon is low—look above the mountain, and you, too, shall see the ghost of the Great White Stag. Na-hoh.

4 When America Was Younger

These stories are little bits of what America has inherited from the past. In them you will find some of the things that make all Americans alike, no matter from what country your ancestors came, no matter when they came, and no matter in what part of the country you live. The kinds of experiences that children and their families had in those early years helped to make us into one country.

It is interesting to see how the boys and girls and the older folks tried to carry on as they had always done in this new world that was so strange in many ways—in a whole chain of new worlds from the first colonies to the farthest frontiers. It is interesting to see how they came to live with other people who were so strange in many ways. And it is interesting to see how different kinds of people, coming from different European countries, were like the Indians whom they found here—and like one another, too.

How did any one of these people, red or white, act when he was afraid or suspicious? How did any of them act toward their own, and how toward those whom they considered their enemies? And how did Americans learn to live as friends with so many different kinds of neighbors?

Abraham Lincoln said once, "This country with its institutions belongs to all the people who inhabit it." If the country is today different from what it was in the past, the inhabitants of the years between have made it what it is. And in a sense we—all of us—can make this country what we want it to be.

THE HOME ON WHEELS

by Alice Dalgliesh

Richard and Ellen could not sleep that first night in the covered wagon. Mother and baby Hugh were fast asleep; one could hear their deep, even breathing. To the two older children it was all so thrilling that they could not settle down. Through the canvas flaps of the wagon they could see the dark sky, studded with stars. Some of the men were still talking by the camp fire. Richard sighed and pulled the blanket closer. It was warm and comfortable in the wagon but he would like to be outside. For a long time the children lay there drowsily, then somehow they fell asleep.

In the morning all kinds of noises awakened them, the bustle of people getting ready to start, loud talk of the trail and of the gold that lay at the end of it, high spirits for the first exciting days of the journey. There was not much room to dress in the wagon, for there was so much of everything in it. Barrels of flour with eggs neatly packed in the middle, other food supplies, tools, clothing, bedding, even the clock that mother prized so highly and would not leave behind. The first breakfast in the open air! The morning was crisp and cool and the bacon sizzled cheerfully. Why did people talk of the hardships of the overland trail?

That night the travelers sat around the camp fire. Luke played on his fiddle. Philip played on his flute. The thin, sad little tune trickled out into the darkness.

"Home, home, sweet, sweet home,
Be it ever so humble there's no place like home!"

There was a choking sound from one of the women. She was thinking of the comfortable home she had left in Iowa. Nothing but a home on wheels for months to come!

"Play something cheery, Luke!" whispered one of the men.

Luke drew the bow across the strings of his fiddle and swung into a rousing tune.

"Oh, Susannah,
Don't you cry for me,
For I'm going to California
With my wash bowl on my knee."

Voices joined in. The fire cracked and the darkness was full of song. Richard and Ellen were sorry when it was time for bed.

Those first days were not unpleasant in spite of bad roads. In the daytime there was a long trail of white-topped wagons with men and cows walking beside them. At night the wagons formed a corral or closed circle for protection in case of an Indian attack. Much to the relief of the older people, but rather to the disappointment of the children, they saw few Indians. One morning as they were breaking camp a small group of Indians did ride up, but they seemed to be merely curious and inclined to be friendly. Richard was standing by the wagon with Hugh in his arms. The morning sun shone on the baby's red-gold curls and one of the Indians gave a grunt of approval. He got down from his horse, pointed to the baby, to himself and then to the horse. He would trade the horse for the baby! Richard held Hugh tightly, shook his head, and stepped back into the shelter of the wagon. When the Indians rode away Richard gave a sigh of relief.

There was often the excitement and danger of crossing rivers. The first river was deep and muddy and there were only two flat boats to ferry hundreds of wagons across. That meant a long wait. Some streams were shallow and could be forded by the wagons. The oxen were urged in and soon the water came up to the tops of the wheels. It was a queer experience to sit in the wagon and watch the water swirling almost at one's feet. If only the stream did not get too deep! The worst crossing was a deep river where there were no ferries. There the men had to take the wagon bodies off the wheels and caulk the seams with tar so that the flat bodies could be used as boats. All the goods and supplies had to be unpacked, taken across the river and packed again.

On and on went the wagons, over roads so thick with dust that one could not see ahead. At night Richard and Ellen slept warmly in the wagon, Ellen wrapped in a blue and white coverlet which her grandmother had woven. Down in the corner of it was her grandmother's name and the date. The coverlet was Ellen's favorite possession and it was going all the way to California. It would make her feel more settled to see its familiar blue and white pattern on the bed in a new home.

On and on! Over roads even worse than before plodded the wagons, over mountains, through valleys, and over barren plains. On and on and on! They came to the grassy meadows before a long desert. Everyone had to turn to and make hay to feed the oxen during the days when there would be no grass. Then the hardest part of the journey was begun. The ground was hard and crusted with alkali. The sun was burning hot. Everyone who could walk beside the wagons did so to spare the oxen. Ellen rode with baby Hugh, Father and Mother and Richard walked. On and on! Now the sand was heavy and deep, the wheels of the wagons sank in it. Deserted wagons and dead oxen told the tale of difficulties met by other emigrants.

"We'll never make it," said the men. "The loads must be lightened."

All the heavy things went first, cook stoves and barrels of supplies. Still the wagon wheels moved heavily and the oxen strained at their yokes. The poor animals were growing tired. If they died there would be no hope of getting out of the desert. Men, women, and children looked worn and anxious.

The day came when everything that could be taken out to lighten the wagons was taken out. Richard and Ellen helped to carry the things to the side of the trail and pile them up. All their cherished belongings, with Mother's clock ticking steadily on top of the pile.

"Oh, Father," said Ellen, "must I leave Grandmother's coverlet? *Please* let me keep it."

"We'll have to leave it," said Father grimly. "It's leave everything now, or die ourselves."

The blue coverlet joined the pathetic pile at the side of the trail, so did Richard's gray blanket. The men made a sign such as they had seen in other places, "Help yourself." Perhaps a lighter wagon would be able to use some of the things they had discarded.

"I hope someone will take my blue coverlet," said Ellen sadly.

"Most likely before the week is out an Indian baby will be wrapped in it," said Richard.

"Don't tease your sister, Richard," said Mother fretfully. "We have troubles enough without that."

They were near the edge of the desert now and it was well, for the water casks were almost empty. A different danger lay ahead, for in the distance were the snow-capped peaks of a great range of mountains. Ellen felt weak and tired. As she lay in her bed at night an endless procession of dreary scenes went through her mind. Burning hot days on the prairies; choking dust; sand, miles and miles of it; the kitchen clock and the blue coverlet by the side of the trail; Bright, their favorite ox, lying dead; heat; thirst, baby Hugh crying pitifully for water; hunger. Now she was sure that she knew all the hardships of the California trail.

Mountain travel was dangerous, but a welcome change. These mountains were worse than those that they had passed. There were times when wagons had to be unpacked and lowered over precipices, or dragged up a steep rocky wall. At other times they toiled up long hills almost too steep for the oxen, or went through deep, gloomy ravines. It was solemn and lonely in the mountains and nights were cold. Everyone longed for the warm coverings left behind in the desert.

At last the road began to go downward. The grass was fresh and green and full of flowers. California was near! The travelers were at the end of the trail, and there was a pleasant grassy valley and a good place to camp. That night there was music and cheery talk around the camp fire. Richard and Ellen listened to a surprising conversation between two of the older men. One of them said solemnly, "Providence has blessed and favored us through this long journey." "Indeed," said the other, "we have avoided accident and disease and have traveled smoothly and quietly." Richard and Ellen gave each other a wondering look. Evidently the journey had been an easy one!

The story might end here with the making of new homes. For Ellen it ended later, when in the cabin of one of the settlers she saw a blue and white coverlet on a bed. Ellen lifted a corner of it and looked. There was the woven name:

ELLEN ADAIR

Her grandmother's name! Ellen dropped the corner of the coverlet without saying a word. The sign had said, "Help yourself"; she had no right to the coverlet now. That was just a part of life on the trail.

FLEET-FOOT ANN

by Elizabeth Coatsworth

Once upon a time in America—about a hundred and fifty years ago—a little girl named Ann was visiting her uncle and aunt at a new settlement on the shores of Lake Erie. Here, on a terrace of land above a creek, seven or eight log cabins had been built. The oldest belonged to the Indian trader, Mr. Winney, who had been there for five or six years. The newest belonged to Ann's young uncle and aunt who had only come to Buffalo Creek a year ago.

Uncle Asa was a sort of Indian trader, too, but he didn't sell the Indians rum and whiskey, knives, red calico, or beads. Uncle Asa sold them beautiful things he made out of silver—headbands to put around their hats when they wore them, and wide bracelets, brooches, and rings.

Just beyond the settlers' cabins were the Indian houses covered with elm bark, and beyond those was the forest, very dark and beautiful, where lived the wolves and bears, the deer, the panthers, and the squirrels.

Across Niagara River, just opposite the little American settlement, was the British fort called Fort Erie. Ann could often hear the fife and drum from the fort and catch a glimpse of the fine scarlet coats of the soldiers. Sometimes the officers had themselves rowed across the river for a council talk with the chiefs of the Seneca village. The officers considered that the village was English; the settlers said it was American, and no one was quite sure what the Indians thought about it, though they probably wished that it was still altogether theirs.

On very still days Ann could sometimes hear the distant roar of the Niagara Falls far away. It was loudest before the weather turned bad. Then it sounded like a humming of troubled bees, a low murmur in the air.

One morning Ann went fishing very early with some of the Indian girls of her own age. She stole out of the cabin before her aunt and uncle were awake, just stopping for a moment to look at little Lydia in her cradle.

Lydia was the first white baby to be born in Western New York State. The squaws often came to look at her, touching her fine yellow hair, laughing when she opened her big blue eyes. Even the chiefs smiled when they saw her; at least when they had not been drinking the trader's rum. Then they were quarrelsome and noisy and tried to push one another into the cooking fires, and their wives quietly hid their weapons until they were sober again.

These things were part of Ann's everyday life. She was not afraid of the fine British officers in their spotless uniforms, nor of the Indian chiefs with their shaved heads and foxtails and feathers fastened in their scalp locks. She was not afraid when she heard the panthers scream like people in trouble through the darkness, nor even when the wolves howled, one answering another.

Ann was like an Indian girl. She wore Seneca moccasins with flowers embroidered on them in beads, and she braided her long brown hair in two thick braids down her back. She could run as fast as any of her friends; she knew how to snare rabbits and squirrels for Aunt Kezia's pies. Once the flocks of pigeons came so thick that when they roosted at night they broke the branches of the trees with their weight. Ann went with the Senecas and knocked them from the trees after dark by torchlight.

"Oh, dear!" cried Aunt Kezia. "You are just like a little Seneca, Ann. Do pray point out your toes, and try to walk sedately. You haven't stitched at your sampler for a week."

"Let Ann alone," laughed Uncle Asa. "Who would get you good fish from the river and fresh meat for your pies if it wasn't for Ann? I'm busy at my silver making, and haven't much time for hunting. It's less trouble to buy a haunch of venison from the Senecas for a ring or a brooch."

But Aunt Kezia shook her head.

"The child is growing to be a little savage," she protested. "There's no church and no school here. In fact, when you think of it, there's no other white child but our precious Lydia, and a baby doesn't count. Ann, dear, remember to bring me the primer after I've done my baking, and I'll set you a task. And don't run whenever you want to go somewhere. No good will come of it."

"Running as Ann runs is a gift of God," said Uncle Asa. He was hammering out a bar of silver on his small silversmith's anvil. All day the cabin was filled with the pleasant, light tap-tapping of his hammer, except when an Indian came to look and bargain.

This morning Ann had risen early. She had a secret plan with some of her friends to go down the river, past the sand hills, until they reached the creek at Black Rock which the white and blue pike frequented. The fishing was best at dawn.

Ann carefully took a couple of fishhooks from a shelf, and a double fishline of twisted linden bark. She closed the cabin door behind her. It was cool and still rather dark outside, and when she came to the outskirts of the Indian village, the fires were all heaps of gray-white ashes which seemed to breathe out a last sigh of smoke. But already there was a stir about. Her friends were stealing out of the community houses where they slept with their families, and here and there a squaw was already going to the spring for water.

There were five Indian girls, all about Ann's age. They set out together, single file, for the creek, running at a steady pace. As they passed the marshes below the settlers' cabins, the ducks and geese flew up out of pools just stained with coming dawn. Across the river the garrison still seemed asleep, though no doubt the sentries were walking to and fro. Among the sand hills the girls came upon three deer playing. They sped away when they saw the girls.

Even in the sand Ann was not tired. Like the others, she trotted on, listening and smelling and watching as she ran. She smelled the sand and the river and the coming morning. She heard the crash of some animal in the bushes beside her. The sky was growing brighter with the cold, false dawn and the girls were wet to the knees with dew as they reached a big black rock which projected into the river.

Soon the sun would appear. They must hurry. Ann seized a basket which one of the girls had brought and waded out into the chilly water. She waited motionless and, then, with a quick jerk, brought the basket to the surface filled with water and minnows. Each child baited her hooks and waded out into the river and then slowly returned to shore. While they were still knee-deep, the sun came up, and the girls waded in gold and roses. Birds sang and called loudly from the trees on the banks, and the river rippled with fish, rising to snatch at moths or flies with wetted wings.

By the time the children had reached the bank, each had at least one fish struggling and thrashing behind her, scattering a rainbow of drops, and some had two. They laughed and chatted. The Seneca children liked Ann as much as she liked them.

"The old men do not understand," one of them said, as they sat cleaning their fish before going home. "Red Jacket says that the whites are our foes, and so do many of the other chiefs. But Farmer's Brother says that the Americans are our friends and that's what I think."

"And I think so," said another one.

"Anyway, *you* are," said a third. "See, I will give you my bead necklace. I wish to make you a present."

"Then I will give you my new ring," said Ann, for she knew that a present must always meet a present half way.

The girls strolled home, talking. There was no hurry, nothing to be done for hours. In the distance, almost at the other bank, they saw a bateau filled with men.

"It looks like our people," said Ann. "Oh, now I remember. Uncle was talking about taking the corn to the mill beyond Fort Erie today. We are out of meal, and so are most of the others."

"You should grind it in a hole in a rock, the way we do," said the girls. "A man should not have to take a journey across the river for squaws' work."

When Ann reached the cabin she found Aunt Kezia looking worried.

"I'm so glad you're back, child," she exclaimed. "What lovely fish! But your frock is very untidy. Never mind. Bring a blanket and we'll put Lydia under the big tree there. She's fretful in the heat. While you mind her, I'll bring out my spinning wheel."

"Has Uncle Asa gone to the mill?" asked Ann, carrying out Lydia who took a good firm hold of her cousin's braids in her two plump fists.

"Yes," said Aunt Kezia, the worried look deepening in her eyes. "He and all the other men, too, except the trader. And from the noise at his place, some of those Indians are buying more rum. I wish your uncle was home, I do."

Ann said quite seriously, "I'll take care of you and Lydia, Aunt Kezia."

Her aunt smiled. "I believe you would, child, if any one could. But I'll be glad when the men return."

It was growing very hot now after the coolness of the early morning. There was no wind, and the birds and animals of the forest were silent in the noontide quiet. Aunt Kezia's spinning wheel hummed drowsily by the door of the cabin. Little Lydia crawled here and there and then went to sleep. Ann was wondering if she should get the forgotten primer and look at the pictures in it, when suddenly a loud sound broke the peace.

A party of eight or nine braves was passing by, their blankets trailing behind them, their feathers askew, their footsteps staggering. Aunt Kezia went on with her spinning, hoping to escape notice. Ann sat, quiet as a wild thing, waiting for them to pass by.

But they didn't pass. They stood around the spinning wheel staring at it—at first, idly.

Then one said, "Rum, you gettum rum!" And they all began to shout and call for rum.

Aunt Kezia shook her head and spread her hands. "No rum!" she said.

She pointed to herself and shook her head. "No gottum rum."

The Indians became very angry. They shouted to her to bring it to them quick. They called her bad names in the Seneca language, and suddenly one of them came over and snatched up Lydia before Ann could even cry out.

"You tell the woman," he said to Ann in Seneca, "bring rum or I will throw her child against a tree for the wolves to eat and the eagles to fight over."

Ann knew this Indian. Usually he was gentle and kind, but a very small glass of rum, which a white man would never notice, drove an Indian crazy. Now little yellow-haired Lydia might as well be in the arms of a bear. What would happen?

She didn't need to tell Aunt Kezia what the brave had said.

Aunt Kezia understood. She got up from her stool. Her face was white as paper, but she smiled.

"Come with me, Ann," she called sweetly. "Yes, yes, I bring rum. Lots of rum. Yes, in one minute."

She drew the child into the darkness of the cabin and closed the door, dropping the heavy bar across it.

Then she began to breathe like a deer driven by the hounds. She hurried with Ann to the back window and opened it and pushed Ann through it.

"Run! Run for your life to the trader's! Quick! Quick!"

As Ann ran she could hear the Indians already growing impatient. They were beating on the door with their tomahawks and yelling like fiends. At any moment she might hear a shriek from Lydia. Ann ran as she had never run before, and arrived breathless at the door of the trader's cabin.

"Quick, Mr. Winney!" she panted. "The Indians are going to kill Lydia!"

If there was one thing precious in that settlement it was Lydia, the first child who had been born there to white people. Mr. Winney could not run as fast as Ann, but he ran fast that day. Man and child, they burst upon the astonished circle of Indians from the rear.

But the trader had not lived with the Indians without learning something of their ways. One glance showed him that the baby was still safe on the lean dark arm that held her. He spoke to the man quickly in his own tongue.

"I am told that my brothers are still thirsty," he explained. "My heart is grieved that I just now told them that my door was closed to them and they should drink no more of the water that burns like fire. Come back, come back, and we will sit by the table and talk and drink together."

He took Lydia from the man and handed her to Ann. Then he led the Indians, shouting and laughing now, toward his own place, as the splintered door of the cabin was flung open and Aunt Kezia threw her arms about her niece and daughter together.

"Thank goodness, you are safe!" she said, laughing and crying. "Oh, Ann, I shall never, never chide you again for running so fast! Lydia, my puppet, my dear, are you all right?"

Lydia was not even crying. She sat on her mother's arm smiling, as she had sat on the Indian's arm. She was perfectly happy. She had a new plaything. Some one had put a silver necklace hung with old French coins about her neck for her to play with, and she was swinging the end of the chain and watching the coins twinkle and dance.

"Pitty," she remarked. It was the first word she had spoken all afternoon.

Aunt Kezia looked about her at the forest, at the creek with its marshes below them, and the endless lake beyond. The Indians at the trader's were singing now, rather solemnly. The ducks were flying back to their pools among the alders for the evening, and a robin was trilling from a branch overhead.

"I don't understand," said Aunt Kezia, straightening the lace cap on her yellow hair, so like little Lydia's. "Was it a dreadful game, all the time? Or wasn't it? Anyhow, your uncle will soon be coming back for his supper and we must build up the fire again and broil your fish. He'll be hungry after all that rowing and walking in the heat."

BENJIE'S HAT*

by Mabel Leigh Hunt

Grandmother's letter had been addressed to the whole family, but Benjie remembered only one surprising paragraph.

"I want Benjie to come and spend the winter with me," wrote Grandmother. "The school house is only a mile through the woods, so that it will be right smart easier for him here than at home. Tell him that I am very lonely since his grandfather died, and that I need a manbody to look after me and keep me company."

Benjie felt that he was the most important person in all of North Carolina. "A manbody!" Well—wasn't he ten years old? Of course he would look after Grandmother!

And, too, he remembered the molasses cookies in the big stone jar in Grandmother's kitchen—always plenty of them.

So Benjie rode back to Guilford County with Peter Kersey, who was Grandmother's good neighbor. It was he who had brought her letter.

Benjie liked living at Grandmother's from the moment of his arrival. In the first place, he loved his grandmother. In the second place, in Grandmother's house he was the only boy, and not one of many, as at home. He was important. In the third place, out of the iron pots slung over the hearthfire, and from the big outdoor oven on baking days, there came the most savory and delicious foods, for Grandmother was famous for her cooking. The molasses cakes were even bigger and browner and better than Benjie remembered.

Grandmother lived in a comfortable old house built of great hand-hewn timbers. The oaken floors were always well scrubbed, the hand-woven coverlets and rugs always bright, the pewter always gleaming, and Grandmother herself, in kerchief and cap, as neat as a plump little sparrow.

On Saturdays Benjie often played with Eliphalet, the ten-year-old son of Hamish and Clemmie, the free Negroes who lived in a cabin on the farm. Together the boys explored the banks of the slow amber-colored river, or gathered nuts and persimmons and the sweet wild muscadines.

Benjie had his chores, too, feeding the chickens, throwing down hay from the loft for the horses, turning the windlass that drew the water up from the covered well. And on wash-days before he left for school there was the enormous outdoor kettle to fill with water from the near-by brook. Grandmother even trusted him to build the careful fire under the smoke-blackened kettle. There was no doubt that Benjie was helping to look after Grandmother.

And in the evenings he would "keep her company." They would talk, or play riddles and guessing games. Finally, Grandmother would read a chapter from the big Bible. Then bed, and the long, long night of sleep.

All through the mild autumn weather Benjie had been running hatless and coatless to school, when Grandmother said one day, "I never saw that thee brought a hat with thee, Benjie."

"I didn't," answered Benjie. "Mother said that I should leave my cap for Brother John. She said that thee would buy me a new one from the general store in Friendship."

"Thee must be provided," agreed Grandmother, "for soon it will be too cold to go with nothing on thy head."

Benjie thought no more of this conversation until one blustery First Day evening, Grandmother said, "Tomorrow thee must wear thy new hat to school. Thee didn't know I had a surprise for thee."

She opened the door of the fireside cupboard, and drew out a hat.

"There, Benjie!" she said. "While thee was at school, I was busy plying my needle. There was no need to spend good money for a cap, when thy grandfather's tall beaver lay unused in its box. See—I cut a mite off the crown, though it was a pity to waste even that bit. I took some pleats in crown and brim, to make it more thy size. Then I sewed them back together again, and there is thy hat!" She held it up proudly.

Benjie stared. "It's a very peculiarsome hat," he murmured, and burst into tears. "The b-b-boys will laugh."

"Tut, tut, Benjamin," scolded Grandmother. "Is thee a girl, to be so vain of thy looks? 'Tis a good hat, and 'twill serve the purpose. And thee should feel honored to wear the hat thy grandfather wore for fifteen years."

Benjie set off to school the next morning, wearing the hat. In spite of Grandmother's careful pleatings, it was still much too large for him, and only his ears held it up. In the wood he put up his hand and felt of it. How smooth and furry it was! No doubt Grandfather had once paid a good round sum for it. Perhaps, after all, the boys would not laugh.

But when he entered the school yard, up went shouts of derision, and soon the whole world, as it seemed to Benjie, was echoing with the chorus.

"Look at Benjie's ha-yat!
Look at Benjie's ha-yat!"

Oh, how red and unhappy Benjie was!

But he laughed as hard as anyone when his tormentors flung the hat upward, and it caught on the limb of a tree. He hoped that it would hang there forever, and went home that evening to tell Grandmother cheerfully that the hat was entirely out of reach. But the next day, while school was keeping, Grandmother and Hamish came with a long pole and lifted it down.

What a craning of necks as the children watched them through the windows! And presently, to the delight of every boy in the room, Grandmother opened the door, and said, "Benjamin, thee will find thy hat hanging in the school entry." For a few hours after that Benjie didn't even *like* his grandmother.

Soon Benjie began to feel that nothing could harm that hat. For instance, it blew off one day in a gust of windy rain. He carried it home hopefully, for it was smeared with the gummy red clay of North Carolina. But Grandmother let it dry, scraped off the dirt, and washed and brushed it carefully. It looked just as good as ever.

"Is this my hat, Grandmother, or is it Grandfather's hat?" asked Benjie.

"It is thy hat now," answered Grandmother.

Therefore Benjie felt that he had a perfect right to give the hat to Eliphalet, for it seemed as if the little colored boy was the only one in all the world, except Grandmother, of course, who did not laugh at Benjie's hat.

"This is a sure 'nough gif'," declared Eliphalet grinning from ear to ear. "That ol' Mister Beaver he's just as smooth an' slick as ever he was."

But when Clemmie saw the hat decorating her son's head, she shouted, "You march straight up to the big house with that hat, an' don't be delayin' yourself. Benjie's grandmother—she's going to be in a big huff when she finds that boy gave ol' dead Massa's hat away. An' ol' dead Massa's going to haunt folks that wear his hat when they're got no right to it."

In a very few moments the hat was lying on Grandmother's doorstep, and Eliphalet was running home with might and main, for fear of the *haunt*.

Whenever Benjie went to First Day Meeting, sitting like a man on the men's side, his ears burned scarlet with mortification, for it was the Quaker custom to wear one's hat throughout the Meeting. He would turn suspiciously, to catch a frosty twinkle in a pair of elderly eyes, or a smothered giggle from some boy.

Therefore one morning as they rode to Meeting, Benjie said sulkily, "I guess *thee* wouldn't wear this hat."

"Indeed, I would," answered Grandmother, tartly, and to Benjie's horror, she removed her bonnet, and put on the hat, sitting very straight in the carriage seat. She looked ridiculous. Oh dear! Grandmother was certainly very difficult to look after. He couldn't have *her* make a laughing-stock out of herself. Personal pride was one thing, but family pride was another. "Never mind, Grandmother," he said meekly, "*I'd* better wear it."

Just then a dog came running out from nowhere, barking furiously. The horse jumped, and thundered down the road, almost shaking Grandmother and Benjie to pieces. Afterward it was discovered that Benjie's hat was missing. He went back to search for it, praying that it had been trampled beyond repair, or that the dog had carried it off. But there it was, lying in a fence-corner, with only one small dent in the brim. "A bit of steaming and pressing will attend to that," said Grandmother.

The next time that Peter Kersey had an errand to Alamance County, Benjie secretly gave him a letter to carry. It said:

DEAR MOTHER:

I am well, and hope thee is the same. I wish thee would send me a Cap, and oblige

Thy obeedyunt son,
BENJAMIN BARNETT.

But when Peter returned, and Benjie unwrapped the eagerly-awaited parcel, there was nothing but an old yarn muffler. To tie up his head like a baby! Oh, it was terribly disappointing!

One evening Benjie sat on a stump in the wood. There was a dark scowl on his face. His lower lip stuck away out. At school that afternoon when Susan Bond was supposed to be doing a sum on the blackboard, she had drawn a picture. First she had made a very tall hat. Beneath that two enormous ears. Then she had drawn a tiny, teeny body, and underneath she had printed BENJIE. She had rubbed it out quickly before the teacher had suspected, but most of the scholars had seen it.

Benjie was mad. He was mad at everybody in the world. Presently Peter Kersey came riding through the wood. He alighted from his horse, and sat down by the boy. Benjie did not speak. He only scowled the darker. Peter picked the hat up and turned it thoughtfully in his hands.

"Thy grandfather was a fine man, Benjie," he began quietly, "one of the finest North Carolina has ever produced. He and I were boys together. He was my great friend. Did thee ever hear about the time thy grandfather—" And straightway Peter began to tell stories about Grandfather Barnett—things Benjie had never heard before. Soon the scowl faded, and the sulky lower lip slipped back. Benjie began to think that perhaps he might wear cheerfully a hat that such a fine grandfather had worn.

"And I'll tell thee, Benjie," said Peter, when he had finished, "thy grandmother is a fine woman, too. But between me and thee, women never understand how a man feels about his hat. A man's hat is his own. Let it be suitable, and he can face the world with his head up."

Even if Peter Kersey was an Elder and sat at the head of the Meeting, he understood a fellow!

But the next morning, Benjie remembered Susan's drawing, and said to himself, "I'll not wear this hat to school if I catch the quinsy and die!" So he took to hiding the hat in the wood, and nobody knew.

One afternoon in the early winter Peter Kersey took his gun into the wood after rabbits. He had bagged three and was just turning homeward, when he saw another plump cottontail bounding ahead. He took aim and missed. The rabbit disappeared into one end of a hollow log just as Peter fired his second shot. He walked forward to investigate. And there in the end of the log was Benjie's hat, with the top of the crown almost torn off by the force of the shot, and the dead rabbit trapped inside.

"Now, I've done it," said Peter ruefully. "I'll have to wait for Benjie to come along this way from school."

When Benjie saw the hat—what joy! "Now I'll never have to wear it again!" he cried.

"Don't thee be too sure of that," warned Peter. "But now we must go and tell thy grandmother what has happened." They walked slowly homeward through the wood, wondering just what they would say. Presently Peter said, "A thought has suddenly occurred to me. Put on the hat, Benjie. And can't thee look a trifle pale?"

Indeed Benjie's cheeks were not as rosy as usual, for what would Grandmother say when she learned that he had been hiding the hat in the wood?

Arrived at the house, Peter confronted Grandmother bravely. He kept Benjie well behind him. His face was long and serious. "I have something to tell thee, Judith," he said. "I hope thee will not take it too hard. This afternoon I was hunting in the woods, and I—I shot thy—thy grandson's hat." He reached around quickly and plucked the hat off Benjie's head.

Grandmother stared at the bullet holes. She saw the stains in the crown. She went white as a sheet. "Oh, Benjie-boy," she cried, "is thee hurt?"

At that Benjie could not keep his face straight a moment longer. He laughed, and Peter laughed. And as soon as Grandmother heard about the rabbit, her relief was so great that she laughed as hard as anyone. "I do declare," said she, "this hat has had so many misfortunes that I'm beginning to believe that the Lord never intended that Benjie should wear it."

"Then thee'll throw it away?" cried Benjie.

"Throw this good hat away?" echoed Grandmother. "Just hearken to him, Peter. I'm sure I don't know where he gets such notions of wastefulness. Everything comes in handy sooner or later, Grandson. Thee knows that old saying—'Keep a thing seven years, and thee will find a use for it.' So *of course* I won't throw the hat away. But I guess thee won't have to wear it any more, Benjie. I always thought it very suitable, but I don't believe thee ever liked it much. Tomorrow, Benjie, we shall drive over to Friendship, and buy thee a new cap!"

Benjie wanted to shout, or clap his hands, or turn a handspring, but thought better of it, for Grandmother's sake. But he ran to the stone jar and selected the very biggest and brownest cooky for his friend Peter Kersey. And the next biggest for himself. As Peter accepted the cooky, he and Benjie looked at each other, as man to man, and smiled.

GRINDING THE AX

by Benjamin Franklin

One cold morning in winter, when I was a little boy, a smiling man with an ax on his shoulder stopped me, saying, "My pretty boy, has your father a grindstone?"

"Yes, sir," said I.

"You are a fine little fellow!" said the man. "Will you let me grind my ax?"

Pleased with the flattery, I answered, "Oh, yes, sir. The grindstone is down in the shop."

Patting me on my head, he said, "Will you get me some hot water?" I ran and brought the hot water.

"How old are you, and what is your name?" he inquired, without waiting for a reply. "I'm sure you are one of the finest lads I have ever seen. Will you turn the grindstone a few minutes for me?"

Tickled with the flattery, I went to work with a will. It was a new ax, and I toiled and tugged till I was almost tired to death. The school bell rang, but I could not get away. My hands were blistered; still the ax was not half ground.

At last, however, it was sharpened. Then the man turned to me and said, "Now, you little rascal, you've played truant! Scud to school, or you'll be sorry!"

Alas! thought I. It was hard enough to turn a grindstone this cold day, but now to be called a rascal is too much.

The memory of turning the grindstone that winter's morning sank deep into my mind. I have thought of it since. Now, whenever I hear words of flattery, I say to myself, "That man has an ax to grind."

ONAWANDAH

by Louisa May Alcott

Long ago when hostile Indians haunted the great forests, and every settlement had its fort for the protection of the inhabitants, in one of the towns on the Connecticut River lived Parson Bain and his little son and daughter. The wife and mother was dead; but an old servant took care of them, and did her best to make Reuben and Eunice good children. Her direst threat, when they were naughty, was, "The Indians will come and fetch you, if you don't behave." So they grew up in great fear of the red men. Even the friendly Indians, who sometimes came for food or powder, were regarded with suspicion by the people. No man went to work without his gun near by. On Sundays, when they trudged to the rude meeting-house, all carried the trusty rifle on the shoulder, and while the pastor preached, a sentinel mounted guard at the door, to give warning if canoes came down the river or a dark face peered from the wood.

One autumn night, when the first heavy rains were falling and a cold wind whistled through the valley, a knock came at the minister's door and, opening it, he found an Indian boy, ragged, hungry, and foot-sore, who begged for food and shelter. In his broken way, he told how he had fallen ill and been left to die by enemies who had taken him from his own people, months before; how he had wandered for days till almost sinking; and that he had come now to ask for help, led by the hospitable light in the parsonage window.

"Send him away, Master, or harm will come of it. He is a spy, and we shall be scalped by the murdering Injuns who are waiting in the wood," said old Becky, harshly; while little Eunice hid in the old servant's ample skirts, and twelve-year-old Reuben laid his hand on his cross-bow, ready to defend his sister if need be.

But the good man drew the poor lad in, saying, with his friendly smile: "Shall not a Christian be as hospitable as a godless savage? Come in, child, and be fed; you sorely need rest and shelter."

Leaving his face to express the gratitude he had no words to tell, the boy sat by the comfortable fire and ate like a famished wolf, while Becky muttered her forebodings and the children eyed the dark youth at a safe distance. Something in his pinched face, wounded foot and eyes full of dumb pain and patience, touched the little girl's tender heart, and, yielding to a pitiful impulse, she brought her own basin of new milk and, setting it beside the stranger, ran to hide behind her father, suddenly remembering that this was one of the dreaded Indians.

"That was well done, little daughter. Thou shalt love thine enemies, and share thy bread with the needy. See, he is smiling; that pleased him, and he wishes us to be his friends."

But Eunice ventured no more that night, and quaked in her little bed at the thought of the strange boy sleeping on a blanket before the fire below. Reuben hid his fears better, and resolved to watch while others slept; but was off as soon as his curly head touched the pillow, and dreamed of tomahawks and war-whoops till morning.

Next day, neighbors came to see the waif, and one and all advised sending him away as soon as possible, since he was doubtless a spy, as Becky said, and would bring trouble of some sort.

"When he is well, he may go whithersoever he will; but while he is too lame to walk, weak with hunger, and worn out with weariness, I will harbor him. He can not feign suffering and starvation like this. I shall do my duty, and leave the consequences to the Lord," answered the parson, with such pious firmness that the neighbors said no more.

But they kept a close watch upon Onawandah, when he went among them, silent and submissive, but with the proud air of a captive prince, and sometimes a fierce flash in his black eyes when the other lads taunted him with his red skin. He was very lame for weeks, and could only sit in the sun, weaving pretty baskets for Eunice, and shaping bows and arrows for Reuben. The children were soon his friends, for with them he was always gentle, trying in his soft language and expressive gestures to show his good will and gratitude; for they defended him against their ruder playmates, and, following their father's example, trusted and cherished the homeless youth.

When he was able to walk, he taught the boy to shoot and trap the wild creatures of the wood, to find fish where others failed, and to guide himself in the wilderness by star and sun, wind and water. To Eunice he brought little offerings of bark and feathers; taught her to make moccasins of skin, belts of shells, or pouches gay with porcupine quills and colored grass. He would not work for old Becky—who plainly showed her distrust—saying: "A brave does not grind corn and bring wood; that is squaw's work. Onawandah will hunt and fish and fight for you, but no more." And even the request of the parson could not win obedience in this, though the boy would have died for the good man.

Winter came, and the settlers fared hardly through the long months, when the drifts rose to the eaves of their low cabins, and the stores, carefully harvested, failed to supply even their simple wants. But the minister's family never lacked wild meat, for Onawandah proved himself a better hunter than any man in the town, and the boy of sixteen led the way on his snow-shoes when they went to track a bear to its den, chase the deer for miles, or shoot the wolves that howled about their homes in the winter nights.

"Be of good cheer, little daughter; I shall be gone but three days, and our brave Onawandah will guard you well," said the parson, one April morning, as he mounted his horse to visit a distant settlement, where the bitter winter had brought sickness and death to more than one household.

The boy showed his white teeth in a bright smile as he stood beside the children, while Becky croaked, with a shake of the head:

"I hope you may n't find you've warmed a viper in your bosom, Master."

Two days later, it seemed as if Becky was a true prophet, and that the confiding minister *had* been terribly deceived; for Onawandah went about to hunt, and, that night, the awful war-whoop woke the sleeping villagers to find their houses burning, while the hidden Indians shot at them by the light of the fires kindled by dusky scouts. In terror and confusion the whites fled to the fort; and, while the men fought bravely, the women held blankets to catch arrows and bullets, or bound up the hurts of their defenders.

It was all over by daylight, and the red men sped away up the river, with several prisoners, and such booty as they could plunder from the deserted houses. Not till all fear of a return of their enemies was over, did the poor people venture to leave the fort and seek their ruined homes. Then it was discovered that Becky and the parson's children were gone, and great was the bewailing, for the good man was much beloved by all his flock.

Suddenly the smothered voice of Becky was heard by a party of visitors, calling dolefully:

"I am here, betwixt the beds. Pull me out, neighbors, for I am half dead with fright and smothering."

The old woman was quickly extricated from her hiding-place, and with much energy declared that she had seen Onawandah, disguised with warpaint, among the Indians, and that he had torn away the children from her arms before she could fly from the house.

"He chose his time well, when they were defenseless, dear lambs! Spite of all my warnings, Master trusted him, and this is the thanks we get. Oh, my poor master! How can I tell him this heavy news?"

There was no need to tell it; for, as Becky sat moaning and beating her breast on the fireless hearth, and the sympathizing neighbors stood about her, the sound of a horse's hoofs was heard, and the parson came down the hilly road like one riding for his life. He had seen the smoke afar off, guessed the sad truth, and hurried on, to find his home in ruins and to learn by his first glance at the faces around him that his children were gone.

When he had heard all there was to tell, he sat down upon his door-stone with his head in his hands, praying for strength to bear a grief too deep for words. The wounded and weary men tried to comfort him with hope, and the women wept with him as they hugged their own babies closer to the hearts that ached for the lost children. Suddenly a stir went through the mournful group, as Onawandah came from the wood with a young deer upon his shoulders, and amazement in his face as he saw the desolation before him. Dropping his burden, he stood an instant looking with eyes that kindled fiercely; then he came bounding toward them, undaunted by the hatred, suspicion, and surprise plainly written on the countenances before him. He missed his playmates, and asked but one question:

"The boy? the little squaw?—where gone?"

His answer was a rough one, for the men seized him and poured forth the tale, heaping reproaches upon him for such treachery and ingratitude. He bore it all in proud silence till they pointed to the poor father whose dumb sorrow was more eloquent than all their wrath. Onawandah looked at him, and the fire died out of his eyes as if quenched by the tears he would not shed. Shaking off the hands that held him, he went to his good friend, saying with passionate earnestness:

"Onawandah is *not* traitor! Onawandah remembers. Onawandah grateful! You believe?"

The poor parson looked up at him, and could not doubt his truth; for genuine love and sorrow ennobled the dark face, and he had never known the boy to lie.

"I believe and trust you still, but others will not. Go, you are no longer safe here, and I have no home to offer you," said the parson, sadly, feeling that he cared for none, unless his children were restored to him.

"Onawandah has no fear. He goes; but he comes again to bring the boy, the little squaw."

Few words, but they were so solemnly spoken that the most unbelieving were impressed; for the youth laid one hand on the gray head bowed before him, and lifted the other toward heaven, as if calling the Great Spirit to hear his vow.

A relenting murmur went through the crowd, but the boy paid no heed, as he turned away, and with no arms but his hunting knife and bow, no food but such as he could find, no guide but the sun by day, the stars by night, plunged into the pathless forest and was gone.

Then the people drew a long breath, and muttered to one another:

"He will never do it, yet he is a brave lad for his years."

"Only a shift to get off with a whole skin, I warrant you. These varlets are as cunning as foxes," added Becky, sourly.

The parson alone believed and hoped, though weeks and months went by, and his children did not come.

Meantime, Reuben and Eunice were far away in an Indian camp, resting as best they could, after the long journey that followed that dreadful night. Their captors were not cruel to them, for Reuben was a stout fellow and, thanks to Onawandah, could hold his own with the boys who would have tormented him if he had been feeble or cowardly. Eunice also was a hardy creature for her years, and when her first fright and fatigue were over, made herself useful in many ways among the squaws, who did not let the pretty child suffer greatly; though she was neglected, because they knew no better.

Life in a wigwam was not a life of ease, and fortunately the children were accustomed to simple habits and the hardships that all endured in those early times. But they mourned for home till their young faces were pathetic with longing, and their pillows of dry leaves were often wet with tears in the night. Their clothes grew ragged, their hair unkempt, their faces tanned by sun and wind. Scanty food and exposure to all weathers tried the strength of their bodies, and uncertainty as to their fate saddened their spirits; yet they bore up bravely, and said their prayers faithfully, feeling sure that God would bring them home to father in His own good time.

One day, when Reuben was snaring birds in the wood,—for the Indians had no fear of such young children venturing to escape,—he heard the cry of a quail, and followed it deeper and deeper into the forest, till it ceased, and, with a sudden rustle, Onawandah rose up from the brakes, his finger on his lips to prevent any exclamation that might betray him to other ears and eyes.

"I come for you and little Laraka," the name he gave Eunice, meaning "Wild Rose." "I take you home. Not know me yet. Go and wait."

He spoke low and fast; but the joy in his face told how glad he was to find the boy after his long search, and Reuben clung to him, trying not to disgrace himself by crying like a girl, in his surprise and delight.

Lying hidden in the tall brakes they talked in whispers, while one told of the capture, and the other of a plan for escape; for, though a friendly tribe, these Indians were not Onawandah's people, and they must not suspect that he knew the children, else they might be separated at once.

"Little squaw betray me. You watch her. Tell her not to cry out, and speak me any time. When I say come, we go,—fast,—in the night. Not ready yet."

These were the orders Reuben received, and, when he could compose himself, he went back to the wigwams, leaving his friend in the wood, while he told the good news to Eunice, and prepared her for the part she must play.

Fear had taught her self-control, and the poor child stood the test well, working off her relief and rapture by pounding corn in the stone mortar till her little hands were blistered, and her arms ached for hours afterward.

Not till the next day did Onawandah make his appearance, and then he came limping into the village, weary, lame, and half starved after his long wandering in the wilderness. He was kindly welcomed, and his story believed, for he told only the first part, and said nothing of his life among the white men. He hardly glanced at the children when they were pointed out to him by their captors, and scowled at poor Eunice, who forgot her part in her joy, and smiled as she met the dark eyes that till now had always looked kindly at her. A touch from Reuben warned her, and she was glad to hide her confusion by shaking her long hair over her face, as if afraid of the stranger.

Onawandah took no further notice of them, but seemed to be very lame with the old wound in his foot, which prevented his being obliged to hunt with the men. He was resting and slowly gathering strength for the hard task he had set himself, while he waited for a safe time to save the children.

At last, in the early autumn, all the men went off on the warpath, leaving only boys and women behind. Then Onawandah's eyes began to kindle, and Reuben's heart to beat fast, for both felt that their time for escape had come.

All was ready, and one moonless night the signal was given. A cricket chirped shrilly outside the tent where the children slept with one old squaw. A strong hand cut the skin beside their bed of fir boughs, and two trembling creatures crept out to follow the tall shadow that flitted noiselessly before them into the darkness of the wood. Not a broken twig, a careless step or a whispered word betrayed them, and they vanished as swiftly and silently as hunted deer flying for their lives.

Till dawn they hurried on, Onawandah carrying Eunice, whose strength soon failed, and Reuben manfully shouldering the hatchet and the pouch of food. At sunrise they hid in a thicket by a spring and rested, while waiting for the friendly night to come again. Then they pushed on, and fear gave wings to their feet, so that by another morning they were far enough away to venture to travel more slowly and sleep at night.

If the children had learned to love and trust the Indian boy in happier times, they adored him now, and came to regard him as an earthly Providence, so faithful, brave and tender was he; so forgetful of himself, so bent on saving them. He never seemed to sleep, ate the poorest morsels or went without any food when provision failed; let no danger daunt him, no hardship wring complaint from him; but went on through the wild forest, led by guides invisible to them, till they began to hope that home was near.

Twice he saved their lives. Once, when he went in search of food, leaving Reuben to guard his sister, the children, being very hungry, ignorantly ate some poisonous berries which looked like wild cherries, and were deliciously sweet. The boy generously gave most of them to Eunice, and soon was terror-stricken to see her grow pale and cold and deathly ill. Not knowing what to do, he could only rub her hands and call wildly for Onawandah.

The name echoed through the silent wood, and, though far away, the keen ear of the Indian heard it, his fleet feet brought him back in time, and his knowledge of wild roots and herbs made it possible to save the child when no other help was at hand.

"Make fire. Keep warm. I soon come," he said, after hearing the story and examining Eunice, who could only lift her eyes to him, full of childish confidence and patience.

Then he was off again, scouring the woods like a hound on the scent, searching everywhere for the precious little herb that would counteract the poison. Any one watching him would have thought him crazy as he rushed hither and thither, tearing up the leaves, creeping on his hands and knees that it might not escape him, and when he found it, springing up with a cry that startled the birds, and carried hope to poor Reuben, who was trying to forget his own pain in his anxiety for Eunice, whom he thought dying.

"Eat, eat, while I make drink. All safe now," cried Onawandah, as he came leaping toward them with his hands full of green leaves, and his dark face shining with joy.

The boy was soon relieved, but for hours they hung over the girl, who suffered sadly, till she grew unconscious and lay as if dead. Reuben's courage failed then, and he cried bitterly, thinking how hard it would be to leave the dear little creature under the pines and go home alone to father. Even Onawandah lost hope for a while, and sat like a bronze statue of despair, with his eyes fixed on his Wild Rose, who seemed fading away too soon.

Suddenly he rose, stretched his arms to the west, where the sun was setting splendidly, and in his own musical language prayed to the Great Spirit. The Christian boy fell upon his knees, feeling that the only help was in the Father who saw and heard them even in the wilderness. Both were comforted, and when they turned to Eunice there was a faint tinge of color on the pale cheeks, as if the evening red kissed her, the look of pain was gone, and she slept quietly without the moans that had made their hearts ache before.

"He hears! he hears!" cried Onawandah, and for the first time Reuben saw tears in his keen eyes, as the Indian boy turned his face to the sky full of a gratitude that no words were sweet enough to tell.

In the morning she was safe, and great was the rejoicing; but for two days the little invalid was not allowed to continue the journey, much as they longed to hurry on. It was a pretty sight, the bed of hemlock boughs spread under a green tent of woven branches, and on the pillow of moss the pale child watching the flicker of sunshine through the leaves, listening to the babble of a brook close by, or sleeping tranquilly, lulled by the murmur of the pines. Patient, loving and grateful, it was a pleasure to serve her, and both the lads were faithful nurses. Onawandah cooked birds for her to eat, and made a pleasant drink of the wild raspberry leaves to quench her thirst. Reuben snared rabbits, that she might have nourishing food, and longed to shoot a deer for provision, that she might not suffer hunger again on their journey. The boyish desire led him deeper into the wood than it was wise for him to go alone, for it was near night-fall, and wild creatures haunted the forest in those days. The fire, which Onawandah kept constantly burning, guarded their little camp where Eunice lay; but Reuben, with no weapon but his bow and hunting knife, was beyond this protection when he at last gave up his vain hunt and turned homeward. Suddenly, the sound of stealthy steps startled him, but he could see nothing through the dusk at first, and hurried on, fearing that some treacherous Indian was following him. Then he remembered his sister, and resolved not to betray her resting-place if he could help it, for he had learned courage of Onawandah, and longed to be as brave and generous as his dusky hero.

So he paused to watch and wait, and soon saw the gleam of two fiery eyes, not behind, but above him, in a tree. Then he knew that it was an "Indian devil," as they called a species of fierce wild-cat that lurked in the thickets and sprang on its prey like a small tiger.

"If I could only kill it alone, how proud Onawandah would be of me," thought Reuben, burning for the good opinion of his friend.

It would have been wiser to hurry on and give the beast no time to spring; but the boy was over bold, and, fitting an arrow to the string, aimed at the bright eye-ball and let fly. A sharp snarl showed that some harm was done, and, rather daunted by the savage sound, Reuben raced away, meaning to come back next day for the prize he hoped he had secured.

But soon he heard the creature bounding after him, and he uttered one ringing shout for help, feeling too late that he had been foolhardy. Fortunately he was nearer camp than he thought. Onawandah heard him and was there in time to receive the wild-cat, as, mad with the pain of the wound, it sprung at Reuben. There was no time for words, and the boy could only watch in breathless interest and anxiety the fight which went on between the brute and the Indian.

It was sharp but short, for Onawandah had his knife, and as soon as he could get the snarling, struggling beast down, he killed it with a skilful stroke. But not before it had torn and bitten him more dangerously than he knew, for the dusk hid the wounds, and excitement kept him from feeling them at first. Reuben thanked him heartily, and accepted his first words of warning with grateful docility; then both hurried back to Eunice, who till next day knew nothing of her brother's danger.

Onawandah made light of his scratches, as he called them, got their supper, and sent Reuben early to bed, for tomorrow they were to start again.

Excited by his adventure, the boy slept lightly, and waking in the night, saw by the flicker of the fire Onawandah binding up a deep wound in his breast with wet moss and his own belt. A stifled groan betrayed how much he suffered; but when Reuben went to him, he would accept no help, said it was nothing, and sent him back to bed, preferring to endure the pain in stern silence, with true Indian pride and courage.

Next morning, they set out and pushed on as fast as Eunice's strength allowed. But it was evident that Onawandah suffered much, though he would not rest, forbade the children to speak of his wounds and pressed on with feverish haste, as if he feared that his strength might not hold out. Reuben watched him anxiously, for there was a look in his face that troubled the boy and filled him with alarm, as well as with remorse and love.

In three days they reached the river, and, as if Heaven helped them in their greatest need, found a canoe, left by some hunter, near the shore. In they sprang, and let the swift current bear them along, Eunice kneeling in the bow like a little figure-head of Hope, Reuben steering with his paddle, and Onawandah sitting with arms tightly folded over his breast, as if to control the sharp anguish of the neglected wound.

Hour after hour they floated down the great river, looking eagerly for signs of home, and when at last they entered the familiar valley, while the little girl cried for joy, and the boy paddled as he had never done before, Onawandah sat erect with his haggard eyes fixed on the dim distance, and sang his death-song in a clear, strong voice—though every breath was pain,—bent on dying like a brave, without complaint or fear.

At last they saw the smoke from the cabins on the hill-side

and, hastily mooring the canoe, all sprung out, eager to be at home after their long and perilous wandering. But as his foot touched the land, Onawandah felt that he could do no more, and stretching his arms toward the parsonage, the windows of which glimmered as hospitably as they had done when he first saw them, he said, with a pathetic sort of triumph in his broken voice: "Go. I can not.—Tell the good father, Onawandah not lie, not forget. He keep his promise."

5

Enchantment and Wonder

Stories like these have been made up by people everywhere, in all languages, and in many different forms. Many of them belong to the whole world, for it is impossible to tell where they began. And of course all the time new ones are being made up everywhere.

These stories do not pretend to be "true" in any sense; they are made up just for the fun of making up something or just to amuse others. And they are made up out of imagination, bits of dreams and wishes, bits of fancy that see human faces and a rhinoceros in a cloud. Anybody, almost, can make up a story about what isn't so. It may be an exaggeration or a pretend-joke about what the fire hydrant said to the letter box while you were waiting for the bus, or recalling how you jumped over a barn when a butterfly chased you—or perhaps the other way around. But really good make-believe stories are very popular, and some of them are constantly being retold and get into all languages.

People, including boys and girls, often wish that things were different; and then we build daydreams or "Spanish castles" about how we should like things to be. Many people seem to be always wondering how things might *be; and this kind of wondering and imagining has brought about some of the greatest achievements and inventions of mankind.*

THE NIGHTINGALE

by Hans Christian Andersen

In China, you must know, the Emperor is a Chinaman, and all whom he has about him are Chinamen, too. It happened a good many years ago, but that's just why it's worth while to hear the story before it is forgotten. The Emperor's palace was the most splendid in the world; it was made entirely of porcelain, very costly, but so delicate and brittle that one had to take care how one touched it. In the garden were to be seen the most wonderful flowers, and to the costliest of them silver bells were tied, which sounded so that nobody should pass by without noticing the flowers. Yes everything in the Emperor's garden was admirably arranged. And it extended so far that the gardener himself did not know where the end was. If a man went on and on he came into a glorious forest with high trees and deep lakes. The wood extended straight down to the sea, which was blue and deep; great ships could sail to and fro beneath the branches of the trees; and in the trees lived a Nightingale, which sang so splendidly that even the poor Fisherman, who had many other things to do, stopped still and listened when he had gone out at night to throw out his nets and heard the Nightingale.

"How beautiful that is!" he said; but he was obliged to attend to his property, and thus forgot the bird. But when on the next night the bird sang again, and the Fisherman heard it, he exclaimed again, "How beautiful that is!"

From all the countries of the world travelers came to the city of the Emperor and admired it and the palace and the garden, but when they heard the Nightingale they said, "That is the best of all!"

And the travelers told of it when they came home; and the

learned men wrote many books about the town, the palace, and the garden. But they did not forget the Nightingale; that was placed highest of all; and those who were poets wrote most magnificent poems about the Nightingale in the wood by the deep lake.

The books went through all the world, and a few of them once came to the Emperor. He sat in his golden chair and read and read; every moment he nodded his head, for it pleased him to peruse the masterly descriptions of the city, the palace, and the garden. "But the Nightingale is the best of all!"—it stood written there.

"What's that?" exclaimed the Emperor. "I don't know the Nightingale at all! Is there such a bird in my empire, and even in my garden? I've never heard of that. To think that I should have to learn such a thing for the first time from books!"

And thereupon he called his Cavalier. This Cavalier was so grand that if anyone lower in rank than himself dared to speak to him or to ask him any question he answered nothing but "P!" —and that meant nothing.

"There is said to be a wonderful bird here called a Nightingale!" said the Emperor. "They say it is the best thing in all my empire. Why have I never heard anything about it?"

"I have never heard him named," replied the Cavalier. "He has never been introduced at court."

"I command that he shall appear this evening and sing before me," said the Emperor. "All the world knows what I possess, and I do not know it myself!"

"I have never heard him mentioned," said the Cavalier. "I will seek for him. I will find him."

But where was he to be found? The Cavalier ran up and down all the staircases, through halls and passages, but no one among all those whom he met had heard talk of the Nightingale. And the Cavalier ran back to the Emperor and said that it must be a fable invented by the writers of books.

"Your Imperial Majesty cannot believe how much is written

that is fiction besides something that they call the black art."

"But the book in which I read this," said the Emperor, "was sent to me by the high and mighty Emperor of Japan, and therefore it cannot be a falsehood. I will hear the Nightingale! It must be here this evening! It has my imperial favor; and if it does not come all the court shall be trampled upon after the court has supped!"

"Tsing-pe!" said the Cavalier; and again he ran up and down all the staircases, and through all the halls and corridors; and half the court ran with him, for the courtiers did not like being trampled upon.

Then there was a great inquiry after the wonderful Nightingale, which all the world knew excepting the people at court.

At last they met with a poor little girl in the kitchen who said: "The Nightingale? I know it well; yes, it can sing gloriously. Every evening I get leave to carry my poor sick mother the scraps from the table. She lives down by the strand, and when I get back and am tired, and rest in the wood, then I hear the Nightingale sing. And then the water comes into my eyes, and it is just as if my mother kissed me!"

"Little Kitchen-girl," said the Cavalier, "I will get you a place in the kitchen, with permission to see the Emperor dine, if you will lead us to the Nightingale, for it is announced for this evening."

So they all went out into the wood where the Nightingale was accustomed to sing; half the court went forth. When they were in the midst of their journey a cow began to low.

"Oh!" cried the court pages, "now we have it! That shows a wonderful power in so small a creature! I have certainly heard it before."

"No, those are cows lowing!" said the little Kitchen-girl. "We are a long way from the place yet."

Now the frogs began to croak in the marsh.

"Glorious!" said the Chinese Court Preacher. "Now I hear it —it sounds just like little church-bells."

"No, those are frogs!" said the little Kitchen-maid. "But now I think we shall soon hear it."

And then the Nightingale began to sing.

"That is it!" exclaimed the little Girl. "Listen, listen! And yonder it sits." And she pointed to a little gray bird up in the boughs.

"Is it possible?" cried the Cavalier. "I should never have thought it looked like that! How simple it looks! It must certainly have lost its color at seeing such grand people around."

"Little Nightingale!" called the little Kitchen-maid, quite loudly, "our gracious Emperor wishes you to sing before him."

"With the greatest pleasure!" replied the Nightingale, and began to sing most delightfully.

"It sounds just like glass bells!" said the Cavalier. "And look at its little throat, how it's working! It's wonderful that we should never have heard it before. That bird will be a great success at court."

"Shall I sing once more before the Emperor?" asked the Nightingale, for it thought the Emperor was present.

"My excellent little Nightingale," said the Cavalier, "I have great pleasure in inviting you to a court festival this evening, when you shall charm his Imperial Majesty with your beautiful singing."

"My song sounds best in the greenwood," replied the Nightingale; still it came willingly when it heard what the Emperor wished.

The Palace was festively adorned. The walls and the flooring, which were of porcelain, gleamed in the rays of thousands of golden lamps. The most glorious flowers which could ring clearly had been placed in the passages. There was a running to and fro and a thorough draught, and all the bells rang so loudly that one could not hear oneself speak.

In the midst of the great hall, where the Emperor sat, a golden perch had been placed, on which the Nightingale was to sit. The whole court was there, and the little Cook-maid had got leave to stand behind the door, as she had now received the title of a real Court Cook. All were in full dress, and all looked at the little gray bird, to which the Emperor nodded.

And the Nightingale sang so gloriously that the tears came into the Emperor's eyes and the tears ran down over his cheeks; and then the Nightingale sang still more sweetly, that went straight to the heart. The Emperor was so much pleased that he said the Nightingale should have his golden slipper to wear round its neck. But the Nightingale declined this with thanks, saying it had already received a sufficient reward.

"I have seen tears in the Emperor's eyes—that is the real treasure to me. An Emperor's tears have a peculiar power. I am rewarded enough!" And then it sang again with a sweet, glorious voice.

"That's the most amiable coquetry I ever saw!" said the ladies who stood round about, and then they took water in their mouths to gurgle when anyone spoke to them. They thought they should be nightingales too. And the lackeys and chambermaids reported that they were satisfied, too; and that was saying a good deal, for they are the most difficult to please. In short, the Nightingale achieved a real success.

It was now to remain at court, to have its own cage, with liberty to go out twice every day and once at night. Twelve servants were appointed when the Nightingale went out, each of whom had a silken string fastened to the bird's leg, which they held very tight. There was really no pleasure in an excursion of that kind.

The whole city spoke of the wonderful bird; and when two people met, one said nothing but "Nightin," and the other said "gale"; and then they sighed and understood each other. Eleven peddlers' children were named after the bird; but not one of them could sing a note.

One day the Emperor received a large parcel on which was written, "The Nightingale."

"There we have a new book about this celebrated bird," said the Emperor.

But it was not a book, but a little work of art contained in a box, an artificial nightingale, which was to sing like a natural one and was brilliantly ornamented with diamonds, rubies, and sapphires. So soon as the artificial bird was wound up he could sing one of the pieces that he really sang, and then his tail moved up and down and shone with silver and gold. Round his neck hung a little ribbon, and on that was written, "The Emperor of China's Nightingale is poor compared with that of the Emperor of Japan."

"That is capital!" said they all; and he who had brought the artificial bird immediately received the title, Imperial-Head-Nightingale-Bringer.

"Now they must sing together. What a duet that will be!"

And so they had to sing together; but it did not sound very well, for the real Nightingale sang in its own way, and the artificial bird sang waltzes.

"That's not his fault," said the Play-master; "he's quite perfect, and very much in my style."

Now the artificial bird was to sing alone. It had just as much success as the real one, and then it was much handsomer to look at—it shone like bracelets and breast-pins.

Three-and-thirty times over did it sing the same piece, and yet was not tired. The people would gladly have heard it again, but the Emperor said that the living Nightingale ought to sing something now. But where was it? No one had noticed that it had flown away out of the open window back to the greenwood.

"But what has become of it?" said the Emperor.

And all the courtiers abused the Nightingale and declared that it was a very ungrateful creature.

"We have the best bird, after all," said they.

And so the artificial bird had to sing again, and that was the thirty-fourth time that they listened to the same piece. For all that they did not know it quite by heart, for it was so very difficult. And the Play-master praised the bird particularly; yes, he declared that it was better than a nightingale, not only with regard to its plumage and the many beautiful diamonds, but inside as well.

"For you see, ladies and gentlemen and, above all, your Imperial Majesty, with a real nightingale one can never calculate what is coming, but in this artificial bird everything is settled. One can explain it; one can open it and make people understand where the waltzes come from, how they go, and how one follows up another."

"Those are quite our own ideas," they all said.

And the speaker received permission to show the bird to the people on the next Sunday. The people were to hear it sing too, the Emperor commanded; and they did hear it, and were as much pleased as if they had all got tipsy upon tea, for that's quite the Chinese fashion; and they all said, "Oh!" and held up their forefingers and nodded. But the poor Fisherman, who had heard the real Nightingale, said:

"It sounds pretty enough, and the melodies are similar; but there's something wanting, though I know not what!"

The real Nightingale was banished from the country and empire. The artificial bird had its place on a silken cushion close to the Emperor's bed; all the presents it had received, gold and precious stones, were ranged about it; in title it had advanced to be the High-Imperial-After-Dinner-Singer, and in rank to number one on the left hand; for the Emperor considered that side the most important on which the heart is placed, and even in an Emperor the heart is on the left side; and the Play-master wrote a work of five-and-twenty volumes about the artificial bird; it was very learned and very long, full of the most difficult Chinese words; but yet all the people declared that they had read it and understood it for fear of being considered stupid and having their bodies trampled on.

So a whole year went by. The Emperor, the court, and all the other Chinese knew every little twitter in the artificial bird's song by heart. But just for that reason it pleased them best—they could sing with it themselves, and they did so. The street-boys sang, "tsi-tsi-tsi-glug-glug!" and the Emperor sang it, too. Yes, that was certainly famous. But one evening, when the artificial bird was singing its best and the Emperor lay in bed listening to it, something inside the bird said, "Whizz!" Something cracked. "Whir-r-r!" All the wheels ran round, and then the music stopped.

The Emperor immediately sprang out of bed and caused his body physician to be called; but what could *he* do? Then they sent for a Watchmaker, and after a good deal of talking and investigation the bird was put into something like order; but the Watchmaker said that the bird must be carefully treated, for the barrels were worn, and it would be impossible to put new ones in in such a manner that the music would go. There was a great lamentation; only once in a year was it permitted to let the bird sing, and that was almost too much. But then the Play-master made a little speech full of heavy words, and said this was just as good as before—and so, of course, it was as good as before.

Now five years had gone by and a real grief came upon the whole nation. The Chinese were really fond of their Emperor, and now he was ill and could not, it was said, live much longer. Already a new Emperor had been chosen, and the people stood out in the street and asked the Cavalier how their old Emperor did.

"P!" said he, and shook his head.

Cold and pale lay the Emperor in his great gorgeous bed; the whole court thought him dead, and each one ran to pay homage to the new ruler. The chamberlains ran out to talk it over, and the ladies'-maids had a great coffee party. All about, in all the halls and passages, cloth had been laid down so that no footstep could be heard, and therefore it was quiet there, quite quiet. But the Emperor was not dead yet; stiff and pale he lay on the gorgeous bed with the long velvet curtains and the heavy gold tassels; high up a window stood open, and the moon shone in upon the Emperor and the artificial bird.

The poor Emperor could scarcely breathe; it was just as if something lay upon his chest; he opened his eyes, and then he saw that it was Death who sat upon his chest, and had put on his golden crown and held in one hand the Emperor's sword and in the other his beautiful banner. And all around from among the folds of the splendid velvet curtains strange heads peered forth; a few very ugly, the rest quite lovely and mild. These were all the Emperor's bad and good deeds that stood before him now that Death sat upon his heart.

"Do you remember this?" whispered one to the other. "Do you remember that?" and then they told him so much that the perspiration ran from his forehead.

"I did not know that!" said the Emperor. "Music! music! the great Chinese drum," he cried, "so that I need not hear all they say!"

And they continued speaking, and Death nodded like a Chinaman to all they said.

"Music! music!" cried the Emperor. "You little precious golden bird, sing, sing! I have given you gold and costly presents; I have even hung my golden slipper around your neck—sing now, sing!"

But the bird stood still; no one was there to wind him up, and he could not sing without that; but Death continued to stare at the Emperor with his great hollow eyes, and it was quiet, fearfully quiet.

Then there sounded from the window, suddenly, the most lovely song. It was the little live Nightingale that sat outside on a spray. It had heard of the Emperor's sad plight and had come to sing to him of comfort and hope. And as it sang the specters grew paler and paler; the blood ran quickly and more quickly through the Emperor's weak limbs; and even Death listened and said:

"Go on, little Nightingale, go on!"

"But will you give me that splendid golden sword? Will you give me that rich banner? Will you give me the Emperor's crown?"

And Death gave up each of these treasures for a song. And the Nightingale sang on and on; and it sang of the quiet churchyard where the white roses grow, where the elder-blossoms smell sweet, and where the fresh grass is moistened by the tears of survivors. Then Death felt a longing to see his garden, and floated out at the window in the form of a cold, white mist.

"Thanks! thanks!" said the Emperor. "You heavenly little bird! I know you well. I banished you from my country and empire, and yet you have charmed away the evil faces from my couch and banished Death from my heart! How can I reward you?"

"You have rewarded me!" replied the Nightingale. "I drew tears from your eyes when I sang the first time—I shall never forget that. Those are the jewels that rejoice a singer's heart. But now sleep and grow fresh and strong again. I will sing you something."

And it sang, and the Emperor fell into a sweet slumber. Ah! how mild and refreshing that sleep was! The sun shone upon him through the windows when he awoke refreshed and restored; not one of his servants had yet returned, for they all thought he was dead; only the Nightingale still sat beside him and sang.

"You must always stay with me," said the Emperor. "You shall sing as you please; and I'll break the artificial bird into a thousand pieces."

"Not so," replied the Nightingale. "It did well as long as it could; keep it as you have done till now. I cannot build my nest in the palace and dwell in it, but let me come when I feel the wish; then I will sit in the evening on the spray yonder by the window and sing you something, so that you may be glad and thoughtful at once. I will sing of those who are happy and of those who suffer. I will sing of good and of evil that remain hidden round about you. The little singing-bird flies far around—to the poor fisherman, to the peasant's roof, to every one who dwells far away from you and your court. I love your heart more than your crown, and yet the crown has an air of sanctity about it. I will come and sing to you—but one thing you must promise me."

"Everything!" said the Emperor; and he stood there in his imperial robes, which he had put on himself, and pressed the sword, which was heavy with gold, to his heart.

"One thing I beg of you: tell no one that you have a little bird who tells you everything. Then it will go all the better."

And the Nightingale flew away.

The servants came in to look to their dead Emperor, and—yes, there he stood; and the Emperor said,

"Good morning!"

HOW CATS CAME TO PURR

by John Bennett

A boy having a Pet Cat which he Wished to Feed, Said to Her, "Come, Cat, Drink this Dish of Cream; it will Keep your Fur as Soft as Silk, and Make you Purr like a Coffee-Mill."

He had no sooner said this than the Cat, with a Great Glare of her Green Eyes, bristled her Tail like a Gun-Swab, and went over the Back Fence, head first—pop!—as Mad as a Wet Hen.

And this is how she came to do so:

The story is an old one—very, very old. It may be Persian; it may be not: that is of very little moment. It is so old that if all the nine lives of all the cats that have ever lived in the world were set up together in a line, the other end of it would just reach back to the time when this occurred.

And this is the story:

Many, many years ago, in a country which was quite as far from anywhere else as the entire distance thither and back, there was a huge cat that ground the coffee in the King's kitchen, and otherwise assisted with the meals.

This cat was, in truth, the actual and very father of all subsequent cats, and his name was Sooty Will, for his hair was as black as a night in a coal-hole. He was ninety years old, and his mustaches were like whisk-brooms. But the most singular thing about him was that in all his life he had never once purred nor humped up his back, although his master often stroked him. The fact was that he never had learned to purr, nor had any reason, so far as he knew, for humping up his back. And being the father of all the cats, there was no one to tell him how. It remained for him to acquire a reason, and from his example to devise a habit which cats have followed from that time forth, and no doubt will forever follow.

The King of the country had long been at war with one of his neighbors; but one morning he sent back a messenger to say that he had beaten his foeman at last, and that he was coming home for an early breakfast as hungry as three bears. "Have batter-cake and coffee," he directed, "hot and plenty of 'em!"

At that the turnspits capered and yelped with glee, for batter-cakes and coffee are not cooked upon spits, and so they were free to sally forth into the city streets and watch the King's home-coming in a grand parade.

But the cat sat down on his tail in the corner and looked cross. "Scat!" said he, with an angry caterwaul. "It is not fair that you should go and that I should not."

"Oh, yes, it is," said the gleeful turnspits; "turn and turn about is fair play: you saw the rat that was killed in the parlor."

"Turn about fair play, indeed!" cried the cat. "Then all of you get to your spits; I am sure that is turn about!"

"Nay," said the turnspits, wagging their tails and laughing. "That is over and over again, which is not fair play. 'Tis the coffee-mill that is turn and turn about. So turn about to your mill, Sooty Will; we are off to see the King!"

With that they pranced out into the court-yard, turning hand-springs, head-springs, and heel-springs as they went, and, after giving three hearty and vociferous cheers in a grand chorus at the bottom of the garden, went capering away for their holiday.

The cat spat at their vanishing heels, sat down on his tail in the chimney-corner, and was very glum indeed.

Just then the cook looked in from the pantry. "Hullo!" he said gruffly. "Come, hurry up the coffee!" That was the way he always gave his orders.

The black cat's whiskers bristled. He turned to the mill with a fierce frown, his long tail going to and fro like that of a tiger in its lair; for Sooty Will had a temper like hot gunpowder, that was apt to go off sizz, whizz, bang! and no one to save the pieces. Yet, at least while the cook was by, he turned the mill furiously, as if with a right goodwill.

Meantime, out in the city, a glorious day came on. The sun went buzzing up the pink-and-yellow sky with a sound like that of a walking-doll's works, or of a big Dutch clock behind a door; banners waved from the castled heights, and bugles sang from every tower; the city gates rang with the cheers of the enthusiastic crowd. Up from cellars, down from lofts, off work-benches, and out at the doors of their masters' shops, dodging the thwacks of their masters' straps, "pop-popping" like corks from the necks of so many bottles, came apprentices, shop-boys, knaves and scullions, crying: "God save the King! Hurrah! Hurrah! Masters and work may go to Rome; our tasks shall wait on our own sweet wills; 'tis holiday when the King comes home. God save the King! Hurrah!"

Then came the procession. There were first three regiments of trumpeters, all blowing different tunes; then fifteen regiments of mounted infantry on coal-black horses, forty squadrons of green-and-blue dragoons, and a thousand drummers and fifers in scarlet and blue and gold, making a thundering din with their rootle-te-tootle-te-tootle-te-rootle; and pretty well up to the front in the ranks was the King himself, bowing and smiling to the populace, with his hand on his breast; and after him the army, all in shining armor, just enough pounded to be picturesque, miles on miles of splendid men, all bearing the trophies of glorious war, and armed with lances, and bows and arrows, falchions, morgensterns, martels-de-fer, and other choice implements of justifiable homicide, and the reverse, such as hautboys and sackbuts and accordions and dudelsacks and Scotch bagpipes—a glorious sight!

And, as has been said before, the city gates rang with the cheers of the crowd, crimson banners waved over the city's pinnacled summits, and bugles blew, trumpets brayed, and drums beat until it seemed that wild uproar and rich display had reached its high millennium.

The black cat turned the coffee-mill. "My oh! My oh!" he said. "It certainly is not fair that those bench-legged turnspits with feet like so much leather should see the King marching home in his glory, while I, who go shod, as it were, in velvet, should hear only the sound through the scullery windows. It is not fair. It is no doubt true that 'The cat may mew, and the dog shall have his day,' but I have as much right to my day as he; and has it not been said from immemorial time that 'A cat may look at a king'? Indeed it has, quite as much as that the dog may have his day. I will not stand it; it is not fair. A cat may look at a king; and if any cat may look at a king, why, I am the cat who may. There are no other cats in the world; I am the only one. Poh! The cook may shout till his breath gives out, he cannot frighten me; for once I am going to have my fling!"

So he forthwith swallowed the coffee-mill, box, handle, drawer-knobs, coffee-well, and all, and was off to see the King.

So far, so good. But, ah! the sad and undeniable truth, that brightest joys too soon must end! Triumphs cannot last forever, even in a land of legends. There comes a reckoning.

When the procession was past and gone, as all processions pass and go, vanishing down the shores of forgetfulness; when barons, marquises, dukes, and dons were gone, with their pennants and banners; when the last lancers had gone prancing past and were lost to sight down the circuitous avenue, Sooty Will, with drooping tail, stood by the palace gate, dejected. He was sour and silent and glum. Indeed, who would not be, with a coffee-mill on his conscience? To own up to the entire truth, the cat was feeling decidedly unwell. When suddenly the cook popped his head in at the scullery entry, crying, "How now, how now, you vagabonds! The war is done, but the breakfast is not. Hurry up, scurry up, scamper and trot! The cakes are all cooked and are piping hot! Then why is the coffee so slow?"

The King was in the dining-hall, in dressing-gown and slippers, irately calling for his breakfast!

The shamefaced, guilty cat ran hastily down the scullery stairs and hid under the refrigerator, with such a deep inward sensation of remorse that he dared not look the kind cook in the face. It now really seemed to him as if everything had gone wrong with the world, especially his own insides. This any one will readily believe who has ever swallowed a coffee-mill. He began to weep copiously.

The cook came into the kitchen. "Where is the coffee?" he said. Then, catching sight of the secluded cat, he stooped, crying, "Where is the coffee?"

The cat sobbed audibly. "Some one must have come into the kitchen while I ran out to look at the King!" he gasped, for there seemed to him no way out of the scrape but by telling a plausible untruth. "Some one must have come into the kitchen and stolen it!" And with that, choking upon the handle of the mill, which projected into his throat, he burst into inarticulate sobs.

The cook, who was, in truth, a very kind-hearted man, sought to reassure the poor cat. "There; it is unfortunate, very; but do not weep; thieves thrive in kings' houses!" he said, and, stooping, he began to stroke the drooping cat's back to show that he held the weeping creature blameless.

Sooty Will's heart leaped into his throat.

"Oh, oh!" he half gasped, "oh, oh! If he rubs his great hands down my back he will feel the corners of the coffee-mill through my ribs as sure as fate! Oh, oh! I am a gone cat!" And with that, in an agony of apprehension lest his guilt and his falsehood be thus presently detected, he humped up his back as high in the air as he could, so that the corners of the mill might not make bumps in his sides and that the mill might thus remain undiscovered.

But, alas! he forgot that coffee-mills turn. As he humped up his back to cover his guilt, the coffee-mill inside rolled over, and, as it rolled, began to grind—*rr-rr-rr-rr-rr-rr-rr-rr-rr-rr!*

"Oh, oh! You have swallowed the mill!" cried the cook.

"No, no," cried the cat, "I was only thinking aloud."

At that out stepped the Genius that Lived under the Great Ovens, and, with his finger pointed at the cat, said in a frightful voice, husky with wood-ashes: "Miserable and pusillanimous beast! By telling a falsehood to cover a wrong you have only made bad matters worse. For betraying man's kindness to cover your shame, a curse shall be upon you and all your kind until the end of the world. Whenever men stroke you in kindness, remembrance of your guilt shall make you hump up your back with shame, as you did to avoid being found out. And in order that the reason for this curse shall never be forgotten, whenever man is kind to a cat the sound of the grinding of a coffee-mill inside shall perpetually remind him of your guilt and shame!"

With that the Genius vanished in a cloud of smoke.

And it was even as he said. From that day Sooty Will could never abide having his back stroked without humping it up to conceal the mill within him; and never did he hump up his back but the coffee-mill began slowly to grind, *rr-rr-rr-rr!* inside him; so that, even in the prime of life, before his declining days had come, being seized upon by a great remorse for these things that might never be amended, he retired to a home for aged and reputable cats, and there, so far as the records reveal, lived the remainder of his days in charity and repentance.

But the curse has come down even to the present day—as the Genius that Lived under the Great Ovens said—and still maintains, though cats have probably forgotten the facts, and so, when stroked, hump up their backs and purr as if these actions were a matter of pride instead of being a blot upon their family record.

THE FORTY THIEVES

FROM THE ARABIAN NIGHTS

by Andrew Lang

In a town in Persia there dwelt two brothers, one named Cassim, the other Ali Baba. Cassim was married to a rich wife and lived in plenty, while Ali Baba had to maintain his wife and children by cutting wood in a neighboring forest and selling it in the town. One day, when Ali Baba was in the forest, he saw a troop of men on horseback, coming toward him in a cloud of dust. He was afraid they were robbers and climbed into a tree for safety. When they came up to him and dismounted, he counted forty of them. They unbridled their horses and tied them to trees.

The finest man among them, whom Ali Baba took to be their captain, went a little way among some bushes and said, "Open, Sesame!" so plainly that Ali Baba heard him. A door opened in the rocks and, having made the troop go in, he followed them and the door shut again of itself.

They stayed some time inside and Ali Baba, fearing they might come out and catch him, was forced to sit patiently in the tree. At last the door opened again and the forty thieves came out. As the captain went in last he came out first, and made them all pass by him; he then closed the door, saying, "Shut, Sesame!" Every man bridled his horse and mounted, the captain put himself at their head, and they returned as they came.

Then Ali Baba climbed down and went to the door concealed among the bushes and said, "Open, Sesame!" and it flew open. Ali Baba, who expected a dull, dismal place, was greatly surprised to find it large and well lighted, and hollowed by the hand of man in the form of a vault, which received the light from an opening in the ceiling. He saw rich bales of merchandise—silk stuffs, brocades, all piled together, gold and silver in heaps, and money in leather purses. He went in and the door shut behind him. He did not look at the silver but brought out as many bags of gold as he thought his asses, which were browsing outside, could carry, loaded them with the bags, and hid it all with fagots. Using the words, "Shut, Sesame!" he closed the door and went home.

Then he drove his asses into the yard, shut the gates, carried the moneybags to his wife and emptied them out before her. He bade her keep the secret and he would bury the gold.

"Let me first measure it," said his wife. "I will borrow a measure of someone while you dig the hole."

So she ran to the wife of Cassim and borrowed a measure. Knowing Ali Baba's poverty, the sister was curious to find out what sort of grain his wife wished to measure and artfully put some suet at the bottom of the measure. Ali Baba's wife went home and set the measure on the heap of gold and filled it and emptied it often, to her great content. She then carried it back to her sister, without noticing that a piece of gold was sticking to it.

Cassim's wife perceived it directly her back was turned. She grew curious and said to Cassim when he came home, "Cassim, your brother is richer than you. He does not count his money, he measures it."

He begged her to explain this riddle, which she did by showing him the piece of money and telling him where she had found it. Then Cassim grew so envious that he could not sleep and went to his brother in the morning before sunrise.

"Ali Baba," he said, showing him the gold piece, "you pretend to be poor and yet you measure gold."

By this Ali Baba perceived that through his wife's folly Cassim and his wife knew his secret, so he confessed all and offered Cassim a share.

"That I expect," said Cassim, "but I must know where to find the treasure, otherwise I will discover all and you will lose all."

Ali Baba, more out of kindness than fear, told him of the cave and the very words to use. Cassim left Ali Baba, meaning to be beforehand with him and get the treasure for himself. He rose early next morning and set out with ten mules loaded with great chests. He soon found the place and the door in the rock. He said, "Open Sesame!" and the door opened and shut behind him.

He could have feasted his eyes all day on the treasures, but he now hastened to gather together as much of it as possible; but when he was ready to go he could not remember what to say for thinking of his great riches. Instead of "Sesame," he said, "Open Barley!" and the door remained fast. He named several other sorts of grain, all but the right one, and the door still stuck fast. He was so frightened at the danger he was in that he had as much forgotten the word as if he had never heard it.

About noon the robbers returned to their cave and saw Cassim's mules roving about with great chests on their backs. This gave them the alarm. They drew their sabers, and went to the door, which opened on their captain's saying, "Open, Sesame!" Cassim, who had heard the trampling of their horses' feet, resolved to sell his life dearly, so when the door opened he leaped out and threw the captain down. In vain, however, for the robbers with their sabers soon killed him. On entering the cave they saw all the bags laid ready, and could not imagine how anyone had got in without knowing their secret. They cut Cassim's body into four quarters and nailed them up inside the cave, in order to frighten anyone who should venture in, and went away in search of more treasure.

As night drew on Cassim's wife grew very uneasy, ran to her brother-in-law and told him where her husband had gone. Ali Baba did his best to comfort her and set out to the forest in search of Cassim. The first thing he saw on entering the cave was his dead brother. Full of horror, he put the body on one of his asses and bags of gold on the other two and, covering all with fagots, returned home. He drove the two asses laden with gold into his own yard and led the other to Cassim's house. The door was opened by the slave Morgiana, whom he knew to be both brave and cunning.

Unloading the ass, he said to her, "This is the body of your master, who was murdered, but whom we must bury as though he had died in his bed. I will speak with you again, but now tell your mistress I am come."

The wife of Cassim, on learning the fate of her husband, broke out into cries and tears, but Ali Baba offered to take her to live with him and his wife if she would promise to keep his counsel and leave everything to Morgiana; whereupon she agreed, and dried her eyes.

Morgiana, meanwhile, sought an apothecary and asked him for some lozenges. "My poor master," she said, "can neither eat nor speak and no one knows what his distemper is." She carried home the lozenges and returned next day weeping, and asked for an essence given only to those just about to die. Thus, by evening, no one was surprised to hear the shrieks and cries of Cassim's wife and Morgiana, telling everyone that Cassim was dead.

The next day Morgiana went to an old cobbler near the gates of the town, who opened his stall early, put a piece of gold in his hand and bade him follow her with his needle and thread. Having bound his eyes with a handkerchief, she took him to the room where the body lay, pulled off the bandage and bade him sew the quarters together, after which she covered his eyes again and led him home.

Then they buried Cassim, and Morgiana, his slave, followed him to the grave weeping and tearing her hair, while Cassim's wife stayed at home uttering lamentable cries. Next day she went to live with Ali Baba, who gave Cassim's shop to his eldest son.

The forty thieves, on their return to the cave, were much astonished to find Cassim's body gone as well as some of their money bags.

"We are certainly discovered," said the captain, "and shall be undone if we cannot find out who it is that knows our secret. Two men must have known it; we have killed one, we must now find the other. To this end one of you who is bold and artful must go into the city, dressed as a traveler, and discover whom we have killed and whether men talk of the strange manner of his death. If the messenger fails he must lose his life, lest we be betrayed."

One of the thieves started up and offered to do this and, after the rest had highly commended him for his bravery, he disguised himself and happened to enter the town at daybreak, just by Baba Mustapha's stall. The thief bade him good day, saying, "Honest man, how can you possibly see to stitch at your age?"

"Old as I am," replied the cobbler, "I have very good eyes, and you will believe me when I tell you that I sewed a dead body together in a place where I had less light than I have now."

The robber was overjoyed at his good fortune and, giving the cobbler a piece of gold, desired to be shown the house where he had stitched up the dead body. At first Mustapha refused, saying that he had been blindfolded. But when the robber gave him another piece of gold he began to think he might remember the turnings if blindfolded as before. This means succeeded. The robber partly led him and was partly guided by him right in front of Cassim's house, the door of which the robber marked with a piece of chalk.

Then, well pleased, he bade farewell to Baba Mustapha and returned to the forest. By and by Morgiana, going out, saw the mark the robber had made, quickly guessed that some mischief was brewing and, fetching a piece of white chalk, marked two or three doors on each side, without saying anything to her master or mistress.

The thief, meanwhile, told his comrades of his discovery. The captain thanked him and bade him show him the house he had marked. But when they came to it they saw that five or six of the houses were chalked in the same manner. The guide was so confounded that he knew not what answer to make, and when they returned to the cave he was at once beheaded for having failed. Another robber was dispatched and, having won over Baba Mustapha, marked the house in red chalk; but Morgiana being again too clever for them, the second messenger was put to death also.

The captain now resolved to go himself but, wiser than the others, he did not mark the house but looked at it so closely he could not fail to remember it. He returned and ordered his men to go into the neighboring villages and buy nineteen mules and thirty-eight leather jars, all empty, except one which was full of oil. The captain put one of his men, fully armed, into each, rubbing the outside of the jars with oil from the full vessel. Then the nineteen mules were loaded with thirty-seven robbers in jars and the jar of oil, and reached the town by dusk.

The captain stopped his mules in front of the house and said to Ali Baba, who was sitting outside for coolness, "I have brought some oil from a distance to sell at tomorrow's market, but it is now so late that I know not where to pass the night, unless you will do me the favor to take me in."

Though Ali Baba had seen the captain of the robbers in the forest he did not recognize him in the disguise of an oil merchant. He bade him welcome, opened his gates for the mules to enter, and went to Morgiana to bid her prepare a bed and supper for his guest. He brought the stranger into his hall, and after they had supped went again to speak to Morgiana in the kitchen, while the captain went into the yard under pretence of seeing after his mules but really to tell his men what to do.

Beginning at the first jar and ending at the last, he said to each man, "As soon as I throw some stones from the window of the chamber where I lie, cut the jars open with your knives and come out, and I will be with you in a trice."

He returned to the house and Morgiana led him to his chamber. She then told Abdallah, her fellow slave, to set on the pot to make some broth for her master, who had gone to bed. Meanwhile her lamp went out and she had no more oil in the house.

"Do not be uneasy," said Abdallah, "go into the yard and take some out of one of those jars."

Morgiana thanked him for his advice, took the oil pot, and went into the yard. When she came to the first jar the robber inside said softly, "Is it time?"

Any other slave but Morgiana, on finding a man in the jar instead of the oil she wanted, would have screamed and made a noise. But she, knowing the danger her master was in, bethought herself of a plan and answered quietly, "Not yet, but presently."

She went to all the jars, giving the same answer, till she came to the jar of oil. She now saw that her master, thinking to entertain an oil merchant, had let thirty-eight robbers into his house. She filled her oil pot, went back to the kitchen and, having lit her lamp, went again to the oil jar and filled a large kettle full of oil. When it boiled she went and poured enough oil into every jar to stifle and kill the robber inside. When this brave deed was done she went back to the kitchen, put out the fire and the lamp, and waited to see what would happen.

In a quarter of an hour the captain of the robbers awoke, got up and opened the window. As all seemed quiet he threw down some little pebbles which hit the jars. He listened and as none of his men seemed to stir, he grew uneasy and went down into the yard. On going to the first jar and saying, "Are you asleep?" he smelt the hot boiled oil and knew at once that his plot to murder Ali Baba and his household had been discovered. He found all the gang were dead and, missing the oil out of the last jar, became aware of the manner of their death. He then forced the lock of a door leading into a garden and, climbing over several walls, made his escape. Morgiana heard and saw all this and, rejoicing at her success, went to bed and fell asleep.

At daybreak Ali Baba arose and, seeing the oil jars there still, asked why the merchant had not gone with his mules. Morgiana bade him look in the first jar and see if there was any oil. Seeing a man, he started back in terror.

"Have no fear," said Morgiana, "the man cannot harm you; he is dead."

Ali Baba, when he had recovered somewhat from his astonishment, asked what had become of the merchant.

"Merchant!" said she, "he is no more a merchant than I am!" and she told him the whole story, assuring him that it was a plot of the robbers of the forest, of whom only three were left, and that the white and red chalk marks had something to do with it. Ali Baba at once gave Morgiana her freedom, saying that he owed her his life. They then buried the bodies in Ali Baba's garden, while the mules were sold in the market by his slaves.

The captain returned to his lonely cave, which seemed frightful to him without his lost companions, and firmly resolved to avenge them by killing Ali Baba. He dressed himself carefully and went into town, where he took lodgings at an inn. In the course of a great many journeys to the forest he carried away many rich stuffs and much fine linen, and set up a shop opposite that of Ali Baba's son. He called himself Cogia Hassan, and as he was both civil and well dressed he soon made friends with Ali Baba's son and through him with Ali Baba, whom he was continually asking to sup with him.

Ali Baba, wishing to return his kindness, invited him into his house and received him smiling, thanking him for his kindness to his son. When the merchant was about to take his leave Ali Baba stopped him saying, "Where are you going, sir, in such haste? Will you not stay and sup with me?"

The merchant refused, saying that he had a reason and, on Ali Baba's asking him what that was, he replied, "It is, sir, that I can eat no victuals that have any salt in them."

"If that is all," said Ali Baba, "let me tell you there shall be no salt in either the meat or the bread that we eat tonight."

He went to give this order to Morgiana, who was much surprised. "Who is this man," she said, "who eats no salt with his meat?"

"He is an honest man, Morgiana," returned Ali Baba, "therefore do as I bid you."

But she could not withstand a desire to see this strange man, so she helped Abdallah carry up the dishes and saw in a moment that Cogia Hassan was the robber captain and carried a dagger under his garment. "I am not surprised," she said to herself, "that this wicked man who intends to kill my master will eat no salt with him, but I will hinder his plans."

She sent up the supper by Abdallah, while she made ready for one of the boldest acts that could be thought on. When the dessert had been served, Cogia Hassan was left alone with Ali Baba and his son, whom he thought to make drunk and then to murder.

Morgiana, meanwhile, put on a head-dress like a dancing girl's and clasped a girdle round her waist, from which hung a dagger with a silver hilt, and said to Abdallah, "Take your tabor, and let us go and divert our master and his guest."

Abdallah took his tabor and played before Morgiana until they came to the door, where Abdallah stopped playing and Morgiana made a low curtsy.

"Come in, Morgiana," said Ali Baba, "let Cogia Hassan see what you can do," and turning to his guest, he said, "She is my housekeeper."

Cogia Hassan was by no means pleased, for he feared that his chance of killing Ali Baba was gone for the present, but he pretended great eagerness to see Morgiana, and Abdallah began to play and Morgiana to dance. After she had performed several dances she drew her dagger and made passes with it, sometimes pointing it at her own breast, sometimes at her master's, as if it were part of the dance. Suddenly, out of breath, she snatched the tabor from Abdallah with her left hand and holding the dagger in her right, held out the tabor to her master. Ali Baba and his son put a piece of gold into it and Cogia Hassan, seeing that she was coming to him, pulled out his purse to make her a present, but while he was putting his hand into it Morgiana plunged the dagger into his heart.

"Unhappy girl!" cried Ali Baba and his son. "What have you done to ruin us?"

"It was to preserve you, master, not to ruin you," answered Morgiana. "See here," opening the false merchant's garment and showing the dagger, "see what an enemy you have entertained!

Remember, he would eat no salt with you; what more would you have? Look at him! He is both the false oil merchant and the captain of the forty thieves."

Ali Baba was so grateful to Morgiana for thus saving his life that he offered her to his son in marriage, who readily consented; and a few days after, the wedding was celebrated with great splendor. At the end of a year Ali Baba, hearing nothing of the two remaining robbers, judged they were dead, and set out to the cave. The door opened on his saying, "Open, Sesame!" He went in and saw that nobody had been there since the captain left it. He brought away as much gold as he could carry and returned to town. He told his son the secret of the cave, which his son handed down in his turn, so the children and grandchildren of Ali Baba were rich to the end of their lives.

THE LAUGHING PRINCE

by Parker Fillmore

There was once a farmer who had three sons and one little daughter. The eldest son was a studious boy who learned so much out of books that the farmer said:

"We must send Mihailo to school and make a priest of him."

The second boy was a trader. Whatever you had he would get it from you by offering you something else for it. And always what he gave you was worth less than what you gave him.

"Jakov will make a fine peddler," the farmer said. "He's industrious and sharp and some day he will probably be a rich man."

But Stefan, the farmer's youngest son, had no special talent and because he didn't spend all his time with his nose in a book and because he never made the best of a bargain his brothers scorned him. Militza, his little sister, loved him dearly for he was kind and jolly and in the evening he was always ready to tell her stories and play with her. But the farmer, of course, listened to the older brothers.

"I don't know about poor Stefan," he used to say. "He's a good boy but he talks nonsense. I suppose he'll have to stay on the farm and work."

Now the truth is the farm was a fine place for Stefan for he was strong and lusty and he liked to plow and harvest and he had a wonderful way with the animals. He talked to them as if they were human beings and the horses all whinnied when he came near, and the cows rubbed their soft noses against his shoulder. And as for the pigs—they loved him so much that whenever they saw him they used to run squealing between his legs.

"Stefan is nothing but a farmer!" Mihailo used to say as though being a farmer was something to be ashamed of.

And Jakov said:

"If the village people could see the pigs following him about, how they'd laugh at him! I hope when I go to the village to live he won't be visiting me all the time!"

Another thing the older brothers couldn't understand about Stefan was why he was always laughing and joking. He did the work of two men but whether he was working or resting you could always hear him cracking his merry jokes and laughing his jolly laugh.

"I think he's foolish!" Mihailo said.

Jakov hoped the village people wouldn't hear about his carryings on.

"They'd laugh at him," he said, "and they'd laugh at us too, because we're his brothers."

But Stefan didn't care. The more they frowned at him, the louder he laughed. And every evening after supper his little sister, Militza, clapped her hands and cried:

"Now, Stefan, tell me a story! Tell me a story!"

"Father," Mihailo would say, "you ought to make him keep quiet! He's foolish and all he does is fill Militza's head with nonsense!"

This always made Militza very indignant and she would stamp her little foot and say:

"He isn't foolish! He knows more than any one! And he can do more things than any one else and he's the handsomest brother in the world!"

You see Militza loved Stefan dearly and when you love a person of course you think that person is wonderful. But the father supposed that Mihailo must be right for Mihailo studied in books. So he shook his head and sighed every time he thought of Stefan.

Now the kingdom in which the three brothers lived was ruled over by a great Tsar who had an only daughter. In disappointment that he had no son, the Tsar was having his daughter brought up as though she were a boy. He sent all over the world for tutors and teachers and had the poor girl taught statecraft and law and philosophy and all the other things that the heir to the throne ought to know.

The Princess because she was an obedient girl and because she loved her father tried to spend all her time in study. But the dry old scholars whom the Tsar employed as teachers were not amusing companions for a young girl and the first lady-in-waiting who was in constant attendance was scarcely any better for she, too, was old and thin and very prim.

If the poor little Princess between her geography lesson and her arithmetic lesson would peep for a moment into a mirror, the first lady-in-waiting would tap her arm reprovingly and say:

"My dear, vanity is not becoming in a princess!"

One day the little Princess lost her temper and answered sharply:

"But I'm a girl even if I am a princess and I love to look in mirrors and I love to make myself pretty and I'd love to go to a ball every night of my life and dance with handsome young men!"

"You talk like the daughter of a farmer!" the first lady-in-waiting said.

Then the Princess, because she lost her temper still further, said something she should not have said.

"I wish I were the daughter of a farmer!" she declared. "Then I could wear pretty ribbons and go dancing and the boys would come courting me! As it is I have to spend all my time with funny old men and silly old women!"

Now even if her tutors and teachers were funny looking old men, even if the first lady-in-waiting was a silly old woman, the Princess should not have said so. It hurt the feelings of the first lady-in-waiting and made her angry and she ran off to the Tsar at once and complained most bitterly.

"Is this my reward after all my years of loving service to your daughter?" she asked. "It is true that I've grown thin and old looking after her manners and now she calls me a silly old woman! And all the wise men and scholars that you have gathered from the far corners of the earth—she calls them funny old men!"

The fact is they were funny looking, most of them, but yet the first lady-in-waiting was right: the Princess should not have said so.

"And think of her ingratitude to yourself, O Tsar!" the first lady-in-waiting continued. "You plan to make her the heir to your throne and yet she says she wishes she were a farmer's daughter so that she could deck herself out in ribbons and have the boys come courting her! A nice thing for a princess to say!"

The Tsar when he heard this fell into an awful rage. (The truth is whatever temper the Princess had she inherited direct from her father.)

"Wow! Wow!" he roared, just that way. "Send the Princess to me at once. I'll soon have her singing another tune!"

So the first lady-in-waiting sent the Princess to her father and as soon as he saw her he began roaring again and saying:

"Wow! Wow! What do you mean—funny old men and silly old women?"

Now whenever the Tsar began roaring and saying, "Wow! Wow!" the Princess always stiffened, and instead of being the sweet and obedient daughter she usually was she became obstinate. Her pretty eyes would flash and her soft pretty face would harden and people would whisper: "Mercy on us, how much she looks like her father!"

"That's just what I mean!" the Princess said. "They're a lot of funny old men and silly old women and I'm tired of them! I want to be amused! I want to laugh!"

"Wow! Wow! Wow!" roared the Tsar. "A fine princess you are! Go straight back to the schoolroom and behave yourself!"

So the little Princess marched out of the throne room holding her head very high and looking so much like the Tsar that the first lady-in-waiting was positively frightened.

The Princess went back to the schoolroom but she did not behave herself. She was really very naughty. When the poor man who knew more than anybody in the world about the influence of the stars upon the destinies of nations came to give her a lesson, she threw his book out the window. When the superannuated old general who was teaching her military manoeuvers offered her a diagram on which the enemy was represented by a series of black dots and our soldiers by a series of red dots, she took the paper and tore it in two. And worst of all when the old scholar who was teaching her Turkish—for a princess must be able to speak all languages—dropped his horn spectacles on the floor, she deliberately stepped on them.

When the Tsar heard all these things he just *wow-wowed* terribly.

"Lock that young woman in her chamber!" he ordered. "Feed her on bread and water until she's ready to apologize!"

But the Princess, far from being frightened by this treatment, calmly announced:

"I won't eat even your old bread and water until you send me some one who will make me laugh!"

Now this frightened the Tsar because he knew how obstinate

the Princess could be. (He ought to know, too, for the Princess had that streak of obstinacy direct from himself.)

"This will never do!" he said.

He hurried to the Princess's chamber. He found her in bed with her pretty hair spread out on the pillow like a golden fan.

"My dear," the Tsar said, "I was joking. You don't have to eat only bread and water. You may have anything you want."

"Thank you," the Princess said, "but I'll never eat another bite of anything until you send me some one who will make me laugh. I'm tired of living in this gloomy old castle with a lot of old men and old women who do nothing but instruct me and with a father who always loses his temper and says, 'Wow! Wow!' "

"But it's a beautiful castle!" the poor Tsar said. "And I'm sure we're all doing our best to educate you!"

"But I want to be amused as well as educated!" the little Princess said. And then, because she felt she was going to cry, she turned her face to the wall and wouldn't say another word.

What was the Tsar to do? He called together his councilors and asked them how was the Princess to be made to laugh. The councilors were wise about state matters but not one of them could suggest a means of amusing the Princess. The Master of Ceremonies did indeed begin to say something about a nice young man but instantly the Tsar roared out such a wrathful, "Wow! Wow!" that the Master of Ceremonies coughed and pretended he hadn't spoken.

Then the Tsar called together the scholars and the teachers and the first lady-in-waiting. He glared at them savagely and roared:

"Wow! Wow! A nice lot you are! I put you in charge of my daughter and not one of you has sense enough to know that the poor child needs a little amusement! Between you all you have about killed my poor child! Now I ask you: With all your learning doesn't one of you know how to make a young girl laugh?"

Apparently not one of them did, for no one answered. "You said you wished me to teach your daughter etiquette. As you said nothing about amusement, quite naturally I confined myself to the subject of behavior. If I do say it myself, no one has ever been more devoted in duty than I. I am constantly saying to her: 'That isn't the way a princess should act!' In fact for years there has hardly been a moment in the day when I haven't corrected her for something!"

"Poor child!" groaned the Tsar. "No wonder she wants a change! Oh, what fools you all are in spite of your learning! Don't you know that a young girl is a young girl even if she is a Princess!"

Well, the scholars weren't any more help to the Tsar than the councilors, and finally in desperation he sent heralds through the land to announce that to anyone who could make the Princess laugh he would give three bags of gold.

Three bags of gold don't grow on the bushes every day and instantly all the youths and men and old men who had stories that their sweethearts and their wives and their daughters laughed at hurried to the castle.

One by one they were admitted to the Princess's chamber. They entered hopefully but when they saw the Tsar sitting at one side of the door muttering, "Wow! Wow!" in his beard, and the old first lady-in-waiting at the other side of the door watching them scornfully, and the Princess herself in bed with her lovely hair spread out like a golden fan on the pillow, they forgot their funny stories and hemmed and hawed and stammered and had finally, one after another, to be turned out in disgrace.

One day went by and two and three and still the Princess refused to eat. In despair the Tsar sent out his heralds again. This time he said that to any one who would make the Princess laugh he would give the Princess's hand in marriage and make him joint heir to the kingdom.

"I had expected to wed her to the son of some great Tsar," he sighed, "but I'd rather marry her to a farmer than see her die of starvation!"

The heralds rode far and wide until every one even the people on the most distant farms had heard of the Tsar's offer.

"I won't try again," said Mihailo, the oldest son of the farmer I've already told you about. "When I went out there the day before yesterday I began telling her a funny story out of my Latin book but instead of laughing she said: 'Oh, send him away!' So now she'll have to starve to death for all of me!"

"Me, too!" said Jakov, the second son. "When I tried to tell her that funny story of how I traded the moldy oats for the old widow's fat pig, instead of laughing she looked me straight in the face and said: 'Cheat!' "

"Stefan ought to go," Mihailo suggested. "Maybe she'd laugh at him! Everybody else does!"

He spoke sneeringly but Stefan only smiled.

"Who knows? Perhaps I will go. If I do make her laugh then, O my brothers, the laugh will be on you for I shall become Tsar and you two will be known as my two poor brothers. Ho! Ho! Ho! What a joke that would be!"

Stefan laughed loud and heartily and his little sister joined him, but his brothers looked at him sourly.

"He grows more foolish all the time!" they told each other.

When they were gone to bed, Militza slipped over to Stefan and whispered in his ear:

"Brother, you must go to the Princess. Tell her the story that begins: *In my young days when I was an old, old man* . . . I think she'll just have to laugh, and if she laughs then she can eat and she must be very hungry by this time."

At first Stefan said no, he wouldn't go, but Militza insisted and, finally, to please her, he said he would.

So early the next morning he dressed himself in his fine Sunday shirt with its blue and red embroidery. He put on his bright red Sunday sash and his long shiny boots. Then he mounted his horse and before his brothers were awake rode off to the Tsar's castle.

There he awaited his turn to be admitted to the Princess's

chambers. When he came in he was so young and healthy and vigorous that he seemed to bring with him a little of the freshness of outdoors. The first lady-in-waiting looked at him askance for without doubt he was a farmer lad and his table manners probably were not good. Well, he was a farmer lad and for that reason he didn't know that she was first lady-in-waiting. He glanced at her once and thought: What an ugly old woman! and thereafter he didn't think of her at all. He glanced likewise at the Tsar and the Tsar reminded him of a bull of his own. He wasn't afraid of the bull, so why be afraid of the Tsar?

Suddenly he saw the Princess lying in bed with her lovely hair spread out on the pillow like a golden fan and for a moment he couldn't speak. Then he knelt beside the bed and kissed her hand.

"Princess," he said, "I'm not learned and I'm not clever and I don't suppose I can succeed where so many wise men have failed. And even if I do make you laugh you won't have to marry me unless you want to because the reason I really came was to please Militza."

"Militza?"

"Yes, Princess, my little sister, Militza. She loves me very much and so she thinks the stories I tell are funny and she laughs at them. Last night she said to me: 'Stefan, you must go to the Princess and tell her the story that begins: *In my young days when I was an old, old man* . . . I think she'll just have to laugh and if she laughs then she can eat and she must be very hungry by this time.' "

"I am," the Princess said, with a catch in her voice. Then she added: "I think I like that little sister of yours and I think I like you too. I wish you would tell me the story that begins: *In my young days when I was an old, old man . . .*"

"But, Princess, it's a very foolish story."

"The foolisher, the better!"

Just here the first lady-in-waiting tried to correct the Princess for of course she should have said: "The more foolish, the better!"

but the Tsar shut her up with a black frown and one fierce, "Wow!"

"Well, then," Stefan began:

In my young days when I was an old, old man I used to count my bees every morning. It was easy enough to count bees but not the beehives because I had too many hives. One day when I finished counting I found that my best bee was missing. At once I saddled a rooster and set out to find him.

"Father!" cried the Princess. "Did you hear what Stefan said? He said he saddled his rooster!"

"Umph!" muttered the Tsar, and the first lady-in-waiting said severely:

"Princess, do not interrupt! Young man, continue."

His track led to the sea which I rode across on a bridge. The first thing I saw on the other side of the sea was my bee. There he was in a field of millet harnessed to a plow. "That's my bee!" I shouted to the man who was driving him. "Is that so?" the man said, and without any words he gave me back my bee and handed me a bag of millet to pay for the plowing. I took the bag and tied it securely to the bee. Then I unsaddled the rooster and mounted the bee. The rooster, poor thing, was so tired that I had to take him by the hand and lead him along beside us.

"Father!" the Princess cried, "did you hear that? He took the rooster by the hand! Isn't that funny!"

"Umph!" grunted the Tsar, and the first lady-in-waiting whispered:

"Hush! Let the young man finish!"

Whilst we were crossing the bridge, the string of the bag broke and all my millet spilled out. When night came I tied the rooster to the bee and lay down on the seashore to sleep. During the night some wolves came and killed my bee and when I woke up I found that all the honey had run out of his body. There was so much honey that it rose up and up until it reached the ankles of the valleys and the knees of the mountains. I took a hatchet and swam down to a forest where I found two deer leaping about on one leg. I shot at the deer with my hatchet, killed them, and skinned them. With the skins I made two leather bottles. I filled these with the honey and strapped them over the rooster's back. Then I rode home. I no sooner arrived home than my father was born. "We must have holy water for the christening," I said. "I suppose I must go to heaven to fetch some." But how was I to get there? I thought of my millet. Sure enough the dampness had made it grow so well that its tops now reached the sky. So all I had to do was to climb a millet stalk and there I was in heaven. Up there they had mown down some of my millet which they baked into a loaf and were eating with boiled milk. "That's my millet!" I said. "What do you want for it?" they asked me. "I want some holy water to christen my father who has just been born." So they gave me some holy water and I prepared to descend again to earth. But on earth there was a violent storm going on and the wind carried away my millet. So there I was with no way of getting down. I thought of my hair. It was so long that when I stood up it covered my ears and when I lay down it reached all the way to earth. So I pulled out a hair, tied it to a tree of heaven, and began descending by it. When it grew dark I made a knot in the hair and just sat where I was. It was cold, so I took a needle which I happened to have in my coat, split it up, and lighted a fire with the chips.

"Oh, father!" the Princess cried, "Stefan says he split a needle into kindling wood! Isn't he funny!"

"If you ask me——" the first lady-in-waiting began, but before she could say any more the Tsar reached over and stepped on her toe so hard that she was forced to end her sentence with a little squeally, "Ouch!" The Princess, you see, was smiling and the Tsar was hoping that presently she would burst into a laugh. So he motioned Stefan to continue.

Then I lay down beside the fire and fell asleep. While I slept a spark from the fire fell on the hair and burned it through. I fell to earth with such force that I sank into the ground up to my chest. I couldn't budge, so I was forced to go home and get a spade and dig myself out. On the way home I crossed a field where the reapers were cutting corn. The heat was so great that they had to stop work. "I'll get our mare," I said, "and then you'll feel cooler." You know our mare is two days long and as broad as midnight and she has willow trees growing on her back. So I ran and got her and she cast such a cool shadow that the reapers were at once able to go back to work. Now they wanted some fresh drinking water, but when they went to the river they found it had frozen over. They came back to me and asked me would I get them some water. "Certainly," I said. I went to the river myself, then. I took off my head and with it I broke a hole in the ice. After that it was easy enough to fetch them some water. "But where is your head?" they asked. "Oh!" I said, "I must have forgotten it!"

"Oh, father!" the Princess cried with a loud laugh, "he says he forgot his head! Then, Stefan, what did you do? What did you do?"

I ran back to the river and got there just as a fox was sniffing at my skull. "Hi, there!" I said, pulling the fox's tail. The fox turned around and gave me a paper on which was written these words:

NOW THE PRINCESS CAN EAT FOR SHE HAS LAUGHED AND STEFAN AND HIS LITTLE SISTER ARE VERY HAPPY.

"What nonsense!" the first lady-in-waiting murmured with a toss of her head.

"Yes, beautiful nonsense!" the Princess cried, clapping her hands and going off into peal after peal of merry laughter. "Isn't it beautiful nonsense, father? And isn't Stefan a dear lad? And, father, I'm awfully hungry! Please have some food sent in at once and Stefan must stay and eat with me."

So the Tsar had great trays of food brought in, roast birds and vegetables and wheaten bread and many kinds of little cakes and honey and milk and fruit. And Stefan and the Princess ate and made merry and the Tsar joined them and even the first lady-in-waiting took one little cake which she crumbled in her handkerchief in a most refined manner.

Then Stefan rose to go and the Tsar said to him:

"Stefan, I will reward you richly. You have made the Princess laugh and besides you have not insisted on her marrying you. You are a fine lad and I shall never forget you."

"But, father," the Princess said, "I don't want Stefan to go. He amuses me and I like him. He said I needn't marry him unless I wanted to but, father, I think I want to."

"Wow! Wow!" the Tsar roared. "What! My daughter marry the son of a farmer!"

"Now, father," the Princess said, "it's no use your *wow-wowing* at me. If I can't marry Stefan I won't marry any one. And if I don't marry any one I'm going to stop eating again. And that's that!" And still holding Stefan's hand, the Princess turned her face to the wall.

What could the poor Tsar do? At first he fumed and raged but as usual after a day or two he came around to the Princess's way of thinking. In fact it soon seemed to him that Stefan had been his choice from the first and when one of his councilors remarked: "Then, Your Majesty, there's no use sending word to the neighboring kings that the Princess has reached a marriageable age and would like to look over their sons," the Tsar flew into an awful temper and roared:

"Wow! Wow! You blockhead! Neighboring kings, indeed, and their good-for-nothing sons! No, siree! The husband I want for my daughter is an honest farmer lad who knows how to work and how to play! That's the kind of son-in-law we need in this kingdom!"

So Stefan and the little Princess were married and from that day the castle was no longer gloomy but rang with laughter and merriment. Presently the people of the kingdom, following the example of their rulers, were laughing, too, and cracking jokes and, strange to say, they soon found they were working all the better for their jollity.

Laughter grew so fashionable that even Mihailo and Jakov were forced to take it up. They didn't do it very well but they practiced at it conscientiously. Whenever people talked about Stefan, they always pushed forward importantly and said:

"Ho! Ho! Ho! Do you mean Stefan, the Laughing Prince? Ha! Ha! Ha! Why, do you know, he's our own brother!"

As for Militza, the Princess had her come to the castle and said to her:

"I owe all my happiness to you, my dear, for you it was who knew that of course I would laugh at Stefan's nonsense! What sensible girl wouldn't?"

WOMAN'S WIT

by Howard Pyle

In the days when the great and wise King Solomon lived and ruled, evil spirits and demons were as plentiful in the world as wasps in summer.

So King Solomon, who was so wise and knew so many potent spells that he had power over evil such as no man has had before or since, set himself to work to put those enemies of mankind out of the way. Some he conjured into bottles, and sank into the depth of the sea; some he buried in the earth; some he destroyed altogether, as one burns hair in a candle-flame.

Now, one pleasant day when King Solomon was walking in his

garden with his hands behind his back, and his thoughts busy as bees with this or that, he came face to face with a Demon, who was a prince of his kind. "Ho, little man!" cried the evil spirit, in a loud voice, "art not thou the wise King Solomon who conjures my brethren into brass chests and glass bottles? Come, try a fall at wrestling with me, and whoever conquers shall be master over the other for all time. What do you say to such an offer as that?"

"I say aye!" said King Solomon, and, without another word, he stripped off his royal robes and stood bare-breasted, man to man with the other.

The world never saw the like of that wrestling-match betwixt the king and the Demon, for they struggled and strove together from the seventh hour in the morning to the sunset in the evening, and during that time the sky was clouded over as black as night, and the lightning forked and shot, and the thunder roared and bellowed, and the earth shook and quaked.

But at last the king gave the enemy an under twist, and flung him down on the earth so hard that the apples fell from the trees; and then, panting and straining, he held the evil one down, knee on neck. Thereupon the sky presently cleared again, and all was as pleasant as a spring day.

King Solomon bound the Demon with spells, and made him serve him for seven years. First, he had him build a splendid palace, the like of which was not to be seen within the bounds of the seven rivers; then he made him set around the palace a garden, such as I for one wish I may see some time or other. Then, when the Demon had done all that the king wished, the king conjured him into a bottle, corked it tightly, and set the royal seal on the stopper. Then he took the bottle a thousand miles away into the wilderness, and, when no man was looking, buried it in the ground, and this is the way the story begins.

Well, the years came and the years went, and the world grew older and older, and kept changing (as all things do but two), so that by and by the wilderness where King Solomon had hid the bottle became a great town, with people coming and going, and all as busy as bees about their own business and other folks' affairs.

Among these townspeople was a little Tailor, who made clothes for many a worse man to wear, and who lived all alone in a little house with no one to darn his stockings for him, and no one to meddle with his coming and going, for he was a bachelor.

The little Tailor was a thrifty soul, and by hook and crook had laid by enough money to fill a small pot, and then he had to bethink himself of some safe place to hide it. So one night he took a spade and a lamp and went out in the garden to bury his money. He drove his spade into the ground—and click! He struck something hard that rang under his foot with a sound as of iron. "Hello!" said he, "what have we here?" and if he had known as much as you and I do, he would have filled in the earth, and tramped it down, and have left the plate of broth for somebody else to burn his mouth with.

As it was, he scraped away the soil, and then he found a box of adamant, with a ring in the lid to lift it by. The Tailor clutched the ring and bent his back, and up came the box with the damp earth sticking to it. He cleaned the mould away, and there he saw, written in red letters, these words:

Open Not.

You may be sure that after he had read these words he was not long in breaking open the lid of the box with his spade.

Inside the first box he found a second, and upon it the same words:

Open Not.

Within the second box was another, and within that still another, until there were seven in all, and on each was written the same words:

Open Not.

Inside the seventh box was a roll of linen, and inside that a bottle filled with nothing but blue smoke; and I wish that bottle had burned the Tailor's fingers when he touched it.

"And is this all?" said the little Tailor, turning the bottle upside down and shaking it, and peeping at it by the light of the lamp. "Well, since I have gone so far I might as well open it, as I have already opened the seven boxes." Thereupon he broke the seal that stoppered it.

Pop! Out flew the cork, and—Puff! Out came the smoke; not all at once, but in a long thread that rose up as high as the stars, and then spread until it hid their light.

The Tailor stared and goggled and gaped to see so much smoke come out of such a little bottle, and, as he goggled and stared, the smoke began to gather together again, thicker and thicker, and darker and darker, until it was as black as ink. Then out from it there stepped one with eyes that shone like sparks of fire, and who had a countenance so terrible that the Tailor's skin quivered and shrivelled, and his tongue clove to the roof of his mouth at the sight of it.

"Who art thou?" said the terrible being, in a voice that made the very marrow of the poor Tailor's bones turn soft from terror.

"If you please, sir," said he, "I am only a little tailor."

The evil being lifted up both hands and eyes. "How wonderful," he cried, "that one little tailor can undo in a moment that which took the wise Solomon a whole day to accomplish, and in the doing of which he well-nigh broke the sinews of his heart!" Then, turning to the Tailor, who stood trembling like a rabbit, "Hark thee!" said he. "For two thousand years I lay there in that bottle, and no one came nigh to aid me. Thou hast liberated me, and thou shalt not go unrewarded. Every morning at the seventh hour I will come to thee, and I will perform for thee whatever task thou mayest command me. But there is one condition attached to the agreement, and woe be to thee if that condition is broken. If any morning I should come to thee, and thou hast no task for me to do, I shall wring thy neck as thou mightest wring the neck of a sparrow." Thereupon he was gone in an instant, leaving the little Tailor half dead with terror.

Now it happened that the prime-minister of that country had

left an order with the Tailor for a suit of clothes, so the next morning, when the Demon came, the little man set him to work on the bench, with his legs tucked up like a journeyman tailor, "I want," said he, "such and such a suit of clothes."

"You shall have them," said the Demon; and thereupon he began snipping in the air, and cutting most wonderful patterns of silks and satins out of nothing at all, and the little Tailor sat and gaped and stared. Then the Demon began to drive the needle like a spark of fire—the like was never seen in all the seven kingdoms, for the clothes seemed to make themselves.

At last, at the end of a little while, the Demon stood up and brushed his hands. "They are done," said he, and thereupon he instantly vanished. But the Tailor cared little for that, for upon the bench there lay such a suit of clothes of silk and satin stuff, sewed with threads of gold and silver and set with jewels, as the eyes of man never saw before; and the Tailor packed them up and marched off with them himself to the prime-minister.

The prime-minister wore the clothes to court that very day, and before evening they were the talk of the town. All the world ran to the Tailor and ordered clothes of him, and his fortune was made. Every day the Demon created new suits of clothes out of nothing at all, so that the Tailor grew rich, and held his head up in the world.

As time went along he laid heavier and heavier tasks upon the Demon's back, and demanded of him more and more; but all the while the Demon kept his own counsel, and said never a word.

One morning, as the Tailor sat in his shop window taking the world easy—for he had little or nothing to do now—he heard a great hubbub in the street below, and when he looked down he saw that it was the king's daughter passing by. It was the first time that the Tailor had seen her, and when he saw her his heart stood still within him, and then began fluttering like a little bird, for one so beautiful was not to be met with in the four corners of the world. Then she was gone.

All that day the little Tailor could do nothing but sit and think of the princess, and the next morning when the Demon came he was thinking of her still.

"What hast thou for me to do today?" said the Demon, as he always said of a morning.

The little Tailor was waiting for the question.

"I would like you," said he, "to send to the king's palace, and to ask him to let me have his daughter for my wife."

"Thou shalt have thy desire," said the Demon. Thereupon he smote his hands together like a clap of thunder, and instantly the walls of the room clove asunder, and there came out four-and-twenty handsome youths, clad in cloth of gold and silver. After these four-and-twenty there came another one who was the chief of them all, and before whom, splendid as they were, the four-and-twenty paled like stars in daylight. "Go to the king's palace," said the Demon to that one, "and deliver this message: The Tailor of Tailors, the Master of Masters, and One Greater than a King asks for his daughter to wife."

"To hear is to obey," said the other, and bowed his forehead to the earth.

Never was there such a hubbub in the town as when those five-and-twenty, in their clothes of silver and gold, rode through the streets to the king's palace. As they came near, the gates of the palace flew open before them, and the king himself came to meet them. The leader of the five-and-twenty leaped from his horse, and, kissing the ground before the king, delivered his message: "The Tailor of Tailors, the Master of Masters, and One Greater than a King asks for thy daughter to wife."

When the king heard what the messenger said, he thought and pondered for a long time. At last he said, "If he who sent you is the Master of Masters, and greater than a king, let him send me an asking gift such as no king could send."

"It shall be as you desire," said the messenger, and thereupon the five-and-twenty rode away as they had come, followed by crowds of people.

The next morning when the Demon came the Tailor was ready

and waiting for him. "What hast thou for me to do today?" said the Evil One.

"I want," said the Tailor, "a gift to send to the king such as no other king could send him."

"Thou shalt have thy desire," said the Demon. Thereupon he smote his hands together, and summoned, not only the five-and-twenty young men, but fifty more youths, all clad in clothes more splendid than the others.

All of the fifty sat upon coal-black horses, with saddles of silver and housings of silk and velvet embroidered with gold. In the midst of all the five-and-seventy there rode a youth in cloth of silver embroidered in pearls. In his hand he bore something wrapped in a white napkin, and that was the present for the king such as no other king could give. So said the Demon: "Take it to the royal palace, and tell his majesty that it is from the Tailor of Tailors, the Master of Masters, and One Greater than a King."

"To hear is to obey," said the young man, and then they all rode away.

When they came to the palace the gates flew open before them, and the king came out to meet them. The young man who bore the present dismounted and prostrated himself in the dust, and, when the king bade him arise, he unwrapped the napkin, and gave to the king a goblet made of one single ruby, and filled to the brim with pieces of gold. Moreover, the cup was of such a kind that whenever it was emptied of its money it instantly became full again. "The Tailor of Tailors, and Master of Masters, and One Greater than a King sends your majesty this goblet, and bids me, his ambassador, to ask for your daughter," said the young man.

When the king saw what had been sent him he was filled with amazement. "Surely," said he to himself, "there can be no end to the power of one who can give such a gift as this." Then to the messenger, "Tell your master that he shall have my daughter for his wife if he will build over yonder a palace such as no man ever saw or no king ever lived in before."

"It shall be done," said the young man, and then they all went away, as the others had done the day before.

The next morning when the Demon appeared the Tailor was ready for him. "Build me," said he, "such and such a palace in such and such a place."

And the Demon said, "It shall be done." He smote his hands together, and instantly there came a cloud of mist that covered and hid the spot where the palace was to be built. Out from the cloud there came such a banging and hammering and clapping and clattering as the people of that town never heard before. Then when evening had come the cloud arose, and there, where the king had pointed out, stood a splendid palace as white as snow, with roofs and domes of gold and silver. As the king stood looking and wondering at this sight, there came five hundred young men riding, and one in the midst of all who wore a golden crown on his head, and upon his body a long robe stiff with diamonds and pearls. "We come," said he, "from the Tailor of Tailors, and Master of Masters, and One Greater than a King, to ask you to let him have your daughter for his wife."

"Tell him to come!" cried the king, in admiration, "for the princess is his."

The next morning when the Demon came he found the Tailor dancing and shouting for joy. "The princess is mine!" he cried, "so make me ready for her."

"It shall be done," said the Demon, and thereupon he began to make the Tailor ready for his wedding. He brought him to a marble bath of water, in which he washed away all that was coarse and ugly, and from which the little man came forth as beautiful as the sun. Then the Demon clad him in the finest linen, and covered him with clothes such as even the emperor of India never wore. Then he smote his hands together, and the wall of the tailor-shop opened as it had done twice before, and there came forth forty slaves clad in crimson, and bearing bowls full of money in their hands. After them came two leading a horse as white as snow, with a saddle of gold studded with diamonds and rubies and emeralds and sapphires. After came a bodyguard of twenty warriors clad in gold armor. Then the Tailor mounted his horse and rode away to the king's palace, and as he rode the slaves scattered the money amongst the crowd, who scrambled for it and cheered the Tailor to the skies.

That night the princess and the Tailor were married, and all the town was lit with bonfires and fireworks. The two rode away in the midst of a great crowd of nobles and courtiers to the palace which the Demon had built for the Tailor; and, as the princess gazed upon him, she thought that she had never beheld so noble and handsome a man as her husband. So she and the Tailor were the happiest couple in the world.

But the next morning the Demon appeared as he had appeared ever since the Tailor had let him out of the bottle, only now he grinned till his teeth shone and his face turned black. "What hast thou for me to do?" said he, and at the words the Tailor's heart began to quake, for he remembered what was to happen to him when he could find the Demon no more work to do—that his neck was to be wrung—and now he began to see that he had all that he could ask for in the world. Yes; what was there to ask for now?

"I have nothing more for you to do," said he to the Demon; "you have done all that man could ask—you may go now."

"Go!" cried the Demon, "I shall not go until I have done all that I have to do. Give me work, or I shall wring your neck." And his fingers began to twitch.

Then the Tailor began to see into what a net he had fallen. He began to tremble like one in an ague. He turned his eyes up and down, for he did not know where to look for aid. Suddenly, as he looked out of the window, a thought struck him. Maybe, thought he, I can give the Demon such a task that even he cannot do it. "Yes, yes!" he cried. "I have thought of something for you to do. Make me out yonder in front of my palace a lake of water a mile long and a mile wide, and let it be lined throughout with white marble, and filled with water as clear as crystal."

"It shall be done," said the Demon. As he spoke he spat in the air, and instantly a thick fog arose from the earth and hid everything from sight. Then presently from the midst of the fog there came a great noise of chipping and hammering, of digging and delving, of rushing and gurgling. All day the noise and the fog continued, and then at sunset the one ceased and the other cleared away. The poor Tailor looked out the window, and when he saw what he saw his teeth chattered in his head, for there was a lake a mile long and a mile broad, lined within with white marble, and filled with water as clear as crystal, and he knew that the Demon would come the next morning for another task to do.

That night he slept little or none, and when the seventh hour of the morning came the castle began to rock and tremble, and there stood the Demon, and his hair bristled and his eyes shone like sparks of fire. "What hast thou for me to do?" said he, and the poor Tailor could do nothing but look at him with a face as white as dough.

"What hast thou for me to do?" said the Demon again, and then at last the Tailor found his wits and his tongue from sheer terror. "Look!" said he, "at the great mountain over yonder; remove it, and make in its place a level plain with fields and orchards and gardens." And he thought to himself when he had spoken, "Surely, even the Demon cannot do that."

"It shall be done," said the Demon, and, so saying, he stamped his heel upon the ground. Instantly the earth began to tremble and quake, and there came a great rumbling like the sound of thunder. A cloud of darkness gathered in the sky, until at last all was as black as the blackest midnight. Then came a roaring and a cracking and a crashing, such as man never heard before. All day it continued, until the time of the setting of the sun, when suddenly the uproar ceased, and the darkness cleared away; and when the Tailor looked out of the window the mountain was gone, and in its place were fields and orchards and gardens.

It was very beautiful to see, but when the Tailor beheld it his knees began to smite together, and the sweat ran down his face in streams. All that night he walked up and down and up and down, but he could not think of one other task for the Demon to do.

When the next morning came the Demon appeared like a whirlwind. His face was as black as ink and smoke, and sparks of fire flew from his nostrils.

"What have you for me to do?" cried he.

"I have nothing for you to do!" piped the poor Tailor.

"Nothing?" cried the Demon.

"Nothing."

"Then prepare to die."

"Stop!" said the Tailor, falling on his knees, "let me first see my wife."

"So be it," said the Demon, and if he had been wiser he would have said "No."

When the Tailor came to the princess, he flung himself on his face, and began to weep and wail. The princess asked him what was the matter, and at last, by dint of question, got the story from him, piece by piece. When she had it all she began laughing. "Why did you not come to me before?" said she, "instead of making all this trouble and uproar for nothing at all? I will give the Monster a task to do." She plucked a single curling hair from her head. "Here," said she, "let him take this hair and make it straight."

The Tailor was full of doubt; nevertheless, as there was nothing better to do, he took it to the Demon.

"Hast thou found me a task to do?" cried the Demon.

"Yes," said the Tailor. "It is only a little thing. Here is a hair from my wife's head; take it and make it straight."

When the Demon heard what was the task that the Tailor had set him to do he laughed aloud; but that was because he did not know. He took the hair and stroked it between his thumb and finger, and when he had done, it curled more than ever. Then he looked serious, and slapped it between his palms, and that did not better matters, for it curled as much as ever. Then he frowned, and began beating the hair with his palm upon his knees, and that only made it worse. All that day he labored and strove at his task trying to make that one little hair straight, and, when the sun set, there was the hair just as crooked as ever. Then, as the great round sun sank red behind the trees, the Demon knew that he was beaten. "I am conquered! I am conquered!" he howled, and flew away, bellowing so dreadfully that all the world trembled.

So ends the story, with only this to say:

Where man's strength fails, woman's wit prevails.

For, to my mind, the princess—not to speak of her husband the little Tailor—did more with a single little hair and her mother wit than King Solomon with all his wisdom.

THE FEAST OF THE LANTERNS

*Anonymous**

Wang Chih was only a poor man, but he had a wife and children to love, and they made him so happy that he would not have changed places with the Emperor himself.

He worked in the fields all day, and at night his wife always had a bowl of rice ready for his supper. And sometimes, for a treat, she made him some bean soup, or gave him a little dish of fried pork.

But they could not afford pork very often; he generally had to be content with rice.

* Author unknown. This story was taken from Kate Douglas Wiggin & Nora Archibald Smith's *Tales of Wonder*, Doubleday 1909 (1929); and there credited to *Books for Bairus*, ed. by Wm. T. Stead, editor of *Review of Reviews* of London, d. 1912, when the *Titanic* sank.

One morning, as he was setting off to his work, his wife sent Han Chung, his son, running after him to ask him to bring home some firewood.

"I shall have to go up into the mountain for it at noon," he said. "Go and bring me my axe, Han Chung."

Han Chung ran for his father's axe, and Ho-Seen-Ko, his little sister, came out of the cottage with him.

"Remember it is the Feast of Lanterns to-night, Father," she said. "Don't fall asleep up on the mountain; we want you to come back and light them for us."

She had a lantern in the shape of a fish, painted red and black and yellow, and Han Chung had got a big round one, all bright crimson, to carry in the procession; and, besides that, there were two large lanterns to be hung outside the cottage door as soon as it grew dark.

Wang Chih was not likely to forget the Feast of Lanterns, for the children had talked of nothing else for a month, and he promised to come home as early as he could.

At noontide, when his fellow-labourers gave up working, and sat down to rest and eat, Wang Chih took his axe and went up the mountain slope to find a small tree he might cut down for fuel.

He walked a long way, and at last saw one growing at the mouth of a cave.

"This will be just the thing," he said to himself. But, before striking the first blow, he peeped into the cave to see if it were empty.

To his surprise, two old men, with long, white beards, were sitting inside playing chess, as quietly as mice, with their eyes fixed on the chessboard.

Wang Chih knew something of chess, and he stepped in and watched them for a few minutes.

"As soon as they look up I can ask them if I may chop down a tree," he said to himself. But they did not look up, and by and by Wang Chih got so interested in the game that he put down his axe, and sat on the floor to watch it better.

The two old men sat cross-legged on the ground, and the chessboard rested on a slab, like a stone table, between them.

On one corner of the slab lay a heap of small, brown objects which Wang Chih took at first to be date stones; but after a time the chess-players ate one each, and put one in Wang Chih's mouth; and he found it was not a date stone at all.

It was a delicious kind of sweetmeat, the like of which he had never tasted before; and the strangest thing about it was that it took his hunger and thirst away.

He had been both hungry and thirsty when he came into the cave, as he had not waited to have his midday meal with the other fieldworkers; but now he felt quite comforted and refreshed.

He sat there some time longer, and noticed that as the old men frowned over the chessboard, their beards grew longer and longer, until they swept the floor of the cave, and even found their way out of the door.

"I hope my beard will never grow as quickly," said Wang Chih, as he rose and took up his axe again.

Then one of the old men spoke, for the first time. "Our beards have not grown quickly, young man. How long is it since you came here?"

"About half an hour, I dare say," replied Wang Chih. But as he spoke, the axe crumbled to dust beneath his fingers, and the second chess-player laughed, and pointed to the little brown sweetmeats on the table.

"Half an hour, or half a century—aye, half a thousand years, are all alike to him who tastes of these. Go down into your village and see what has happened since you left it."

So Wang Chih went down as quickly as he could from the mountain, and found the fields where he had worked covered with houses, and a busy town where his own little village had been. In vain he looked for his house, his wife, and his children.

There were strange faces everywhere; and although when evening came the Feast of Lanterns was being held once more, there was no Ho-Seen-Ko carrying her red and yellow fish, or Han Chung with his flaming red ball.

At last he found a woman, a very, very old woman, who told him that when she was a tiny girl she remembered her grandmother saying how, when *she* was a tiny girl, a poor young man had been spirited away by the Genii of the mountains, on the day of the Feast of Lanterns, leaving his wife and little children with only a few handfuls of rice in the house.

"Moreover, if you wait while the procession passes, you will see two children dressed to represent Han Chung and Ho-Seen-Ko, and their mother carrying the empty rice-bowl between them: for this is done every year to remind people to take care of the widow and fatherless," she said. So Wang Chih waited in the street; and in a little while the procession came to an end; and the last three figures in it were a boy and a girl, dressed like his own two children, walking on either side of a young woman carrying a rice-bowl. But she was not like his wife in anything but her dress, and the children were not at all like Han Chung and Ho-Seen-Ko; and poor Wang Chih's heart was very heavy as he walked away out of the town.

He slept out on the mountain, and early in the morning found his way back to the cave where the two old men were playing chess.

At first they said they could do nothing for him, and told him to go away and not disturb them; but Wang Chih would not go, and they soon found the only way to get rid of him was to give him some really good advice.

"You must go to the White Hare of the Moon, and ask him for a bottle of the elixir of life. If you drink that you will live forever," said one of them.

"But I don't want to live forever," objected Wang Chih. "I wish to go back and live in the days when my wife and children were here."

"Ah, well! For that you must mix the elixir of life with some water out of the sky-dragon's mouth."

"And where is the sky-dragon to be found?" inquired Wang Chih.

"In the sky, of course. You really ask very stupid questions. He lives in a cloud-cave. And when he comes out of it he breathes fire, and sometimes water. If he is breathing fire you will be burnt up, but if it is only water, you will easily be able to catch some in a little bottle. What else do you want?"

For Wang Chih still lingered at the mouth of the cave.

"I want a pair of wings to fly with, and a bottle to catch the water in," he replied boldly.

So they gave him a little bottle; and before he had time to say "Thank you!" a white crane came sailing past, and lighted on the ground close to the cave.

"The crane will take you wherever you like," said the old men. "Go now, and leave us in peace."

So Wang Chih sat on the white crane's back, and was taken up, and up, and up through the sky to the cloud-cave where the sky-dragon lived. And the dragon had the head of a camel, the horns of a deer, the eyes of a rabbit, the ears of a cow and the claws of a hawk.

Besides this, he had whiskers and a beard, and in his beard was a bright pearl.

All these things show that he was a real, genuine dragon, and if you ever meet a dragon who is not exactly like this, you will know he is only a make-believe one.

Wang Chih felt rather frightened when he perceived the cave in the distance, and if it had not been for the thought of seeing his wife again, and his little boy and girl, he would have been glad to turn back.

While he was far away the cloud-cave looked like a dark hole in the midst of a soft, white, woolly mass, such as one sees in the sky on an April day; but as he came nearer he found the cloud was as hard as a rock, and covered with a kind of dry white grass.

When he got there, he sat down on a tuft of grass near the cave, and considered what he should do next.

The first thing was, of course, to bring the dragon out, and the next to make him breathe water instead of fire.

"I have it!" cried Wang Chih at last; and he nodded his head so many times that the white crane expected to see it fall off.

He struck a light, and set the grass on fire, and it was so dry that the flames spread all around the entrance to the cave, and made such a smoke and crackling that the sky-dragon put his head out to see what was the matter.

"Ho! ho!" cried the dragon, when he saw what Wang Chih had done, "I can soon put this to rights." And he breathed once, and the water came out his nose and mouth in three streams.

But this was not enough to put the fire out. Then he breathed twice, and the water came out in three mighty rivers, and Wang Chih, who had taken care to fill his bottle when the first stream began to flow, sailed away on the white crane's back as fast as he could, to escape being drowned.

The rivers poured over the cloud rock, until there was not a spark left alight, and rushed down through the sky into earth below.

Fortunately, the sea lay right underneath the dragon's cave, else they would have done some nice mischief. As it was the people on the coast looked out across the water toward Japan, and saw three inky-black clouds stretching from the sky into the sea.

"My word! There is a fine rain-storm out at sea!" they said to each other.

But, of course, it was nothing of the kind; it was only the sky-dragon putting out the fire Wang Chih had kindled.

Meanwhile, Wang Chih was on his way to the moon, and when he got there he went straight to the hut where the Hare of the Moon lived, and knocked at the door.

The Hare was busy pounding the drugs which make up the elixir of life; but he left his work, and opened the door, and invited Wang Chih to come in.

He was not ugly, like the dragon; his fur was quite white and soft and glossy, and he had lovely, gentle brown eyes.

The Hare of the Moon lives a thousand years, as you know, and when he is five hundred years old he changes his colour, from brown to white, and becomes, if possible, better tempered and nicer than he was before.

As soon as he heard what Wang Chih wanted, he opened two windows at the back of the hut, and told him to look through each of them in turn.

"Tell me what you see," said the Hare, going back to the table where he was pounding the drugs.

"I can see a great many houses and people," said Wang Chih, "and streets—why, this is the town I was in yesterday, the one which has taken the place of my old village."

Wang Chih stared, and grew more and more puzzled. Here he was up in the moon, and yet he could have thrown a stone into the busy street of the Chinese town below his window.

"How does it come here?" he stammered, at last.

"Oh, that is my secret," replied the wise old Hare. "I know how to do a great many things which would surprise you. But the question is, do you want to go back there?"

Wang Chih shook his head.

"Then close the window. It is the window of the Present. And look through the other, which is the window of the Past."

Wang Chih obeyed, and through this window he saw his own dear little village, and his wife, and Han Chung and Ho-Seen-Ko jumping about her as she hung up the coloured lanterns outside the door.

"Father won't be in time to light them for us, after all," Han Chung was saying.

Wang Chih turned, and looked eagerly at the White Hare.

"Let me go to them," he said. "I have got a bottle of water from the sky-dragon's mouth, and——"

"That's all right," said the White Hare. "Give it to me."

He opened the bottle, and mixed the contents carefully with a few drops of the elixir of life, which was clear as crystal, and of which each drop shone like a diamond as he poured it in.

"Now, drink this," he said to Wang Chih, "and it will give you the power of living once more in the past, as you desire."

Wang Chih held out his hand, and drank every drop.

The moment he had done so, the window grew larger, and he saw some steps leading from it down into the village street.

Thanking the Hare, he rushed through it, and ran toward his own house, arriving in time to take the taper from his wife's hand with which she was about to light the red and yellow lanterns which swung over the door.

"What has kept you so long, father? Where have you been?" asked Han Chung, while little Ho-Seen-Ko wondered why he kissed and embraced them all so eagerly.

But Wang Chih did not tell them his adventures just then; only when darkness fell, and the Feast of Lanterns began, he took his part in it with a merry heart.

THE GREAT QUILLOW

by James Thurber

Once upon a time, in a far country, there lived a giant named Hunder. He was so enormous in height and girth and weight that little waves were set in motion in distant lakes when he walked. His great fingers could wrench a clock from its steeple as easily as a child might remove a peanut from its shell. Every morning he devoured three sheep, a pie made of a thousand apples, and a chocolate as high and as wide as a spinning wheel. It would have taken six ordinary men to lift the great brass key to his front door, and four to carry one of the candles with which he lighted his house.

It was Hunder's way to strip a town of its sheep and apples and chocolate, its leather and cloth, its lumber and tallow and brass, and then move on to a new far village and begin his depredations again. There had been no men strong enough to thwart his evil ways in any of the towns he had set upon and impoverished. He had broken their most formidable weapons between his thumb and forefinger, laughing like the hurricane. And there had been no men cunning enough in any of the towns to bring about his destruction. He had crushed their most ingenious traps with the toe of his mammoth boot, guffawing like a volcano.

One day Hunder strode hundreds and hundreds of leagues and came to a little town in a green valley. It was a staunch little town and a firm little valley, but they quaked with the sound of his coming. The houses were narrow and two stories high; the streets were narrow and cobbled. There were not many people in the town: a hundred men, a hundred women, a hundred children.

Every Tuesday night at seven o'clock a council of ten met to administer the simple affairs of the community. The councilors were the most important tradesmen and artisans of New Moon Street, a short, narrow, cobbled street that ran east and west. These men were the tailor, the butcher, the candymaker, the blacksmith, the baker, the candlemaker, the lamplighter, the cobbler, the carpenter, and the locksmith. After the small business of the tranquil town had been taken care of, the council members sat around and speculated as to the number of stars in the sky, discussed the wonderful transparency of glass, and praised the blueness of violets and the whiteness of snow. Then they made a little fun of Quillow, the toymaker (whose work they considered a rather pretty waste of time), and went home.

Quillow, the toymaker, did not belong to the council but he attended all its meetings. The councilmen were fond of Quillow because of the remarkable toys he made, and because he was a droll and gentle fellow. Quillow made all kinds of familiar playthings on his long and littered workbench: music boxes, jumping jacks, building blocks; but he was famous for a number of little masterpieces of his own invention: a clown who juggled three marbles, a woodman who could actually chop wood, a trumpeter who could play seven notes of a song on a tiny horn, a paperweight in which roses burst into bloom in falling snow.

Quillow was as amusing to look at as any of his toys. He was the shortest man in town, being only five feet tall. His ears were large, his nose was long, his mouth was small, and he had a shock of white hair that stood straight up like a dandelion clock. The lapels of his jacket were wide. He wore a red tie in a deep-pointed collar, and his pantaloons were baggy and unpressed. At Christmastime each year Quillow made little hearts of gold for the girls of the town and hearts of oak for the boys. He considered himself something of a civic figure, since he had designed the spouting dolphins in the town fountain, the wooden animals on the town merry-go-round, and the twelve scarlet men who emerged from the dial of the town clock on the stroke of every hour and played a melody on little silver bells with little silver hammers.

It was the custom of Quillow's colleagues to shout merrily, "Why, here comes the Great Quillow!" when the toymaker appeared. The lamplighter or the tailor or the locksmith would sometimes creep up behind him and pretend to wind a key in his back as if he were a mechanical figure of his own devising. Quillow took all this in good part, and always, when the imaginary key in his back was turned, he would walk about stiff-legged, with jerky movements of his arms, joining in the fun and increasing the laughter.

It was different on the day the giant arrived. Laughter was hushed and the people hid in their houses and talked in frightened whispers when Hunder's great bulk appeared like a cyclone in the sky and the earth shook beneath him. Panting a little after his thousand-league walk, Hunder pulled up four trees from a hillside to make room for his great hulk, and sat down. Hunder surveyed the town and grunted. There was no one to be seen in the streets. Not even a cat crept over the cobblestones.

"Ho, town!" bawled Hunder. The doors shook and the windows rattled. "Ho, town! Send me your clerk that you may hear Hunder's will!"

The town clerk gathered up quill and ink and parchment. "There are ninety-nine other men in town," he grumbled, "but it's the town clerk this, and the town clerk that, and the town clerk everything." He walked out of his house, still grumbling, and trudged across the valley to hear the giant's will.

An hour later the town clerk sat at the head of a long table in the council room and began to call the roll. "We're all here," snapped the blacksmith. "You can see that."

The clerk continued with the roll call.

"Baker," he called. "Here," said the baker. "Blacksmith," he droned. "Here," said the blacksmith sourly.

The clerk finished calling the roll and looked over his spectacles. "We have a visitor tonight, as usual," he said, "Quillow, the toymaker. I will make the proper entry in the minutes."

"Never mind the minutes," said the blacksmith. "Read us the demands of Hunder the giant."

The clerk entered Quillow's name in the minutes. "Now," he said, "I will read the minutes of the last meeting."

The candymaker stood up. "Let's dispense with the minutes of the last meeting," he said.

The clerk looked over his spectacles. "It must be properly moved and duly seconded," he said. It was properly moved and duly seconded. "Now read the demands of Hunder the giant!" shouted the blacksmith.

The clerk rapped on the table with his gavel. "Next," he said, "comes unfinished business. We have before us a resolution to regulate the speed of merry-go-rounds."

"Dispense with it!" bawled the blacksmith.

"It must be properly moved and duly seconded," said the clerk.

It was properly moved and duly seconded and the clerk at last unrolled a long scroll of parchment. "We come now," he said, "to the business of the day. I have here the demands of Hunder the giant. The document is most irregular. It does not contain a single 'greeting' or 'whereas' or 'be it known by these presents'!"

Everyone sat motionless as the clerk began to read the scroll. "I, Hunder, must have three sheep every morning," he read.

"That would use up all the sheep in the valley in a week and a fortnight," said the butcher, "and there would be no mutton for our own people."

"I, Hunder, must have a chocolate a day as high and as wide as a spinning wheel," read the town clerk.

"Why, that would exhaust all the chocolate in my storeroom in three days!" cried the candymaker.

The town clerk read from the parchment again. "I, Hunder, must have a new jerkin made for me in a week and a fortnight."

"Why, I would have to work night and day to make a jerkin in a week and a fortnight for so large a giant," gasped the tailor, "and it would use up all the cloth on my shelves and in my basement."

"I, Hunder," went on the town clerk, "must have a new pair of boots within a week and a fortnight."

The cobbler moaned as he heard this. "Why, I would have to work night and day to make a pair of boots for so large a giant in a week and a fortnight," he said. "And it would use up all the leather in my workshop and in my back room."

The council members shook their heads sadly as each demand was read off by the town clerk. Quillow had folded his arms and crossed his legs and shut his eyes. He was thinking, but he looked like a sleeping toy.

"I, Hunder," droned the town clerk, "must have an apple pie each morning made of a thousand apples."

The baker jumped from his chair. "Why, that would use up all the apples and flour and shortening in town in a week and a fortnight," he cried. "And it would take me night and day to make such a pie, so that I could bake no more pies or cakes or cookies, or blueberry muffins or cinnamon buns or cherry boats or strawberry tarts or plum puddings for the people of the town."

All of the councilmen moaned sadly because they loved the list of good things the baker had recited. Quillow still sat with his eyes closed.

"I, Hunder," went on the town clerk, "must have a house to live in by the time a week and a fortnight have passed."

The carpenter wept openly. "Why, I would have to work night and day to build a house for so large a giant in a week and a fortnight," sobbed the carpenter. "All my nephews and uncles and cousins would have to help me, and it would use up all the wood and pegs and hinges and glass in my shop and in the countryside."

The locksmith stood up and shook his fist in the direction of the hillside on which the giant lay snoring. "I will have to work night and day to make a brass key large enough to fit the keyhole in the front door of the house of so large a giant," he said. "It will use up all the brass in my shop and in the community."

"And I will have to make a candle for his bedside so large it will use up all the wick and tallow in my shop and the world!" said the candlemaker.

"This is the final item," said the town clerk. "I, Hunder, must be told a tale each day to keep me amused."

Quillow opened his eyes and raised his hand. "I will be the teller of tales," he said. "I will keep the giant amused."

The town clerk put away his scroll.

"Does anyone have any idea of how to destroy the giant Hunder?" asked the candymaker.

"I could creep up on him in the dark and set fire to him with my lighter," said the lamplighter.

Quillow looked at him. "The fire of your lighter would not harm him any more than a spark struck by a colt-shoe in a meadow," said Quillow.

"Quillow is right," said the blacksmith. "But I could build

secretly at night an enormous catapult which would cast a gigantic stone and crush Hunder."

Quillow shook his head. "He would catch the stone as a child catches a ball," said Quillow, "and he would cast it back at the town and squash all our houses."

"I could put needles in his suit," said the tailor.

"I could put nails in his boots," said the cobbler.

"I could put oil in his chocolates," said the candymaker.

"I could put stones in his mutton," said the butcher.

"I could put tacks in his pies," said the baker.

"I could put gunpowder in his candles," said the candlemaker.

"I could make the handle of his brass key as sharp as a sword," said the locksmith.

"I could build the roof of his house insecurely so that it would fall on him," said the carpenter.

"The plans you suggest," said Quillow, "would merely annoy Hunder as the gadfly annoys the horse and the flea annoys the dog."

"Perhaps the Great Quillow has a plan of his own," said the blacksmith with a scornful laugh.

"Has the Great Quillow a plan?" asked the candymaker, with a faint sneer.

The little toymaker did not answer. The councilors got up and filed slowly and sadly from the council room. That night none of them wound the imaginary key in Quillow's back.

Quillow did not leave the council chamber for a long time, and when he walked through New Moon Street, all the shops of the councilmen were brightly lighted and noisily busy. There was a great ringing and scraping and thumping and rustling. The blacksmith was helping the locksmith make the great brass key for Hunder's house. The carpenter was sawing and planing enormous boards. The baker was shaping the crust for a gigantic pie, and his wife and apprentice were peeling a thousand apples. The butcher was dressing the first of the three sheep. The tailor was cutting the cloth for Hunder's jerkin. The cobbler was fitting together mammoth pieces of leather for Hunder's boots. The candymaker was piling all his chocolate upon his largest table, while his wife and his daughter made soft filling in great kettles. The candlemaker had begun to build the monumental candle for Hunder's bedside.

As Quillow reached the door of his shop, the town clock in its steeple began to strike, the moon broke out of a patch of cloud, and the toymaker stood with his hand on the door latch to watch the twelve little men in scarlet hats and jackets and pantaloons emerge, each from his own numeral, to make the night melodious with the sound of their silver hammers on the silver bells of the round white dial.

Inside his shop, Quillow lighted the green-shaded lamp over his workbench, which was littered with odds and ends and beginnings and middles of all kinds of toys. Working swiftly with his shining tools, Quillow began to make a figure eight inches high out of wire and cloth and leather and wood. When it was finished it looked like a creature you might come upon hiding behind a tulip or playing with toads. It had round eyes, a round nose and a wide mouth, and no hair. It was blue from head to foot. Its face was blue, its jacket was blue, its pantaloons were blue, and its feet were blue.

As Quillow stood examining the toy, the lamplighter stuck his head in the door without knocking, stared for a moment, and went away. Quillow smiled with satisfaction and began to make another blue man. By the time the first cock crowed he had made ten blue men and put them away in a long wooden chest with a heavy iron clasp.

The lamplighter turned out the last street light, the sun rose, the crickets stopped calling and the clock struck five. Disturbed by the changing pattern of light and sound, the giant on the hillside turned in his sleep. Around a corner into New Moon Street tiptoed the town crier. "Sh!" he said to the lamplighter. "Don't wake the giant."

"Sh!" said the lamplighter. "His food may not be ready."

The town crier stood in the cobbled street and called softly, "Five o'clock, and all's well!"

All the doors in New Moon Street except Quillow's flew open.

"The pie is baked," said the baker.

"The chocolate is made," said the candymaker.

"The sheep are dressed," said the butcher.

"I worked all night on the great brass key," said the locksmith, "and the blacksmith helped me with his hammer and anvil."

"I have scarcely begun the enormous candle," said the candlemaker.

"I am weary of sawing and planing," said the carpenter.

"My fingers are already stiff," said the tailor, "and I have just started the giant's jerkin."

"My eyes are tired," said the cobbler, "and I have hardly begun to make his boots."

The sun shone full on the giant's face, and he woke up and yawned loudly. The councilors jumped, and a hundred children hid in a hundred closets.

"Ho!" roared Hunder. It was the sign the blacksmith had waited for. He drove his wagon drawn by four horses into New Moon Street and climbed down.

"Ho!" roared the giant.

"Heave," grunted the councilors as they lifted the sheep onto the wagon.

"Ho!" roared the giant.

"Heave," grunted the councilors, and up went the pie.

"Ho!" roared the giant.

"Heave," grunted the councilors, and they set the great chocolate in place.

Hunder watched the loading of the wagon, licking his lips and growling like a cave full of bulldogs.

The councilors climbed up on the wagon and the blacksmith yelled "Giddap!", and then "Whoa!" He glared about him. "Where is Quillow?" he demanded. "Where is that foolish little fellow?"

"He was in his shop at midnight," said the lamplighter, "making toys."

The nine other councilors snorted.

"He could have helped with the key," said the locksmith.

"The pie," said the baker.

"The sheep," said the butcher.

"The boots," said the cobbler.

At this, Quillow bounced out of his shop like a bird from a clock, bowing and smiling.

"Well!" snarled the blacksmith.

"Ho!" roared Hunder.

"Good morning," said Quillow. He climbed up on the wagon and the blacksmith spoke to each horse in turn. (Their names were Lobo, Bolo, Olob, and Obol.)

"I worked all night with my hammer and anvil," said the blacksmith as the horses lurched ahead, "helping the locksmith with the great brass key." He scowled at Quillow. "The lamplighter tells us *you* spent the night making toys."

"Making toys," said Quillow cheerily, "and thinking up a tale to amuse the giant Hunder."

The blacksmith snorted. "And a hard night you must have spent hammering out your tale."

"And twisting it," said the locksmith.

"And leveling it," said the carpenter.

"And rolling it out," said the baker.

"And stitching it up," said the tailor.

"And fitting it together," said the cobbler.

"And building it around a central thread," said the candlemaker.

"And dressing it up," said the butcher.

"And making it not too bitter and not too sweet," said the candymaker.

When the wagon came to a stop at Hunder's feet, the giant clapped his hands, and Quillow and the councilors were blown to the ground. Hunder roared with laughter and unloaded the wagon in half a trice.

"Tell me your silly names," said Hunder, "and what you do."

The new slaves of Hunder, all except Quillow, bowed in turn and told the giant who they were and what they did. Quillow remained silent.

"You, smallest of men, you with the white hair, who are you?" demanded Hunder.

"I am Quillow, the teller of tales," said the toymaker, but unlike the others he did not bow to the giant.

"Bow!" roared Hunder.

"Wow!" shouted Quillow.

The councilors started back in dismay at the toymaker's impertinence, their widening eyes on Hunder's mighty hands, which closed and then slowly opened. The black scowl cleared from the giant's brow and he laughed suddenly.

"You are a fairly droll fellow," he said. "Perhaps your tales will amuse me. If they do not, I will put you in the palm of my hand and blow you so far it will take men five days to find you. Now be off to your work, the rest of you!"

As the wagon carried the frightened councilors back to town, Quillow sat on the ground and watched the giant eat a sheep as an ordinary man might eat a lark. "Now," said Hunder, "tell me a tale."

"Once upon a time," began Quillow, crossing his legs and tickling a cricket with a blade of grass, "a giant came to our town from a thousand leagues away, stepping over the hills and rivers. He was so mighty a giant that he could stamp upon the ground with his foot and cause the cows in the fields to turn flip-flops in the air and land on their feet again."

"Garf," growled Hunder, "I can stamp upon the ground with my foot and empty a lake of its water."

"I have no doubt of that, O Hunder," said Quillow, "for the thunder is your plaything and the mountains are your stool. But the giant who came over the hills and rivers many and many a year ago was a lesser giant than Hunder. He was weak. He fell ill of a curious malady. He was forced to run to the ocean and bathe in the yellow waters, for only the yellow waters in the middle of the sea could cure the giant."

"Rowf," snarled Hunder, picking up another sheep. "That giant was a goose, that giant was a grasshopper. *Hunder* is never sick." The giant smote his chest and then his stomach mighty blows without flinching, to show how strong he was.

"This other giant," said Quillow, "had no ailment of the chest or the stomach or the mouth or the ears or the eyes or the arms or the legs."

"Where else can a giant have an ailment?" demanded Hunder.

Quillow looked dreamily across the green valley toward the town, which was bright in the sun. "In the mind," said Quillow, "for the mind is a strange and intricate thing. In lesser men than Hunder, it is subject to mysterious maladies."

"Wumf," said the giant, beginning his third sheep. "Hunder's mind is strong like the rock." He smote himself heavily across the forehead without wincing.

"No one to this day knows what brought on this dreadful disease in the mind of the other giant," said Quillow. "Perhaps he killed a turtle after sundown, or ran clockwise thrice around a church in the dark of the moon, or slept too close to a field of asphodel."

Hunder picked up the pie and began to devour it. "Did this goose, this grasshopper, have pains in his head?" he asked. "Look, teller of tales!" Hunder banged his head savagely against a tree, and the trunk of the tree snapped in two. The giant grinned, showing his jagged teeth.

"This other giant," said Quillow, "suffered no pain. His symptoms were marvelous and dismaying. First he heard the word. For fifteen minutes one morning, beginning at a quarter of six, he heard the word."

"Harumph!" said Hunder, finishing his pie and reaching for

his chocolate. "What was the word the giant heard for fifteen minutes one day?"

"The word was 'woddly,'" said Quillow. "All words were one word to him. All words were 'woddly.'"

"All words are different to Hunder," said the giant. "And do you call this a tale you have told me? A blithering goose of a giant hears a word and you call that a tale to amuse Hunder?"

Quillow arose as the clock in the steeple struck six and the scarlet figures came out to play the silver bells.

"I hear all words," said Hunder. "This is a good chocolate; otherwise I should put you in the palm of my hand and blow you over the housetops."

"I shall bring you a better tale tomorrow," said Quillow. "Meanwhile, be sure to see the first star over your left shoulder, do not drink facing downstream, and always sleep with your heart to the east."

"Why should Hunder practice this foolish rigmarole?" asked the giant.

"No one knows to this day," said Quillow, "what caused the weird illness in the mind of the other giant." But Hunder gave only a murmurous growl in reply, for he had lain down again on the hillside and closed his eyes. Quillow smiled as he saw that the giant lay with his heart to the east.

The toymaker spent the day making twenty more little blue men and when the first owl hooted he stood in the doorway of his shop and whistled. The hundred children collected in the cobbled street before the toyshop from every nook and corner and cranny and niche of the town. "Go to your homes," said Quillow, "each Sue and John of you, each Nora and Joe, and tell your fathers and mothers to come to the merry-go-round in the carnival grounds one quarter-hour before the moon comes over the hill. Say that Quillow has a plan to destroy the giant Hunder."

The group of children broke like the opening of a rose and the cobbled streets rang with the sound of their running.

Even the scowling blacksmith, the scornful lamplighter, the

mumbling town crier, and the fussy town clerk (who had spent the day searching for an ancient treaty the people of the town had once signed with a giant) came at the appointed hour to hear what Quillow had to say.

"What is this clown's whim that brings us here like sheep?" demanded the blacksmith.

Quillow climbed up on the merry-go-round, sat on a swan, and spoke. At first there was a restless stir like wind in the grass, but as Quillow explained his plan, even the chattering wives fell silent. Quillow finished speaking as the moon peeped over the hill, and the hundred men and the hundred women and the hundred children straggled away from the carnival grounds.

"It will never work," said the lamplighter.

"It is worth trying," said the candymaker.

"I have a better plan," said the town crier. "Let all the women and all the children stand in the streets and gaze sorrowfully at the giant, and perhaps he will go away."

His wife took him by the arm and led him home. "We will try Quillow's plan," she said. "He has a magic, the little man."

The next morning, just as the clock in the steeple struck five, the weary blacksmith, with Quillow sitting beside him, drove the wagon loaded with three sheep and a fresh apple pie and another monster chocolate to where the giant sat on the hillside. Hunder unloaded the wagon in a third of a trice, placed the food beside him on the hill, and began to gnaw at a sheep. "Tell me a tale, smallest of men," he said, "and see to it that I do not nod, or I shall put you in the palm of my hand and blow you through yonder cloud."

"Once upon a time," began Quillow, "there was a king named Anderblusdaferafan, and he had three sons named Ufabrodoborobe, Quamdelrodolanderay, and Tristolcomofarasee."

"Those names are hard names," said Hunder. "Tell me those names again that I may remember them." So Quillow started over slowly with "Once upon a time," and again the giant made him repeat the names.

"Why did this king and his sons have such long and difficult names?" demanded Hunder, eating his second sheep.

"Ah," said Quillow, "it was because of the king's mother, whose name was Isoldasadelofandaloo."

"Tell me her name once more," said Hunder, "that I may remember it." So Quillow told him the name again slowly.

Thus the wily Quillow, who really had thought of no tale to tell, wasted the long minutes as the hands of the clock in the steeple crept around the dial. As they neared a quarter of six o'clock, Quillow went on. "One day as the king and his sons were riding through the magical forest," he said, "they came upon a woddly. Woddly woddly woddly. Woddly woddly woddly."

The giant's eyes grew narrow, then wide.

"Woddly woddly woddly," said Quillow, "woddly woddly woddly woddly."

The giant dropped the chocolate he was eating. "Say it with words!" he bellowed. "You say naught but 'woddly.'"

Quillow looked surprised. "Woddly woddly woddly woddly woddly woddly woddly woddly," he said. "Woddly woddly woddly."

"Can this be the malady come upon me?" cried the giant. He caught the toymaker up in his hand. "Or do you seek to frighten Hunder?" he roared.

"Woddly woddly woddly," said Quillow, trembling in spite of himself, as he pointed to a farmer in a field and to a child gathering cowslips and to the town crier making his rounds. "Woddly woddly woddly," repeated Quillow.

The giant dropped Quillow and arose. He strode to where the farmer stood and picked him up. "Say words!" bawled Hunder. "Say many words!"

"Woddly," said the farmer, and Hunder dropped him in the field and turned to the child.

"What is your name?" roared Hunder.

"Woddly woddly," said the child.

Hunder stepped over to the town crier. "What is the time of day?" he bellowed.

"Woddly woddly," said the town crier.

Then Hunder shouted questions at men and women and children who came running into the streets. He asked them how old they were, and what day it was, and where they were going, and how they were feeling. And they said "Woddly" and "Woddly woddly" and "Woddly woddly woddly."

Hunder strode back across the green valley to where Quillow sat brushing flies off the half-eaten chocolate. "It is the malady! I have heard the word! It is the malady!" cried Hunder. "What am I to do to cure the malady?"

Just then the clock in the steeple struck six, and as the scarlet men came out to play the bells, Quillow spoke reproachfully. "I was telling you how the king and his three sons rode through the magical forest," he said, "when you picked me up and flung me to the earth and ran away, leaving your chocolate uneaten."

The giant sat on the ground, panting heavily, his lower teeth showing. "I heard the word," he said. "All men said the word."

"What word?" asked Quillow.

"Woddly," said the giant.

"That is but the first symptom," said Quillow reassuringly, "and it has passed. Look at the chimneys of the town. Are they not red?"

Hunder looked. "Yes, the chimneys are red," said Hunder. "Why do you ask if the chimneys are red?"

"So long as the chimneys are red," said Quillow, "you have no need to worry, for when the second symptom is upon you, the chimneys of the town turn black."

"I see only red chimneys," said the giant. "But what could have caused Hunder to hear the word?" he asked as he hurled the half-eaten chocolate far away over the roofs of the town.

"Perhaps," said Quillow, "you stepped on a centaur's grave or waked the sleeping unicorn or whistled on Saint Nillin's Day."

Hunder the giant rested badly on the hillside that night, twisting and turning in his sleep, tormented by ominous dreams. While he slept, the youngest and most agile men of the town, in black smocks and slippered feet, climbed to the roofs of the houses and shops, each carrying a full pail and a brush, and painted all the chimneys black.

Quillow, the toymaker, worked busily all night, and by the dark hour before the dawn, had made twenty more blue men so that he now had fifty blue men in all. He put the new ones with the others he had made, in the large chest with the iron clasp.

As the first birds twittered in the trees, the lamplighter and the town crier came into the toyshop. Quillow was repairing a doll for a little girl who was ill. He smiled and bowed to his friends confidently, but the palms of their hands were moist and the roofs of their mouths were dry.

"Perhaps he will detect your trick," said the lamplighter.

"Perhaps he will smash all our houses," said the town crier.

As the three men talked, they heard the giant stirring on the hillside. He rubbed his eyes with his great knuckles, yawned with the sound of a sinking ship, and stretched his powerful arms. The toymaker and the lamplighter and the town crier watched through a window and held their breath.

Hunder sat up, staring at the ground and running his fingers through his hair. Then slowly he lifted his head and looked at the town. He closed his eyes tightly and opened them again and stared. His mouth dropped open and he lurched to his feet. "The chimneys!" he bellowed. "The chimneys are black! The malady is upon me again!"

Quillow began to scamper through the cobbled streets and across the green valley as the giant's eyes rolled and his knees trembled. "Teller of tales, smallest of men!" bellowed Hunder. "Tell me what I must do. The chimneys are black!" Quillow reached the feet of the giant, panting and flushed. "Look, teller of tales," said the giant, "name me fairly the color of yonder chimneys."

Quillow turned and looked toward the town. "The chimneys

are red, O Hunder," he said. "The chimneys are red. See how they outdo the red rays of the sun."

"The rays of the sun are red," said Hunder, "but the chimneys of the town are black."

"You tremble," said Quillow, "and your tongue hangs out, and these are indeed the signs of the second symptom. But still there is no real danger, for you do not see the blue men. Or do you see the blue men, O Hunder?" he asked.

"I see the men of the town standing in the streets and staring at me," said Hunder. "But their faces are white and they wear clothes of many colors. Why do you ask me if I see blue men?"

Quillow put on a look of grave concern. "When you see the blue men," he said, "it is the third and last symptom of the malady. If that should happen, you must rush to the sea and bathe in the yellow waters or your strength will become the strength of a kitten." The giant groaned. "Perhaps if you fast for a day and a night," said Quillow, "the peril will pass."

"I will do as you say, teller of tales," said the giant, "for you are wise beyond the manner of men. Bring me no food today, tell me no tale." And with a moan Hunder sat back upon the hillside and covered his eyes with his hands.

When Quillow returned to the town, the people cheered him softly and the children flung flowers at his feet. But the blacksmith was skeptical. "The giant is still there on the hillside," he said. "I shall save my cheers and my flowers until the day he is gone, if that day shall ever come." And he stalked back to his smithy to help the locksmith make the great brass key for Hunder's front door.

That noon there was enough mutton and pie and chocolate for all the people of the town, and they ate merrily and well.

Hunder the giant fretted and worried so profoundly during the day that he fell quickly to sleep as the night came. It was a night without moon or stars, as Quillow had hoped. A town owl who lived on the roof of the tavern—at the Sign of the Clock and Soldier—was surprised at the soft and shadowy activities of the toymaker. The bat and the firefly hovered about him in wonder as he worked secretly and swiftly in the green valley at the feet of the snoring giant. The squirrel and the nightingale watched like figures in a tapestry as he dug and planted in the woods at the giant's head. If the giant thrashed suddenly in his sleep or groaned, the cricket and the frog fell silent in high anxiety. When Quillow's work was finished and he returned to his shop, the bat and the firefly moved in dreamy circles, the squirrel and the nightingale stirred freely again, and the cricket and the frog began to sing. The owl on the roof of the Clock and Soldier nodded and slept. Quillow lay down on his workbench and closed his eyes.

When the scarlet men played the bells of five o'clock, and the first birds twittered in the trees and the gray light came, Quillow awoke and opened his door. The town crier stood in the cobbled street in front of the shop. "Cry the hour," said Quillow. "Cry all's well."

"Five o'clock!" cried the town crier. "Five o'clock and all's well!"

The people crept out of their houses and on the hillside across the green valley, Hunder the giant stirred and yawned and stretched and rubbed his eyes and sat up. He saw that the chimneys were still black, but he grinned at them and winked. "The malady passes," said Hunder. "I see men with white faces wearing clothes of many colors, but I see no blue men." He flexed the muscles of his powerful arms and he smote himself mighty blows upon his brow and chest and stomach. "Ho, councilors!" roared Hunder, "bring me my sheep and my pie and my chocolate, for I have a vast hunger."

The people fled from the streets, and behind the barred doors and shuttered windows of their houses they listened and trembled. The baker, the butcher, and the candymaker hid under their beds. They had prepared no meal for the giant and they were afraid for their lives. But the brave little toymaker, his white hair flowing like the dandelion clock in the morning wind, ran through the cobbled streets and across the green valley and stood at the giant's feet.

"Behold, I am still a whole man!" bellowed the giant, thumping his brow. "I have heard the word and I have seen the black chimneys, but I have not beheld the blue men."

"That is well," said Quillow, "for he who beholds the blue men must bathe in the yellow waters in the middle of the sea, or else he will dwindle, first to the height of the pussy willow, then to the height of the daffodil, then to the height of the violet, until finally he becomes a small voice in the grass, lost in the thundering of the crickets."

"But *I* shall remain stronger than the rock and taller than the oak," said Hunder, and he clapped his hands together.

"If you are stronger than the rock and taller than the oak," said Quillow, "then stamp on the ground and make yonder cow in the field turn a flip-flop."

Hunder stood up and chortled with glee. "Behold, smallest of men," he said, "I will make the cow turn twice in the air." He brought his right foot down upon the earth sharply and heavily. The cow turned a double flip-flop in the field, Quillow bounced as high as the giant's belt, and great boughs fell from trees. But the giant had no eyes for these familiar wonders. He stared at something new under the sun, new and small and terrible. The blue men had come. The blue men were popping high into the air. They popped up in the valley and they popped up in the woods. They popped up from behind stones and they popped up from behind cowslips. They popped up in front of Hunder and they popped up behind him and under him and all around him.

"The blue men!" cried Hunder. "The blue men have come! The world is filled with little blue men!"

"I see no blue men," said Quillow, "but you have begun to shrink like the brook in dry weather, and that is the sign of the third symptom."

"The sea! The sea! Point me the sea!" bellowed Hunder, who now stood shivering and shaking.

"It is many leagues to the east," said Quillow. "Run quickly toward the rising sun and bathe in the yellow waters in the middle of the sea."

Hunder the giant ran toward the rising sun, and the town trembled as he ran. Pictures fell from walls and plates from plate rails and bricks from chimneys. The birds flew and the rabbits scampered. The cows turned flip-flops in the fields and the brook jumped out of its bed.

A fortnight later a traveler from afar, stopping at the Sign of the Clock and Soldier, told the innkeeper a marvelous tale of how a giant, panting and moaning like a forest on fire, had stumbled down out of the mountains and plunged into the sea, flailing and threshing, and babbling of yellow waters and black chimneys and little blue men; and of how he had floundered farther and farther out to sea until at last he sank beneath the waves, starting a mighty tide rolling to the shore and sending up water spouts as high as the heavens. Then the giant was seen no more, and the troubled waters quieted as the sea resumed its inscrutable cycle of tides under the sun and the moon.

The innkeeper told this tale to the blacksmith, and the blacksmith told it to the locksmith, and the locksmith told it to the baker, and the baker told it to the butcher, and the butcher told it to the tailor, and the tailor told it to the cobbler, and the cobbler told it to the candymaker, and the candymaker told it to the candlemaker, and the candlemaker told it to the town crier, and the town crier told it to the lamplighter, and the lamplighter told it to the toymaker.

As the lamplighter spoke, Quillow put the finishing touches on a new toy, whistling softly, his eyes sparkling. The lamplighter saw that the toy was a tiny replica of Quillow himself.

"What do you do with that?" he asked.

"You put it in the palm of your hand, like this," said Quillow, and he put the figure in the palm of his hand. "And then you blow, like this." He blew, and the miniature Quillow floated slowly through the air and drifted gently to the floor. "I think it will amuse the children," said the little toymaker. "I got the idea from a giant."

THE FUN THEY HAD*

by Isaac Azimov

Margie even wrote about it that night in her diary. On the page headed May 17, 2157, she wrote, "Today Tommy found a real book!"

It was a very old book. Margie's grandfather once said that when he was a little boy *his* grandfather told him that there was a time when all stories were printed on paper.

They turned the pages, which were yellow and crinkly, and it was awfully funny to read words that stood still instead of moving the way they were supposed to—on a screen, you know. And then, when they turned back to the page before, it had the same words on it that it had had when they read it the first time.

"Gee," said Tommy, "what a waste. When you're through with the book, you just throw it away, I guess. Our television screen must have had a million books on it and it's good for plenty more. I wouldn't throw *it* away."

"Same with mine," said Margie. She was eleven and hadn't seen as many telebooks as Tommy had. He was thirteen.

She said, "Where did you find it?"

"In my house." He pointed without looking, because he was busy reading. "In the attic."

* Used by permission from *Young Folks* children's page, copyright by Newspaper Enterprise Association.

"What's it about?"

"School."

Margie was scornful. "School? What's there to write about school? I hate school."

Margie always hated school, but now she hated it more than ever. The mechanical teacher had been giving her test after test in geography and she had been doing worse and worse until her mother had shaken her head sorrowfully and sent for the County Inspector.

He was a round little man with a red face and a whole box of tools with dials and wires. He smiled at Margie and gave her an apple, then took the teacher apart. Margie had hoped he wouldn't know how to put it together again, but he knew how all right, and, after an hour or so, there it was again, large and black and ugly, with a big screen on which all the lessons were shown and the questions were asked. That wasn't so bad. The part Margie hated most was the slot where she had to put homework and test papers. She always had to write them out in a punch code they made her learn when she was six years old, and the mechanical teacher calculated the mark in no time.

The Inspector had smiled after he was finished and patted Margie's head. He said to her mother, "It's not the little girl's fault, Mrs. Jones. I think the geography sector was geared a little too quick. Those things happen sometimes. I've slowed it up to an average ten-year level. Actually, the over-all pattern of her progress is quite satisfactory." And he patted Margie's head again.

Margie was disappointed. She had been hoping they would take the teacher away altogether. They had once taken Tommy's teacher away for nearly a month because the history sector had blanked out completely.

So she said to Tommy, "Why would anyone write about school?"

Tommy looked at her with very superior eyes. "Because it's not our kind of school, stupid. This is the old kind of school that they had hundreds and hundreds of years ago." He added loftily, pronouncing the word carefully, "*Centuries* ago."

Margie was hurt. "Well, I don't know what kind of school they had all that time ago." She read the book over his shoulder for a while, then said, "Anyway, they had a teacher."

"Sure they had a teacher, but it wasn't a *regular* teacher. It was a man."

"A man? How could a man be a teacher?"

"Well, he just told the boys and girls things and gave them homework and asked them questions."

"A man isn't smart enough."

"Sure he is. My father knows as much as my teacher."

"He can't. A man can't know as much as a teacher."

"He knows almost as much, I betcha."

Margie wasn't prepared to dispute that. She said, "I wouldn't want a strange man in my house to teach me."

Tommy screamed with laughter. "You don't know much, Margie. The teachers didn't live in the house. They had a special building and all the kids went there."

"And all the kids learned the same thing?"

"Sure, if they were the same age."

"But my mother says a teacher has to be adjusted to fit the mind of each boy and girl it teaches and that each kid has to be taught differently."

"Just the same they didn't do it that way then. If you don't like it, you don't have to read the book."

"I didn't say I didn't like it," Margie said quickly. She wanted to read about those funny schools.

They weren't even half-finished when Margie's mother called, "Margie! School!"

Margie looked up. "Not yet, Mamma."

"Now!" said Mrs. Jones. "And it's probably time for Tommy, too."

Margie said to Tommy, "Can I read the book some more with you after school?"

"Maybe," he said nonchalantly. He walked away whistling, the dusty old book tucked beneath his arm.

Margie went into the schoolroom. It was right next to her bedroom, and the mechanical teacher was on and waiting for her. It was always on at the same time every day except Saturday and Sunday, because her mother said little girls learned better if they learned at regular hours.

The screen was lit up, and it said: "Today's arithmetic lesson is on the addition of proper fractions. Please insert yesterday's homework in the proper slot."

Margie did so with a sigh. She was thinking about the old schools they had when her grandfather's grandfather was a little boy. All the kids from the whole neighborhood came, laughing and shouting in the schoolyard, sitting together in the schoolroom, going home together at the end of the day. They learned the same things, so they could help one another on the homework and talk about it.

And the teachers were people. . . .

The mechanical teacher was flashing on the screen: "When we add the fractions ½ and ¼——"

Margie was thinking about how the kids must have loved it in the old days. She was thinking about the fun they had.

6 Humor and Tall Tales

We all like a story that makes us laugh. Among the many kinds of laugh-making stories, the "tall tale" has been very popular in this country, although some of the best ones come from abroad. The tall tale produces its funny effect by stretching some feature to make it so far out of proportion that the whole seems ridiculous. It is an exaggeration that is too great to deceive anyone or even to astonish one. The British speak of telling tall tales as "stretching the long bow."

Some of the simplest funny stories are made up of nothing more important than nonsense or of somebody acting silly or of somebody being awkward. Many kinds of funny stories give you a surprise or have an unexpected twist that makes you laugh.

So far as we can tell, human beings are the only living things that can laugh. It is a distinctive and an important thing to be able to see the humor in various kinds of situations—and to be able to laugh at ourselves sometimes.

OSCAR ON ROLLER SKATES

by Mabel Neikirk

"I'm tired of balancing colored balls," said Oscar, the seal, to Mr. Zabriski. "I need a rest."

"Now, Oscar, be reasonable," said Mr. Zabriski. "Here we are giving a show in the theater every afternoon and every evening. We can't disappoint all the people who come to see you act. Tell me, why are you tired of balancing?"

"Because I have to stand so very still while I'm holding things on my nose," Oscar replied. "I'd like to cut loose and swoop and swish this fine weather."

"Oh, now I understand," said Mr. Zabriski. "You don't need a rest; you need exercise. If it were winter, I'd buy you a sled."

"Or skates," said Oscar, mournfully. "But there's no ice."

"Yes," Mr. Zabriski agreed, "skates are fine for swooping." Then his face brightened up. "You've given me an idea! And it's just right for spring. What about roller skates?"

"Roller skates!" cried Oscar. "Do you really mean it?" And without waiting for an answer, he began building air castles. "I'll smoothly slide and glide to dance music," he murmured. "I'll even learn to do tricks on skates. And I'll wear," he planned enthusiastically, "a snappy little knitted cap with a red tassel."

Mr. Zabriski bought the skates that day. He hired a man to change them so that they would fit a seal. And soon Oscar began to spend his mornings practicing on the empty stage, rolling a foot or two, then sitting down unexpectedly, while the other actors laughed and gave advice.

"You should use teamwork, Oscar," said Tommy Thomas, the band leader. "One flipper sets out for the North Pole while the other starts for China. Make up your mind which way you're going and pull yourself together."

"That's what I'm trying to do," said the seal, swaying helplessly. "But I never knew I was so undecided." Then his skates spread even farther apart, and *smack*, he went down, taking another wallop from the floor.

"Clumsy lummox!" snapped a peppery-tongued actress named Mimi Paprica. "Why doesn't he stick to balancing?"

But no one paid any attention to Mimi. She had bad manners and was always grumbling.

Finally Tommy called his band together. "Perhaps a little music will help Oscar get the swing of it," he said. "Strike up a tune, boys. And whenever he falls, pound the drums like all get out. Ready now!" he directed. "One, two! One, two! Down he goes! Bang! Bang! Up he gets! One, two! Down again! Bang! Bang!"

The rhythm did make the skating easier. Even falling down was fun when accompanied by the booming drums. And soon, with Tommy's help, Oscar began to give a very amusing performance. In fact, the other actors enjoyed his practicing so much that Tommy suggested replacing Oscar's balancing act with a skating exhibition.

"All he has to do," Tommy told Mr. Zabriski, "is to go out there before the footlights with that silly cap on and fall down real hard a few times, and the people will laugh their heads off."

"I've been thinking the same thing," said Mr. Zabriski. "But the act is a little short. It needs something more, perhaps a joke or two. Have you any ideas?"

"Have I!" was Tommy's enthusiastic reply. "My head is just buzzing with ideas. You wait and see."

And the next morning Tommy proudly presented a surprise. He handed it to Oscar, saying, "This will add to the fun."

"What fun?" said the seal, rubbing a sore spot. "I ache all over! Go away!"

"Look," Tommy urged. "It's a song that I wrote for your new act. Try humming it."

"So you want me to sing," Oscar groaned. "It isn't enough that my flippers are going places every minute whether I tell them to or not, but now I must wag my tongue at the same time."

"Oh, come on, Oscar," said Tommy. "You know you're really enjoying yourself."

"Well, it's a change from taking baths," Oscar admitted with a grin. "But whoever heard of anybody singing while being spanked. That's not natural."

However, after trying out the song, Oscar agreed that it was well suited to his way of skating. The words were easily learned, and the next afternoon the seal appeared before the large theater audience.

Over one ear he wore the little knitted cap and tied around his middle, for front and rear bumpers, were two fat pillows. While he skated, the orchestra banged out a lively tune, and whenever he hit the floor the drums thundered and the cymbals clashed.

The new act was an immediate success. And after the final curtain, the other players, the acrobats and the magician came rushing to Oscar, offering congratulations. But Mimi Paprica, the song and dance artist, stayed away. She was a jealous person, so Oscar's triumph put her in a bad humor. And later, just before the evening performance, when the trumpet player in Tommy's orchestra was taken ill, Mimi flew into a rage.

"I ask you," she demanded. "How am I going to sing with only half an orchestra?"

Her remark was so unreasonable that Oscar overhearing it said indignantly, "*Well!* The poor fellow couldn't help getting sick! He didn't do it on purpose!"

"He could, too, help it," Mimi pitched into Oscar. "Don't contradict me, you flip-flipping frankfurter!"

After that outburst the stage manager hastened to calm Mimi down. "Oh, Miss Paprica," he called. "It's a full house tonight."

Mimi put her eye to a hole in the curtain and was in a good humor at once. "Why, there's Sandy Campbell in the second row!" she exclaimed. "He's the Scotchman who runs the Sea Breeze Park."

"Do you mean that nice place where they have the merry-go-round and skating rink?" one of the actors asked.

"Uh-huh!" Mimi grunted rudely, adding, "I'll bet Sandy is looking for entertainers."

"Oh, boy!" Oscar spoke up. "I wish he'd give me a job."

"You!" sneered the actress. "What a joke! Mr. Campbell has come to see *my* performance. I am the main attraction here. And I'm going to sing a Scotch song especially for him." Then Mimi remembered the missing trumpet player and started scolding again. "And now," she raged, "the orchestra has begun to fall apart."

Everyone was glad when she flounced off to her dressing room.

"Selfish creature!" Oscar muttered as she disappeared. "If she stubs her toe, she'll blame it on Tommy. I wish I could do something to help him out." And then came an idea. "Why, I *can* help," he whispered. "Now everything will be all right." And he set to work making a change in the stage furniture.

When the curtain rose for Mimi's act, a table stood at one side of the stage. It was covered with a large cloth that hung almost to the floor. And under the table was Oscar, and under Oscar's flipper was his trumpet.

Mimi wore a Scotch costume, and her act began with a dance. As she moved toward the footlights, the orchestra, seated at the back of the stage, struck up a Scotch melody. Under the table, Oscar struck up no melody at all, just a tuneless hubbub of ear-splitting screeches.

Immediately Mimi was thrown out of step. She boiled with fury inside, but outwardly she had to look happy. So she stopped for a moment, nodded pleasantly to Tommy for a new start, and began dancing again. But it was no use. The cat-fight yowls coming from under the table cover drowned out the orchestra, and the actress finally gave up.

"That Tommy Thomas wants to ruin my act," Mimi raged inwardly. "But I'll show him! I'll sing *without* his band!" Then she signaled to the orchestra, and the players laid down their instruments, all except the player under the table who couldn't see what was going on.

Mimi forced a smile onto her face and started her Scotch song. "My Bonnie . . ." she began warbling.

"Peep! Peep!" Oscar began blowing.

"Lies over the ocean," rolled from Mimi's throat.

"Toodle-oo! Toodle-oo! Toodle-oo!" rolled from the throat of the trumpet.

A hasty glance showed Mimi that the orchestra was not playing, so she began to dance about the stage while she sang, hunting the distracting noise.

"My Bonnie lies over the sea," she bellowed, trying to smother the trumpet.

"I'll have to toot louder," the seal decided. And he puffed so violently that the table cover began flapping in the breeze. Then, when Oscar's shiny horn was seen for a moment by the audience, a roar of laughter arose, and some boys in the front row began playing a game with the flustered actress.

When Mimi danced to the far side of the stage they called, "You're cold! You're cold!" and when she danced nearer to Oscar they cried, "You're getting warm!"

Finally Mimi saw the trumpet. She rushed to the table and just as the audience yelled, "You're hot!" she snatched off the cover. But in her wrath Mimi pulled too hard. She lost her balance and down she went on the floor all wrapped up in the table cover.

Cheers and laughter filled the air as Oscar hastened out of his little shelter. Naturally he tried to assist Mimi, but he was still wearing his skates. And no sooner had the actress scrambled to a standing position than Oscar's flippers shot out from under him. He scored a direct hit on Mimi. And again she was laid flat with a *bang!*

Now Mimi wasn't used to tumbling, but she was used to quarreling. So she jumped to her feet and rushed into battle. And having no other weapons, she began hurling words as fast as she could.

"*You sea-going tank! You fur-covered submarine!*" she fired at Oscar.

"Wow!" yelled a man in the audience.

"I only wanted to help," Oscar started to explain.

Mimi's face turned purple. She stamped her foot. "You! You!" she sputtered. And then unable to think of any more names she rushed from the stage, leaving Oscar to bow and wave his cap at the delighted audience.

When the clapping and cheers did not stop, Oscar decided to put on his roller skating act. So he skated and fell down and skated and fell down.

Here is the song that he sang as he tumbled about the stage:

"Oh, I have a pair of wandering feet
They never ever plan to meet.
One starts for the East, one starts for the West,
But I can't decide which way is best.
And how can I follow when I don't know
Whether right or left my skates will go?
So to get anywhere with my heels in the air,
I sit down and slide from here to there."

After the show Sandy Campbell came back stage and offered Oscar a job.

"But I must explain," Mr. Zabriski spoke up. "My seal is only learning to skate. Mostly, he falls."

"That's just fine," said Sandy. "Then all the beginners who are skinning their knees won't get discouraged. They'll laugh at Oscar and keep on trying. He's going to be the star attraction at my skating rink."

HOW THEY BRING BACK THE VILLAGE OF CREAM PUFFS WHEN THE WIND BLOWS IT AWAY

by Carl Sandburg

A Girl named Wing Tip the Spick came to the Village of Liver-and-Onions to visit her uncle and her uncle's uncle on her mother's side and her uncle and her uncle's uncle on her father's side.

It was the first time the four uncles had a chance to see their little relation, their niece. Each of the four uncles was proud of the blue eyes of Wing Tip the Spick.

The two uncles on her mother's side took a long deep look into her blue eyes and said, "Her eyes are so blue, such a clear light blue, they are the same as cornflowers with blue raindrops shining and dancing on silver leaves after a sun shower in any of the summer months."

And the two uncles on her father's side, after taking a long deep look into the eyes of Wing Tip the Spick, said, "Her eyes are so blue, such a clear light shining blue, they are the same as cornflowers with blue raindrops shining and dancing on the silver leaves after a sun shower in any of the summer months."

And though Wing Tip the Spick didn't listen and didn't hear what the uncles said about her blue eyes, she did say to herself when they were not listening, "I know these are sweet uncles and I am going to have a sweet time visiting my relations."

The four uncles said to her, "Will you let us ask you two questions, first the first question and second the second question?"

"I will let you ask me fifty questions this morning, fifty questions tomorrow morning, and fifty questions any morning. I like to listen to questions. They slip in one ear and slip out of the other."

Then the uncles asked her the first question first, "Where do you come from?" and the second question second, "Why do you have two freckles on your chin?"

"Answering your first question first," said Wing Tip the Spick, "I come from the Village of Cream Puffs, a little light village on the upland corn prairie. From a long ways off it looks like a little hat you could wear on the end of your thumb to keep the rain off your thumb."

"Tell us more," said one uncle. "Tell us much," said another uncle. "Tell it without stopping," added another uncle. "Interruptions nix nix," murmured the last of the uncles.

"It is a light little village on the upland corn prairie many miles past the sunset in the west," went on Wing Tip the Spick. "It is light the same as a cream puff is light. It sits all by itself on the big long prairie where the prairie goes up in a slope. There on the slope the winds play around the village. They sing it wind songs, summer wind songs in summer, winter wind songs in winter.

"And sometimes like an accident, the wind gets rough. And when the wind gets rough it picks up the little Village of Cream Puffs and blows it away off in the sky—all by itself."

"O-o-h-h," said one uncle. "Um-m-m-m," said the other three uncles.

"Now the people in the village all understand the winds with their wind songs in summer and winter. And they understand the rough wind who comes sometimes and picks up the village and blows it away off high in the sky all by itself.

"If you go to the public square in the middle of the village you will see a big roundhouse. If you take the top off the roundhouse you will see a big spool with a long string winding up around the spool.

"Now whenever the rough wind comes and picks up the village and blows it away off high in the sky all by itself then the string winds loose off the spool, because the village is fastened to the string. So the rough wind blows and blows and the string on the spool winds looser and looser the farther the village goes blowing away off into the sky all by itself.

"Then at last when the rough wind, so forgetful, so careless, has had all the fun it wants, then the people of the village all come together and begin to wind up the spool and bring back the village where it was before."

"O-o-h-h," said one uncle. "Um-m-m-m," said the other three uncles.

"And sometime when you come to the village to see your little relation, your niece who has four such sweet uncles, maybe she will lead you through the middle of the city to the public square and show you the roundhouse. They call it the Roundhouse of the Big Spool. And they are proud because it was thought up and is there to show when visitors come."

"And now will you answer the second question second—why do you have two freckles on your chin?" interrupted the uncle who had said before, "Interruptions nix nix."

"The freckles are put on," answered Wing Tip the Spick. "When a girl goes away from the Village of Cream Puffs her mother puts on two freckles, on the chin. Each freckle must be the same as a little burnt cream puff kept in the oven too long."

"Oh-h-h-h," said one uncle. "Um-m-m-m," said the other three uncles. And they talked among each other afterward, the four uncles by themselves, saying:

"She has a gift. It is her eyes. They are so blue, such a clear light blue, the same as cornflowers with blue raindrops shining and dancing on silver leaves after a sun shower in any of the summer months."

At the same time Wing Tip the Spick was saying to herself, "I know for sure now these are sweet uncles and I am going to have a sweet time visiting my relations."

JOHNNIE INKSLINGER AND HIS MAGIC PEN

by Dell J. McCormick

One day a visitor asked Paul Bunyan how many men were in camp. Paul didn't know. There was Hot Biscuit Slim and his two hundred cooks. Ole the Big Swede, Blackie, Tiny Tim, and hundreds more.

Paul tried to count them one day at dinner, but they kept coming and going for hours. He asked Cream Puff Fatty how many desserts he had made. "Eight thousand," said Cream Puff Fatty.

"Good!" said Paul. "Then we must have eight thousand men."

"No," said Cream Puff Fatty, "because some of the men don't eat desserts, and Ole the Big Swede eats seven, except when it is strawberry shortcake. Then he eats ten."

So Paul gave up even trying to count the men and sent for Johnnie Inkslinger to do the arithmetic for the camp. Johnnie Inkslinger was the best bookkeeper in the North Woods—a tall sad-looking man with a bald head. He always wore a large pair of eyeglasses perched at the end of his long, thin nose.

He added and subtracted and multiplied endless rows of figures day and night. He became the fastest bookkeeper in the world and never made a mistake. One night he counted all the stars in the sky and never missed one. Johnnie Inkslinger kept track of everything, even down to the last ear of corn in the kitchens.

His magic pen never ran out of ink. A long rubber hose connected it to a ten-gallon barrel of ink, and that is how the fountain pen was invented. Johnnie Inkslinger wrote so fast that the barrel of ink had to be filled every two days.

"You are using too much ink," said Paul one day. "We cannot buy it fast enough." So Johnnie Inkslinger thought of a plan. He quit dotting his "i's" and crossing his "t's" and from then on saved nine gallons of ink a week.

Johnnie Inkslinger invented new ways of adding and subtracting that are used to this day. He wrote every number down twice so as not to make a single mistake.

He also invented the mistake eraser. This was a large rubber sponge to be rubbed over a page of figures. It erased only the mistakes and left all the rest of the figures as they were. Johnnie finally had no use for it as he made no mistakes. He gave it to Hot Biscuit Slim.

Hot Biscuit Slim used it for a while, but he never liked it. The magic sponge erased almost every figure he made. He gave it to Ole the Big Swede. Ole tried it just once and it erased the whole sheet of paper until there was only a blank space where all the figures had been. It seems Ole was very poor at arithmetic, and no matter how many times he added two and two it always came out six.

Johnnie Inkslinger once tried to figure out how much it cost to feed Babe the Blue Ox, but he finally had to give it up. Every time he added up the figures he found that Babe had eaten another barnful of hay. Then he would have to start all over again. This made him so angry that he told Paul he would quit doing arithmetic forever. Nevertheless, Johnnie Inkslinger remained with Paul during all his years of adventure in the woods.

HOW PAT GOT GOOD SENSE

by Charles J. Finger

Pat was a lad who was always ready to laugh, even at himself, and he was willing to lend a hand when any one asked him. The only trouble with him was that while he could put two and two together as well as the next, he often put them together at the wrong time. For instance, see how it was when he went to work for Farmer O'Grady.

"Take the dog," says the farmer, "and gather the sheep on yon hillside and put them through the gate into the meadow beyond."

"Sure, I'll do it and just as you say," answered Pat.

So Pat took a rope and tied it to the dog's neck and went dragging the dog after him, the dog mighty annoyed, too. Indeed, never was a better sheep dog, but there he was at the end of a rope being dragged up hill and down, with the lad at the other end of the rope, shouting at the sheep and taking an hour to do what the dog could do in five minutes.

Pat, with the dog still on the rope, was taking a drink at the pump when O'Grady came up.

"A fine to-do," says O'Grady, "all that leg work for nothing."

"'Twas the dog that made most of the trouble," says Pat.

"Trouble, indeed," says O'Grady. "By the Great Horn Spoon, it's you who made the trouble, dragging a good dog at the rope's end when a word would have sent the dog to do the job for you."

"Didn't you say, 'Take the dog?'" answered Pat. "And how could I take it and send it, too?"

"You're right there," said O'Grady. "However, it's as well to remember that four legs can travel faster than two."

"I'll remember and thank you kindly," says Pat.

"There's nothing much to do till meal time except odd jobs, so you may as well amuse yourself doing them," says O'Grady.

So Pat did nothing much except pull weeds, carry wood and water to the house, clean the pig pen, gather peat, sweep the chicken house, dig potatoes, tidy the barn loft, run messages for the housewife and do what Betty the maid told him. So the time passed quickly, and Pat had an appetite and was ready for the noon meal when O'Grady came up.

"There's nothing like exercise before meals," says the farmer. "Do you, while you're waiting for dinner, run into the village and bring out a table the carpenter has made by my order."

"With all the good will in the world," says Pat and off he went at a lively trot down the dusty road. The carpenter was just going to his dinner when he arrived, but there was the table ready. So, in a couple of minutes Pat was on his way to the farm with the table on his back, and a clumsy load it was. After a mile Pat sat down to rest in the shade of a big tree. Then it was that an idea struck him.

"Why," says he, "the table's got four legs, and what did Mister O'Grady tell me but that a thing with four legs could travel faster than two legs. So we'll see how that works out."

With that off went Pat at a good clip, hungry for his dinner, and got to the farm house just when Betty was clearing away the dinner things.

"And where's the table?" asked O'Grady.

"It's on the road and will soon be here," answered Pat, then told how things were.

"Ochone!" says O'Grady when he heard the story. "Was there ever such a fellow! What I had in mind when I spoke about a thing with four legs was a dog, or a horse, or a rabbit. Well, what you don't have in your head, you'll have to have in your heels. So back you go and bring the table home, and next time put two and two together. You should have hitched the horse to the cart and carried the table that way."

"Thank you," said Pat. "I'll remember next time. But how about dinner?"

"Hunger is the best sauce," says O'Grady. "When you get back you'll have a fine appetite."

So off went Pat, found the table where he had left it, carried it to the farm, sat down to the scraps of dinner that were left, and played a very good knife and fork, as the saying is. But no sooner had he finished than Betty the maid came running.

"There's never a match in the house," says she. "Do you, like a good lad, run to the village and bring a box."

"Nothing could please me better than pleasing you," says he, and off he went to the stable where he put harness on the horse, put the horse in the shafts, and drove to the village, as happy a lad as ever whistled a tune. Then he put the box of matches in the cart and drove back singing merrily, picking up a beggar man on the road.

"And, now, what's this. What's this?" asked O'Grady when he saw Pat drive up with the beggar man and the matches.

"Didn't you tell me to take the horse and cart?" answered Pat.

"And what's your pocket for?" asked O'Grady.

"I see. I see," said Pat. "I'll do it next time."

"You'll get sense knocked into your head some day," says O'Grady. "In the meanwhile get busy."

So Pat turned the hay, fed the pigs, tended a sick cow, chopped down and chopped up a dead oak, dug a ditch at the pigsty and was wondering when all the odd jobs would be done when Betty came.

"Run like a good lad," says she, "over to Farmer Murphy's place. Tell him to let us have a pint of honey and be quick about it."

Off went Pat and found Farmer Murphy sitting in the shade. When Pat had told his message, Farmer Murphy said, "Go, Pat, to the milk house and take what you need."

Now, what with butter, milk, cheese and apples, Pat found the milk house a good place to be in. So he drank his fill of milk, ate a slice of cheese, munched a couple of apples, and then found the honey.

"'Tis a good man who tells me to take what I need," said Pat. "And lucky a lad am I to have a pocket for the honey as Farmer O'Grady told me." With that he poured the honey into his trouser pocket and turned his face farmwards, as happy a lad as ever whistled a tune. But a terrible pother there was when he got to the kitchen door with nothing to show but a wet and sticky pocket. And when the farmer's wife saw how matters were, she set up a scream that brought Farmer O'Grady.

"Now, I begin to believe that if you had a staircase in front of you, you'd look for a rope to go down it," said he. "Anyway, 'tis a long road that has no turn, and you'll get sense knocked into you some day. Why didn't you take a jar and put the honey in that? You ought to have thought that honey runs when you pour it, so a jar would be better than your pocket to carry it home."

"True enough," said Pat. "I'll think of that next time."

So the farmer went one way and Pat another, and Pat's job was working round the house, piling firewood and peat, cleaning out the rain barrel, splitting kindling wood, cleaning out the attic and, also, cleaning out the dog house. While he was doing the last, Betty came and said, "Now, Pat, never was there a better working lad than you."

"Thank you kindly," says Pat, "but too much praise is a burden. What is it you want me to do now?"

"Why," says she, "there's a puppy over at O'Brien's which was promised me. Do you run over and get it."

"If 'twould please you, 'twould delight me," says Pat.

"If you hurry you'll be back by pudding time," says she.

Off went Pat and when he was at the O'Brien place he found the farmer unloading hay from his wagon.

When Pat told his message, Farmer O'Brien pointed to the dog house, told Pat to help himself, then drove away to the stable.

"Now," says Pat, "let me do the errand right. It's got four legs but I can't tell it to go where it ought to go because I can't tell it the way. I can't carry it in the wagon because there's never a wagon here. I can't put it in my pocket because never a pocket have I that is large enough. But it can run, and, sure enough, Farmer O'Grady says, says he, 'When anything runs, put it in a jar.' "

So Pat found a jar, put the pup in it, clapped on the top and went his way singing and whistling.

And "O, whirra! whirra! what shall I do with a dead dog," cried Betty when she found the puppy in the jar, dead as could be.

"Send the lad about his business and tell him never to show his face here again," said the housewife. "Such a fellow would try to lock a door with a boiled carrot," she went on, her voice getting higher and higher, and her face redder and redder. "He's silly enough to try to carry water in a basket."

"Well, wife, the wisest are not always wise," said the farmer. "What you should have done, Pat, was to tie a string to it and lead it saying, 'Come on, little fellow. Come on.'"

"There's a lot to learn in the world and I thank you," said Pat.

"You'll get sense knocked into your head some day," said the farmer.

So Pat went to work again on this and that, going down into the well to get a bucket that had been dropped, carrying stones to mend a hole in the road, driving a pig out of the turnip patch, trimming a hedge, clearing a nettle patch out of the garden, cutting down briars from behind the cow-house and driving up the cows to be milked.

It was while Pat was milking the cows that Betty came and said, "Do you, Pat, run over the hill to the O'Leary place, and bring back a shin of beef to make soup for tomorrow."

"Nothing would please me better," said Pat and off he went.

"Go and cut what you need," said O'Leary when Pat had told his tale. And a fine joint of beef it was that Pat cut, sure enough. To the shank of it he tied Mrs. O'Leary's clothesline, then went off down the road, singing and whistling, dragging the leg of beef and saying, in a kind voice, "Come on, little fellow. Come on."

And hearing the call, Connolly's big dog came sniffing after the meat and began to make a running feast of it. And Parnell's hound came too, and MacManus's yellow dog, and O'Connor's white dog. Then other dogs came until a pack of them were following, and still more came as Pat cried, "Come on, little fellow. Come on."

There were ten of them, then a dozen, then a score, and a fine time they had, yelping, biting, barking, snatching at the meat and tearing off great pieces, stealing one from another and going back to get more. There were terriers, bull dogs, hounds; dogs with short legs and dogs with long ones; dogs that were good for sheep and dogs that were good for nothing; pet dogs and dogs that nobody liked; dogs with curly hair and dogs with straight hair and dogs with no hair at all; and every dog had an appetite.

So there was a terrible to-do when Pat and four dozen dogs got to the farm and nothing was left of the beef but a bone. The farmer's wife was all for sending Pat about his business then and there.

"I tell you he's a fool," says she.

"Well, he isn't all that he might be," said the farmer. "Come to that, neither is anyone of us. Still, he lends a willing hand."

"Sure, there's none without a fault," says Betty, "and while the two of you are talking about him, he might as well run down to the village and get a bag of sugar."

"And you don't need the horse and cart," says the farmer.

"And you don't pour it in your pocket," added Betty. "You carry the sack on your shoulder."

"And you don't let the wild creatures eat up what you ought to eat yourself, like you did with the beef," said the patient O'Grady.

"Sure, and I never make the same mistake twice," said Pat, and off he went. And a fine lad he looked, too, on his way back with the sack of sugar on his shoulder. Whistling and singing, he was, and thinking it a very good world, indeed, since it was as free for a fly as for an eagle. It was while thinking that very thing that he saw how flies by the hundreds were on the sugar sack, and that the sugar was trickling out of a hole. Just then he was passing the school with the children coming out to go home.

"Pat," cried one and the other, "the sugar is leaking out."

"Why, so it is," said Pat. "And there's flies helping themselves, sure enough. And didn't Mister O'Grady tell me that the wild creatures should never eat what I ought to eat, myself?"

With that Pat sat down, helped himself to the sugar, called on the young children to help themselves, and very soon nothing was left but an empty sack.

"Well," says Pat, "at any rate it's all the easier to carry, so I'll get back all the sooner."

Now, to this very day in County Meath they tell of the scolding that Mister O'Grady gave Pat when he got back with the empty sack. The farmer said things that were bad enough, then others that were worse, while Pat sat and listened, so that at last Farmer O'Grady had nothing more to say and felt sorry that he had said so much, and still more sorry for Pat. So, after all that scolding and ranting, and all those hard words, Pat says, easy like, "And what would you have done, sir?"

"What I always do when I see a fly," answered O'Grady.

"And what's that?" asked Pat. "There's one on my head this very moment."

"I always hit it," says O'Grady.

"Then do so," says Pat as he thrust his head forward.

"With all the good will in the world," says O'Grady. With that he gave Pat a clout on the side of the head that killed the fly and made the lad see stars. And, they say, it knocked sense into his head at the same moment.

JUAN CIGARRON

Which means, in English, Johnny Cigar

by Ruth Sawyer

Once there was a poor couple who had many children.

The eldest was a clever rascal, always plaguing the younger ones, always turning a trick to benefit himself. At last when the thirteenth child was born, the father said to the eldest, "Juan Cigarron, you are a clever rascal. You can do your own whistling. Go and seek your fortune. There is no longer enough in the house to eat."

So into God's world went Juan Cigarron. As he followed this road and that, he said to himself, "I am such a good rascal, I will make a better wizard." So he served as an apprentice to all the wizards in Spain until he could beat them all at their game. He bore himself like one who consorted with magic. He fooled the world to perfection. Everybody believed in him because everybody wanted to believe in him; and so he became famous.

Now, it happened one day in the King's palace that all the silver plate disappeared. One day it was there and the King was eating from it, just as he had eaten from it every day. The next day, the silver was gone—plates, goblets, trenchers, and tankards—as if the earth had swallowed them.

"Send for Juan Cigarron," said the King. "I have heard that he is the greatest wizard in Spain. I believe that he may be the greatest rascal. We will try him."

So a messenger was sent and Juan Cigarron was brought to the palace, straight to the hall where the King sat eating from a common clay dish.

"The royal silver is gone—stolen. You are to discover it, and who stole it," said the King. "But you will make your discovery locked in the deepest dungeon in the palace. Being a great wizard you can manage there as well as anywhere else to find it. If you should turn out to be a cheating rascal instead of a wizard, we will have you there safe, hide and hair, to hand as a fine example. Three days you shall have to find the royal silver."

The guards led Juan Cigarron to the dungeon. They fastened an iron ball and chain to his feet. They locked him in with a key as large as his thigh bone. They left him alone all day that he might better practice his magic, and all day his heart grew heavier.

"I am well caught," thought Juan Cigarron to himself. "There never was a wizard who died comfortably in his bed. Already, I feel a hempen collar about my throat. Ah, me!"

At the end of the day there came one of the King's pages to bring him food. In despair Juan Cigarron watched the jailor unlock the door for him to enter. He watched the page place the food on the bench before him, and watched him turn away. All the time he was thinking, "I have paid dearly for my whistle.

Three days of life granted me—no more, no less—and already one is completed." And he groaned aloud as the jailor unlocked the door for the page to go his way.

"Ay, by San Bruno, this is no fun;
Of the three—there goes one!"

Whereupon, hearing those words, the page took to his heels and ran as if the devil himself were after him. Finding the King's two other pages waiting for him in a corner of the palace wall, he told them breathlessly what Juan Cigarron had said. "Not a doubt of it. He is the greatest wizard on earth. He knows we three have stolen the silver and buried it in the graveyard. We are wholly undone. Let us go to him and confess."

"Never," said one of the others. "You are a weakling. Your ears did not hear right. Tomorrow I will carry his supper to him and then we shall see."

At the end of the second day the heart of Juan Cigarron had become as heavy as the irons on his feet. With what agony did he watch the second page enter his dungeon, leave his food, and depart. Counting off another day of life he groaned aloud:

"Now by San José, honest and true,
Of the three—I've counted two."

If one devil had been at the heels of the first page, a score were hounding the second. "He knows—he knows!" he screamed to the two waiting for him. "We are lost."

"Not yet," said the third and oldest page. "We wait. I myself will carry his supper tomorrow night. I shall not run from the cell. I shall stand beside him and mark his words with care."

At the end of the third day, so tightly could he feel the rope drawn about his neck, Juan Cigarron could not eat his supper for choking. Looking up from his bench and seeing the third page still at his elbow he thought—"Here is a lad who feels pity for me." And aloud he said:

"Good San Andras, counsel me.
They've come and gone—all three!"

The page threw himself at the jailed feet of Juan Cigarron. He groveled there. "Master wizard, pity us! Have compassion. Do not tell the King that it is his three pages who have stolen the silver. We will have our necks wrung tomorrow like so many cockerels if you do. Spare us and we will tell you where it lies buried and never, never again, will we commit such an indiscretion."

With great dignity Juan Cigarron rose to his feet. "Do you know that young rascals have a way of turning into old rascals. How do I know that by saving your necks now I shall not be sending you to purgatory later with more sins to atone for! Enough groveling. I will pardon you this time. But you must swear by all the saints never to steal again—not so much as an *ochavito*. Tomorrow when I appear before the King, bring the silver in secret to the dungeon here, every last piece of it."

So on the morrow Juan Cigarron was not hung. He told the King where the silver plate would be found; and there it was, sure enough. The king was more pleased than nothing. He embraced Juan Cigarron and kissed him on both cheeks.

"I did you a great wrong, but I will make restitution. From now on you shall be, not a wizard to all the world, but my own particular, royal wizard. You shall live with me always, in the palace, where you will be handy to turn a trick of magic when the occasion arises. You are great . . . stupendous . . . magnificent . . . more magnificent than all the wizards," and he embraced him again.

So Juan Cigarron lived in the palace, eating with the King, sleeping in his antechamber, going where the King went; and growing thinner and paler and more dejected every day. "What will I do when the next calamity falls. Ah me!" groaned Juan Cigarron, as each new hour in the day struck.

At last there came an evening when the King happened to be walking alone in his garden. He was smoking and thinking that it was time Juan Cigarron should have his wits and his magic put to the test again. Thinking to practice a clever trick on him, the King took from his mouth the cigar and from his pocket his wallet.

Into the wallet he stuffed his cigar; and back into his pocket went both of them. Then he sent a page for the wizard.

When Juan Cigarron stood before him, the King put him this question: "What did I have in my mind that I took out of my mouth and put for safe keeping in my wallet?" Meaning that he had been thinking of Cigarron, smoking cigarron and had put cigarron in his pocket.

But Juan Cigarron was in terror of his life. Here was the moment of his doom descending upon him. Hardly knowing that he spoke he muttered, more to himself than to the King:

"What a fool is man to pretend—
Poor Juan Cigarron has met a bad end!"

How the King did laugh at that. He clapped his hand to his pocket, drew out the wallet and showed the cigar snuffed out, quite dead. Casting it from him, he embraced Juan Cigarron for a third time and said, "That was as clever an answer as ever I heard. I will grant for that, any wish that is yours to make."

"Any wish?" asked Juan Cigarron.

"Any wish," confirmed the King.

"Then I wish to end my days as a wizard tonight—and begin them tomorrow as a simple man."

THE LADY WHO PUT SALT IN HER COFFEE

by Lucretia P. Hale

This was Mrs. Peterkin. It was a mistake. She had poured out a delicious cup of coffee, and, just as she was helping herself to cream, she found she had put in salt instead of sugar! It tasted bad. What should she do? Of course she couldn't drink the coffee; so she called in the family, for she was sitting at a late breakfast all alone. The family came in; they all tasted, and looked, and wondered what should be done, and all sat down to think.

At last Agamemnon, who had been to college, said, "Why don't we go over and ask the advice of the chemist?" (For the chemist lived over the way, and was a very wise man.)

Mrs. Peterkin said, "Yes," and Mr. Peterkin said, "Very well," and all the children said they would go too. So the little boys put on their india-rubber boots, and over they went.

Now the chemist was just trying to find out something which should turn everything it touched into gold; and he had a large glass bottle into which he put all kinds of gold and silver, and many other valuable things, and melted them all up over the fire, till he had almost found what he wanted. He could turn things into almost gold. But just now he had used up all the gold that he had round the house, and gold was high. He had used up his wife's gold thimble and his great-grandfather's gold-bowed spectacles; and he had melted up the gold head of his great-great-grandfather's cane; and, just as the Peterkin family came in, he was down on his knees before his wife, asking her to let him have her wedding-ring to melt up with all the rest, because this time he knew he should succeed, and should be able to turn everything into gold; and then she could have a new wedding-ring of diamonds, all set in emeralds and rubies and topazes, and all the furniture could be turned into the finest of gold.

Now his wife was just consenting when the Peterkin family burst in. You can imagine how mad the chemist was! He came near throwing his crucible—that was the name of his melting-pot—at their heads. But he didn't. He listened as calmly as he could to the story of how Mrs. Peterkin had put salt in her coffee.

At first he said he couldn't do anything about it; but when Agamemnon said they would pay in gold if he would only go, he packed up his bottles in a leather case, and went back with them all.

First he looked at the coffee, and then stirred it. Then he put in a little chlorate of potassium, and the family tried it all round; but it tasted no better. Then he stirred in a little bichlorate of magnesia. But Mrs. Peterkin didn't like that. Then he added some tartaric acid and some hypersulphate of lime. But no; it was no better. "I have it!" exclaimed the chemist,—"a little ammonia is just the thing!" No, it wasn't the thing at all.

Then he tried, each in turn, some oxalic, cyanic, acetic, phosphoric, chloric, hyperchloric, sulphuric, boracic, silicic, nitric, formic, nitrous nitric, and carbonic acids. Mrs. Peterkin tasted each and said the flavor was pleasant, but not precisely that of coffee. So then he tried a little calcium, aluminum, barium, and strontium, a little clear bitumen, and a half of a third of a sixteenth of a grain of arsenic. This gave rather a pretty color; but still Mrs. Peterkin ungratefully said it tasted of anything but coffee. The chemist was not discouraged. He put in a little belladonna and atropine, some granulated hydrogen, some potash, and a very little antimony, finishing off with a little pure carbon. But still Mrs. Peterkin was not satisfied.

The chemist said that all he had done ought to have taken out the salt. The theory remained the same, although the experiment had failed. Perhaps a little starch would have some effect. If not, that was all the time he could give. He should like to be paid, and go. They were all much obliged to him, and willing to give him $1.37½ in gold. Gold was now 2.69¾, so Mr. Peterkin found in the newspaper. This gave Agamemnon a pretty little sum. He sat himself down to do it. But there was the coffee! All sat and thought awhile, till Elizabeth Eliza said, "Why don't we go to the herb-woman?" Elizabeth Eliza was the only daughter. She was named after her two aunts,—Elizabeth, from the sister of her father; Eliza, from her mother's sister. Now, the herb-woman was an old woman who came round to sell herbs, and knew a great deal. They all shouted with joy at the idea of asking her, and Solomon John and the younger children agreed to go and find her too. The herb-woman lived down at the very end of the street; so the boys put on their india-rubber boots again, and they set off. It was a long walk through the village, but they came at last to the herb-woman's house, at the foot of a high hill. They went through her little garden. Here she had marigolds and hollyhocks, and old maids and tall sunflowers, and all kinds of sweet-smelling herbs, so that the air was full of tansy-tea and elder-blow. Over the porch grew a hop-vine, and a brandy-cherry tree shaded the door, and a luxuriant cranberry-vine flung its delicious fruit across the window. They went into a small parlor, which smelt very spicy. All around hung little bags full of catnip, and peppermint, and all kinds of herbs; and dried stalks hung from the ceiling; and on the shelves were jars of rhubarb, senna, manna, and the like.

But there was no little old woman. She had gone up into the woods to get some more wild herbs, so they all thought they would follow her,—Elizabeth Eliza, Solomon John, and the little boys. They had to climb up over high rocks, and in among huckleberry-bushes and blackberry vines. But the little boys had their india-rubber boots. At last they discovered the little old woman. They knew her by her hat. It was steeple-crowned without any vane. They saw her digging with her trowel round a sassafras bush. They told her their story,—how their mother had put salt in her coffee, and how the chemist had made it worse instead of better, and how their mother couldn't drink it, and wouldn't she come and see what she could do? And she said she would, and took up her little old apron, with pockets all round, all filled with everlasting and pennyroyal, and went back to her house.

There she stopped, and stuffed her huge pockets with some of all the kinds of herbs. She took some tansy and peppermint, and caraway-seed and dill, spearmint and cloves, pennyroyal and sweet marjoram, basil and rosemary, wild thyme and some of the other time,—such as you have in clocks,—sappermint and oppermint, catnip, valerian, and hop; indeed, there isn't a kind of herb you can think of that the little old woman didn't have done up in her little paper bags, that had all been dried in her little Dutch-oven. She packed these all up, and then went back with the children, taking her stick.

Meanwhile Mrs. Peterkin was getting quite impatient for her coffee.

As soon as the little old woman came she had it set over the fire, and began to stir in the different herbs. First she put in a little hop for the bitter. Mrs. Peterkin said it tasted like hop-tea, and not at all like coffee. Then she tried a little flagroot and snake-root, then some spruce gum, and some caraway and some dill, some rue and rosemary, some sweet marjoram and sour, some oppermint and sappermint, a little spearmint and peppermint, some wild thyme, and some of the other tame time, some tansy and basil, and catnip and valerian, and sassafras, ginger, and pennyroyal. The children tasted after each mixture, but made up dreadful faces. Mrs. Peterkin tasted, and did the same. The more the old woman stirred, and the more she put in, the worse it all seemed to taste.

So the old woman shook her head, and muttered a few words, and said she must go. She believed the coffee was bewitched. She bundled up her packets of herbs, and took her trowel, and her basket, and her stick, and went back to her root of sassafras, that she had left half in the air and half out. And all she would take for pay was five cents in currency.

Then the family were in despair, and all sat and thought a great while. It was growing late in the day, and Mrs. Peterkin hadn't had her cup of coffee. At last Elizabeth Eliza said, "They say that the lady from Philadelphia, who is staying in town, is very wise. Suppose I go and ask her what is best to be done." To this they all agreed, it was a great thought, and off Elizabeth Eliza went.

She told the lady from Philadelphia the whole story,—how her mother had put salt in the coffee; how the chemist had been called in; how he tried everything but could make it no better; and how they went for the little old herb-woman, and how she had tried in vain, for her mother couldn't drink the coffee. The lady from Philadelphia listened very attentively, and then said,

"Why doesn't your mother make a fresh cup of coffee?" Elizabeth Eliza started with surprise. Solomon John shouted with joy; so did Agamemnon, who had just finished his sum; so did the little boys, who had followed on. "Why didn't we think of that?" said Elizabeth Eliza; and they all went back to their mother, and she had her cup of coffee.

AGAINST THE WIND*

FROM MIGUEL DE CERVANTES

by Leighton Barrett

Those seasoned adventurers, Don Quixote and Rosinante, clattered out of town, one dark and windy night. Close behind them, Sancho Panza rode like a patriarch on his little donkey Dapple, who was the delight of his lazy short legs.

Fastened to Sancho's saddle was a wallet of the largest size. It held not only money for their journey, but also lint, ointment, bread, cheese, and clean shirts. Sancho favored more victuals and less laundry, but he consoled himself with the thought that his island would be brimful of all good things to eat.

At the first glimmer of daylight, he noticed that instead of going anywhere in particular they were wandering wherever Rosinante's fancy happened to stray. Sancho knew very little about islands, but he was sure Rosinante was not a good guide to them. "Sir!" He jogged Don Quixote's elbow until it clanked, "Do you see any islands in the mist?"

* Reprinted from *The Adventures of Don Quixote*, adapted by Leighton Barrett, by permission of Alfred A. Knopf, Inc. Copyright, 1939, by Warren Chappell.

Aroused so suddenly from his knightly meditations, Don Quixote saw not islands but enemies all about him. "Sancho," he cried, "our fortune is better than we could wish. We'll get enormous booty when I overthrow those huge giants ahead of us."

"What giants?" Sancho stopped in his tracks.

Don Quixote pointed with no uncertain finger. "See their long arms stretched to bar our path? I've read that giants can reach out and catch people two leagues away."

"Then we're much too close." Sancho made himself small on Dapple's back and peeped between the donkey's upstanding ears. "It seems to me," he said cautiously, "that those things you're pointing at are windmills. They can't do us any harm."

"You know very little about giants to be mistaking them for windmills." Don Quixote gathered up the slack of his reins. "I tell you they are giants, and if you are afraid, go say your prayers. I'll ride them down alone."

Which he set out to do, with Sancho bawling after him, "Windmills! Lord look out for him. What's he up to now?"

"Stand your ground, cowardly giants," Don Quixote shouted. "I'm only one knight, anxious to engage all of you in unequal combat."

Just then the wind freshened, and Don Quixote thought his enemies were threatening him with their long arms. Leveling his lance at the first of them, he thundered his watchword, "Dulcinea," and charged full tilt.

"Windmill!" Sancho couldn't see it any other way.

Strangely enough, Sancho was perfectly right. The wind blew strong and the turning mill broke Don Quixote's lance to splinters. Rosinante took a glancing blow on the shoulder, and down he toppled. As for Don Quixote, he executed the most spectacular maneuvers. Whirling sails caught him up and cartwheeled him across the field.

"I told you they couldn't do us any harm," Sancho gasped, "but how was I to know you'd go frolicking with them?"

Don Quixote opened his helmet and took a reproachful look

at the world around him. "Fortune of war," he sadly proclaimed. "Black magic, in fact. Probably a trick of that same necromancer who turned my good books into smoke."

Sancho didn't know enough about magic to argue the point. He hove Rosinante upright again, and helped Don Quixote back in the saddle, asking him how they were to mend the shattered lance.

Don Quixote recalled what other knights used to do in such a fix. "They tore up whole trees by the roots," he said. "Remind me to do the same when we come to the first large oak."

Before Don Quixote found a tree large enough to satisfy him, the sun was hot overhead. He managed with Sancho's help, not exactly to uproot the oak, but to break off a reasonably straight branch of it as a shaft for his lance head.

Sancho was thinking more of carving knives than of lances. "It's dinnertime," he announced. "We mustn't forget to eat. We mustn't forget to drink, either."

Don Quixote said he had no appetite.

"What a terrible sign." Sancho wondered how such a thing was possible. "Why, you must be nearly dead, but you're so quiet that I never would have suspected it."

"I can't tell you how much I ache," said Don Quixote, "because it's against all the rules of knighthood to complain of any bruise."

"I hope it's not against the rules of squirehood," Sancho bothered. "I groan easy, and I love to complain at the slightest scratch."

"Complain then, even before you are hurt," Don Quixote gave him leave.

For the life of him, Sancho Panza could think of nothing at all to complain about, as he trotted behind the lean knight. With one hand dipping into the overstuffed wallet, and the other one busy lifting the bottle, he munched and he swigged until his little donkey found him heavy indeed.

FATHER TEACHES ME TO BE PROMPT*

by Clarence Day

Father made a great point of our getting down to breakfast on time. I meant to be prompt, but it never occurred to me that I had better try to be early. My idea was to slide into the room at the last moment. Consequently, I often was late.

My brothers were often late, too, with the exception of George. He was the only thoroughly reliable son Father had. George got down so early, Father pointed out to me, that he even had time to practice a few minutes on the piano.

The reason George was so prompt was that he was in a hurry to see the sporting page before Father got hold of the newspaper, and the reason he then played the piano was to signal to the rest of us, as we dressed, which team had won yesterday's ball game. He had made up a code for this purpose, and we leaned over the banisters, pulling on our stockings and shoes, to hear him announce the results. I don't remember now what the titles were of the airs he selected, but the general idea was if he played a gay, lively air it meant that the Giants had won, and when the strains of a dirge of lament floated up to us, it meant that Pop Anson had beaten them.

As Father didn't approve of professional baseball, we said nothing to him about this arrangement. He led his life and we led ours, under his nose. He took the newspaper away from George the moment he entered the room, and George said good morning to him and stepped innocently into the parlor. Then, while Father watched him through the broad doorway and looked over the political headlines, George banged out the baseball news for us on

* From *Life With Father* by Clarence Day, by permission of Alfred A. Knopf, Inc. Copyright, 1934, 1935, by Clarence Day.

the piano. Father used to admonish him with a chuckle not to thump so hard, but George felt that he had to. We were at the top of the house, and he wanted to be sure that we'd hear him even if we were brushing our teeth. George always was thorough about things. He not only thumped the piano as hard as he could but he hammered out the tune over and over besides, while Father impatiently muttered to himself, "*Trop de zèle.*"

Upstairs, there was usually some discussion as to what kind of news George was sending. He had not been allowed to learn popular tunes, which it would have been easy for us to recognize, and the few classic selections which were available in his little music book sounded pretty much alike at a distance. George rendered these with plenty of good will and muscle but not a great deal of sympathy. He regarded some of the rules of piano-playing as needlessly complicated.

The fact remained that he was the one boy who was always on time, and Father was so pleased by this that he bought a watch for him with "George Parmly Day, Always on Time" engraved on the back. He told me that as I was the eldest he had meant to give me a watch first, and he showed me the one he had bought for me. It was just like George's except that nothing had been engraved on it yet. Father explained that to his regret he would have to put it away for a while, until I had earned it by getting down early to breakfast.

Time went on, without much improvement on my part. Dawdling had got to be a habit with me. Sometimes my lateness was serious. One morning, when breakfast was half over and I had nothing on but a pair of long woolen drawers, Father called up from the front hall, napkin in hand, that he wouldn't stand it and that I was to come down that instant. When I shouted indignantly that I wasn't dressed yet, he said he didn't care. "Come down just as you are, confound it!" he roared. I was tempted to take him at his word, but thought there might be some catch in it and wouldn't, though I hurried, of course, all I could. Father ate his usual hearty breakfast in a stormy mood, and I ate my usual hearty breakfast in a guilty and nervous one. Come what might, we always ate heartily. I sometimes wished afterward that I hadn't, but it never seemed to hurt Father.

Mother told Father that if he would give me the watch, she was sure I'd do better. He said that he didn't believe it, and that that was a poor way to bring a boy up. To prove to him that he was wrong, Mother at last unlocked her jewel box and gave me a watch which had belonged to one of her elderly cousins. It was really too valuable a watch for a boy to wear, she said, and I must be very careful of it. I promised I would.

This watch, however, turned out to be painfully delicate. It was old, I was young. We were not exactly made for each other. It had a back and front of thin gold, and as Mother had had the former owner's monogram shaved off the front cover, that cover used to sink in the middle when pressed. Also, the lid fitted so closely that there was barely room for the glass crystal over the face. Such a very thin crystal had to be used that any pressure on the lid broke it.

I didn't press on the lid, naturally, after the first time this happened. I was careful, and everything would have gone well enough if other boys had been careful, too. It was not practicable, however, for me to make them be careful enough. When I had a fight, friendly or otherwise, I used to ask my opponent if he would be so kind as not to punch me on the left side of my stomach. He might or might not listen. If he and I were too excited and kept on long enough, the watch crystal broke anyway. There was never time to take off my watch first, and anyhow there was no place to put it. A watch that goes around the streets in a boy's pocket has to take life as it comes. This watch had never been designed for any such fate.

The first two crystals I broke Mother paid for, as Father disapproved of the whole business and would have nothing to do with it. Mother was always short of small change, however, and I hated to trouble her—and she hated to be troubled, too. "Oh, Clarence dear! You haven't broken your watch again?" she cried when I opened the cover the second time, to show her the shattered fragments. She was so upset that I felt too guilty to tell her the next time it happened, and from then on I was reduced to the necessity of paying for the damage myself.

My pocket money never exceeded a dollar a month. Every new crystal cost twenty-five cents. It was a serious drain.

Wrestling and rolling around on the floor with Sam Willets, my watch quite forgotten, I would suddenly hear a faint tinkle and know that I was once more insolvent. I would pick out the broken glass and leave the watch with no crystal till I had twenty-five cents on hand, but these delays made me nervous. I knew that Mother wanted to feel sure I was taking good care of the watch, and that she might look at it any evening. As soon as I had the money, I hurried over to Sixth Avenue, where two old Germans kept a tiny watch shop, and left it there to be fixed. One of my most dismal memories is of that stuffy little shop's smell of sauerkraut, and how tall the glass counter then seemed, and the slowness of those two old Germans. When I got there late and they made me leave the watch overnight, I didn't have one easy moment until I got it back the next day. Again and again I argued with them that twenty-five cents was too much, especially for a regular customer, but they said it didn't pay them to do the work even for that, because those thin old-fashioned crystals were hard to get.

I gave up at last. I told Mother I didn't want to wear the watch any more.

Then I found, to my amazement, that this way out of my troubles was barred. The watch was an heirloom. And an heirloom was a thing that its recipient must value and cherish. No good Chinese, I read later on in life, fails to honor his ancestors; and no good boy, I was told in my youth, fails to appreciate heirlooms.

I left Mother's room in low spirits. That night, as I wound up my watch with its slender key, I envied George. Father had selected the right kind for George; he knew what a boy needed. It had a thick nickel case, it had an almost unbreakable crystal, and it endured daily life imperturbably, even when dropped in the bathtub.

It seemed to me that I was facing a pretty dark future. The curse of great possessions became a living thought to me, instead of a mere phrase. The demands that such possessions made on their owners for upkeep were merciless. For months I had had no money for marbles. I couldn't even afford a new top. In some way that I didn't fully understand I was yoked to a watch I now hated—a delicate thing that would always make trouble unless I learned to live gingerly.

Then I saw a way out. All this time I had kept on being late for breakfast at least once a week, out of habit, but it now occurred to me that if I could reform, perhaps Father might relent and give me that reliable nickel watch he had bought. I reformed. I occasionally weakened in my new resolution at first, but every time that crystal got broken I was spurred on to fresh efforts. When I had at length established a record for promptness that satisfied Father, he had my name engraved on the watch he had bought, and presented it to me. He was a little surprised at the intense pleasure I showed on this occasion, and as he watched me hopping around the room in delight he said "There, there" several times. "Don't be so excited, confound it," he added. "You'll knock over that vase."

Mother said she couldn't see why Father should give me a nickel watch when I had a gold one already, but he laughed and told her that "that old thing" was no kind of a watch for a boy. She reluctantly laid it way again to rest in her jewel box.

Her parting shot at Father was that anyhow she had been right; she had said all along that a watch was what I needed to teach me how to be prompt.

HOW PECOS BILL WON AND LOST HIS BOUNCING BRIDE

by Carl Carmer

The story Arizona cowboys like most to tell when they've finished their day's ride, emptied the chuck wagon, and are seated in the flickering light of the campfire, is the tale of Pecos Bill. Every time somebody or other tells about Bill the story gets longer. If you were to listen tonight along the banks of the Turkey River or the Blue, you'd be pretty sure to hear some buckaroo telling about how Pecos Bill licked a mountain lion barehanded, jumped astride his back and rode him into camp, using a rattlesnake he had picked up along the way as a quirt. And some broncobuster from over Chloride way or maybe from Diversion or Sandwater may be telling about the perpetual motion ranch. And after that one's been told, somebody will start up one of the songs that Pecos Bill made up while he was riding the range, *The Chisholm Trail* maybe, or *The Trail to Mexico*, or maybe *The Strawberry Roan*.

Pecos Bill thought he was a coyote until he was almost a grown man. When he was a little boy he had fallen off the end of the big wagon in which he and his sixteen brothers and sisters were being carried westward in a wagon train. When Bill's parents counted noses that night, they realized their loss and tried to find him on the back trail, but they never did. For Bill had been taken up by the coyotes and they had asked him to go home with them. The coyotes taught Bill to sit and howl at the moon just as they did and he soon forgot about being a human being. It wasn't until Bill was eighteen that he realized he wasn't a real coyote. Then he met a cowboy who said:

"Well, if you're a coyote, where's your tail?"

That convinced Bill, and so he left his four-footed friends and went to live in an Arizona town.

One day Bill was riding along beside the Salt River when he saw a pretty girl riding towards him on the back of a rearing, bucking, plunging catfish. Although it was a small catfish for the Salt, hardly larger than a whale, Bill was so pleased at the way the girl handled it with only a surcingle for harness that he fell in love with her and asked her to marry him.

She said her name was Sue and she would be pleased to marry him if he would grant her two requests. Bill was so in love with her he said "yes" before asking what they were.

The first thing she asked for was a bustle to wear on her wedding day. Now, a bustle was a very fashionable article of wearing apparel in the time she asked for it. Every fine lady wore one under her skirt just below her waist in the back and hoped it would give her a big curve just at the place where ladies now hope they have no curves at all. Bill bought Sue the finest bustle in the country—made of steel wire and whalebone—and they were both very happy over it.

But Bill was troubled about Sue's second request. She wished to ride Bill's horse, Widow-Maker, on her wedding day. Though she could ride a bucking catfish, Bill doubted if she could ride Widow-Maker. Still, he had promised, and so after the wedding ceremony he let her get on the horse and start to ride.

Widow-Maker was not accustomed to skirts about his ribs and he bucked so hard that Sue fell off and landed on the bustle—and bounced. The first bounce took her over the lower horn of the new moon. When she came back down that bustle hit on the Rocky Mountains and bounced her back into the sky and completely over the moon.

Bill kept begging her not to be so nervous and he tried mighty hard to figure out some way of stopping her bouncing, but he has never been able to. She is still bouncing out there, and every once in a while on a clear night Arizonians can see her pass across the face of the moon.

When he found out he could never claim his bride, Bill sat

down and began to cry. He is still crying, and it is his flowing tears that made the river that Arizona folks call the Silver.

THE STAG AND THE CHERRY STONES

by Baron Munchausen

You have heard, I dare say, of the hunter's and sportsman's saint and protector St. Hubert; and of the noble stag, which appeared to him in the forest, with the holy cross between his antlers. I have paid my homage to that saint every year in good fellowship, and seen this stag a thousand times, either painted in churches, or embroidered in the stars of his knights; so that, upon the honor and conscience of a good sportsman, I hardly know whether there may not have been formerly, or whether there are not such crossed stags even at this present day. But let me rather tell what I have seen myself.

Having one day spent all my shot, I found myself unexpectedly in the presence of a stately stag, looking at me as unconcernedly as if he had known of my empty pouches. I charged immediately with powder, and upon it a good handful of cherry stones, for I had sucked the fruit as far as the hurry would permit. Thus I let fly at him, and hit him just on the middle of the forehead, between his antlers; it stunned him—he staggered—yet he made off.

A year or two after, being with a party in the same forest, I beheld a noble stag with a fine full-grown cherry-tree above ten feet high between his antlers. I immediately recollected my former adventure, looked upon him as my property, and brought him to the ground by one shot, which at once gave me the haunch and cherry-sauce; for the tree was covered with the richest fruit, the like I had never tasted before. Who knows but some passionate holy sportsman, or sporting abbot, or bishop, may have shot, planted, and fixed the cross between the antlers of St. Hubert's stag, in a manner similar to this? They have always been, and still are, famous for plantations of crosses and antlers; and in a case of distress or dilemma, which too often happens to keen sportsmen, one is apt to grasp at any thing for safety, and to try any expedient, rather than miss the favorable opportunity. I have many times found myself in that trying situation.

What do you say of this, for example? Daylight and powder were spent one day in a Polish forest. When I was going home, a terrible bear made up to me in great speed, with open mouth ready to fall upon me; all my pockets were searched in an instant for powder and ball, but in vain. I found nothing but two spare flints; one I flung with all my might into the monster's open jaws, down his throat. It gave him pain and made him turn about, so that I could level the second at his back-door, which, indeed, I did with wonderful success; for it flew in, met the first flint in the stomach, struck fire, and blew up the bear with a terrible explosion. Though I came off safe that time, yet I should not wish to try it again, or venture against bears with no other ammunition.

There is a kind of fatality in it. The fiercest and most dangerous animals generally came upon me when defenceless, as if they had a notion or an instinctive intimation of it. Thus a frightful wolf rushed upon me so suddenly, and so close, that I could do nothing but follow mechanical instinct, and thrust my fist into his open mouth. For safety's sake I pushed on and on, till my arm was fairly in up to the shoulder. How should I disengage myself? I was not much pleased with my awkward situation—with a wolf face to face—our ogling was not of the most pleasant kind. If I withdrew my arm, then the animal would fly the more furiously upon me; that I saw in his flaming eyes. In short, I laid hold of his tail, turned him inside out like a glove, and flung him to the ground, where I left him.

The same expedient would not have answered against a mad-dog, which soon after came running against me in a narrow street at St. Petersburgh. Run who can, I thought; and to do this the better, I threw off my fur-cloak, and was safe withindoors in an instant. I sent my servant for the cloak, and he put it in the wardrobe with my other clothes. The day after I was amazed and frightened by Jack's bawling, "For God's sake, sir, your fur-cloak is mad!" I hastened up to him, and found almost all my clothes tossed about and torn to pieces. The fellow was perfectly right in his apprehensions about the fur-cloak's madness. I saw him myself just then falling upon a fine full-dress suit, which he shook and tossed in an unmerciful manner.

POOR MR. FINGLE

by Margery Williams Bianco

As soon as you step inside the door of the hardware store you can smell that nice funny hardware smell, the smell of varnish and rope and new oil stoves and straw and packing cases. There is no other place that smells just like it. Even if you were set down there suddenly, with your eyes tight shut, you would know at once that you were standing in the hardware store.

It is the one store where no one is ever in a hurry. People drop in there and potter about for hours and wander out again, and no one any the wiser. In fact, if ever you lose any of your family in town, and don't know where to look for them, the very best place to go to is the hardware store. Sooner or later you are sure to find them there, poking about in the nail bins or reading the tickets on the mowing machines.

It doesn't matter how long you may have to wait in the hardware store, for time passes here very quickly. There is so much to look at. There are all the gardening tools and wheelbarrows and can openers and scissors; there are the families and families of jugs and saucepans, from the big father and mother saucepans down to the youngest and babiest saucepan of all; there are nails enough to nail everything in town, and all different sizes, sorted out in bins and barrels; there are the books of different kinds of wallpapers, and the cards that show you what color your paint is going to be after you get it home, and there too, in endless rows of drawers and boxes, are all the knobs and bolts and screws and gadgets that have ever been invented since the world began.

No one ever gets bored in the hardware store. There are too many things to look at. But if ever you want to buy something there you must be very careful and write it down beforehand, on a piece of paper, and never, never lose it. Otherwise, the same thing might happen to you that happened to Mr. Fingle.

Everyone knows Mr. Fingle. He is always there. No one pays any attention to him. No one ever asks him what he wants. They know it isn't any use. Poor Mr. Fingle!

No matter what time of day you happen to go to the hardware store, there wandering about somewhere among the bins and the barrels and the paint pots and the stoves, you will come upon Mr. Fingle.

If you hear something rustling at your elbow, or see a shadow moving in the dusk of the store, no need to turn around. It is only Mr. Fingle. There he is, a little white mouse of a man, creeping softly about, picking things up, laying them down again, peering here and there in his gentle short-sighted way, and every little while just standing still for a moment, with his finger in his mouth, thinking.

He thinks and he thinks, but all his thinking won't help him. He *can't* remember what he wanted to buy!

Years and years ago Mr. Fingle used to live in the little white house up the road, past the shoe store. He had a front porch and a wife and a lawn mower, just like everybody else, and every morning, if it was summer time, you would see him out mowing his front lawn, or if it was winter you would hear him tinkering away somewhere inside the house. For Mr. Fingle had one great passion in life.

He loved to fix things.

If there happened to be a leaky faucet or a door that wouldn't shut or a latch that wouldn't latch, Mr. Fingle knew just what to do about it. He would fetch out his box of tools, and he would look over all the nails and sort out all the screws, and then he would consider a moment, with his head on one side, and he'd say:

"Now, I know the very thing that's needed to fix *that!*"

He'd rush off to the hardware store, and rush back again, and before he knew it, the thing was done.

And as in every house there are about a million things that need fixing, if anyone really wants to fix them, Mr. Fingle was usually busy from morning to night. He'd tinker in the bathroom and he'd tinker in the kitchen, and when he got through there he would wander down cellar, or up in the attic. There was always something to do.

But one unlucky morning, just as Mr. Fingle was going out to fix the lawn mower, his wife called to him. She said:

"Sometime, when you've got a minute to spare, dear, I do wish you'd fix *this!*"

"I'll fix it right away," said Mr. Fingle, "while I think of it."

And he got out his tools and his nail box, and he looked through everything once, and he looked through everything twice. There were all sorts of gadgets there, but there didn't happen to be the particular gadget he wanted. So he said:

"Well, I can't do it right now. I need a thingamabob, and I haven't got one."

His wife said: "Can't you use a screw driver?"

"It isn't *that,*" said Mr. Fingle. "I've got all the tools I want.

But it's no use trying to fix it with screws. It ought to have one of those little what-you-may-call-'ems, right there, see? Then it will be all right. Remind me next time I go to the hardware store."

"You'd better get several," said his wife, who was a practical woman, "and then we'll have them in the house."

Just then the telephone bell rang, and by the time he had answered the call lunch was ready, and what with one thing and another it was late in the afternoon before Mr. Fingle put on his hat and strolled out into the town. He bought his newspaper and he ordered the groceries, and then he remembered the hardware store.

"While I think of it," he said to himself, "I'll just step over and buy that thingamabob."

So he went into the hardware store. While he was waiting to be served he looked at the hammers and the chisels, and that reminded him that he needed a new pipe wrench, and then he wanted a few yards of copper wire. And while he was about it, how about getting that paint for the kitchen floor?

The hardware man laid all these things out on the counter, one, two, three, and then he asked Mr. Fingle:

"Is there anything else, sir?"

Mr. Fingle thought a moment, and he said: "Why, bless me, yes! I was forgetting the very thing I came for!"

"And what is that?" asked the young man.

"Why, I wanted a . . . a . . . now what on earth was it," asked Mr. Fingle, "that I *did* want?"

The young man couldn't help him, though he did his best. All his suggestions only made poor Mr. Fingle more and more muddled. It wasn't tacks, and it wasn't sandpaper, and it wasn't a washer, or even a nut and bolt. It was one of these thingamies, but for the life of him he couldn't remember what kind of a thingamy it was.

"I must just think a minute," said Mr. Fingle.

So he began to stroll about the store, looking at this and looking at that, and every little while pausing to say to himself: "Now, what *was* it?"

He went over everything he could possibly think of, in his mind, but it wasn't any of them. All he knew was that it was something very important, and that nothing else would quite take its place. It was something to fix the . . . to fix the . . .

He couldn't even remember what it was he had been going to fix!

Back rushed Mr. Fingle to his little white house. His wife was making peach shortcake for supper. But she was no help at all.

"Why, yes, dear," she said. "I do seem to remember asking you to fix something for me. I was in the kitchen here, and you were just going out, and I said . . ."

"Yes?" said Mr. Fingle breathlessly. "Yes?"

"I *know* it was something we use all the time, and I was always thinking: 'Now, when Henry has a minute I'll ask him to fix this,' and so I did. Don't you remember?"

"But what *was* it?" Mr. Fingle shouted.

"I tell you how you'll remember," said Mrs. Fingle. "Don't you know you said you couldn't do it till you got one of these little thingamies, and I even said to you, 'you'd better get several,' I said, 'and then we'll always have them ready.' And you said you would. *Now* don't you remember?"

But oddly enough, Mr. Fingle couldn't remember at all!

That was the beginning of it.

All that night poor Mr. Fingle lay awake and tossed, and first thing next morning, there he was back at the hardware store again.

"All I need to do," he said to himself, "is just to look about me quietly, and then as soon as I see it I shall remember what it was!"

That, as I say, was a long, long time ago.

Days went by, and weeks went by, and now years have gone by, and still Mr. Fingle goes wandering about the hardware store. Everyone has grown so used to the sight of him that now they pay no attention to him whatever. At first they used to shoo him out every evening at closing time, but now they just let him alone. He sleeps somewhere down in the cellar, curled up among the door mats and the wire netting, and there he is perfectly happy.

Poor Mr. Fingle.

7

Of Man's Best Friends: Horses and Dogs

Horses and dogs have been man's best friends among the animals. Even today, when one rarely sees a horse in any of our cities, and dogs mostly on a leash, boys and girls seem to care more about these animals than about any others.

One reason for this favored position of dogs and horses is that of all the animals which man has cultivated or kept around his home for one reason or another, these two respond more to our desires and to our moods. You can feel that a horse or a dog likes you or understands you, much more at least than a cow or a cat or a sheep—all very useful in their ways but not very warm as companions.

For over fifty years automobiles have been displacing the family horse in cities and towns, but boys and girls remain interested in horses. And as more of us live along paved city streets or in apartments, which have no place for dogs, the dog remains a favorite still. Very few boys and girls can really get close to live horses or dogs. Reading about the doings of these animals seems to be the next best thing to seeing them and playing with them.

These horse and dog stories are "real" even though some of them are imaginary, since each one tells about the kind of actions that real dogs or horses might carry out.

BILLY, THE DOG THAT MADE GOOD

by Ernest Thompson Seton

He was the biggest fool pup I ever saw—chock-full of life and spirits; always going at racing speed; generally into mischief; nearly breaking his neck over some small matter; breaking his heart if his master did not notice him; chewing up clothing, hats, and boots; digging up garden stuff that he could not eat; going direct from the pigsty to frolic in the baby's cradle; getting kicked in the ribs by horses and tossed by cows; but still the same, hilarious, rollicking, good-natured pup, and given by common consent the name of Silly Billy.

It was maddening to find on the first cold morning that he had chewed up one's leather glove; but it was worse to have that good-natured little idiot come wagging his tail, offering the remaining glove as much as to say that one glove was enough for anyone. You had to forgive him, and it did not matter much whether you did or not, for the children adored him. Their baby arms were around his neck as much of the time as he could spare from his duties, and, in a sense, those protecting arms were around him all the time. The father realized this fact when one day the puppy pulled down a piece of sacking that hung on the smoke-house pipe, upsetting the stove and burning up the smoke-house and all the dry meat in it. Bob Yancy was furious, for his whole winter's meat stock was gone. He took his shotgun and went forth determined to put that fool dog forever out of mischief. But he met the unexpected. He found his victim with two baby arms about his fuzzy neck; little Ann Yancy was hugging her "doggy," and what could *he* do? "It's my Billy! You shan't touch him! Go away, you naughty daddy!" And the matter ended in a disastrous defeat for daddy.

Every member of the family loved Silly Billy, but they wished that he might soon develop at least a glimmer of common dog sense, for he was already past the time when with most bull terriers puppyhood is ended. Although he was in time to take a place among his master's hunting dogs, he was not yet ready for this honor.

Bob Yancy was a hunter, a professional. His special line was killing bears, mountain lions, lynxes, wolves, and other "varmints" for whose destruction the state pays a bounty. He was ever ready to increase the returns by taking with him amateur hunters who paid him well for the privilege of being present.

Much of this hunting was done on what is commonly called the chase. The morning rally, the far search for a trail, the warming hunt, the hot pursuit, and the finish with a more or less thrilling fight—that was ideal. But it was seldom fully realized. The mountains were too rough. The game either ran off altogether, or, by crossing some impassable barrier, got rid of the hunters, and then turned on the dogs to scatter them in flight.

That was the reason for the huge bear traps that were hanging in Yancy's barn. Those dreadful things would not actually hold the bear prisoner, but when, with a convenient log, they were gripped on his paw, they held him back so that the hunters, even on foot, could overtake the victim.

The dogs, however, were the interesting part of the pursuit. Three kinds were needed: perfect trailers, whose noses could follow with sureness the oldest, coldest trail; swift runners for swift game; and intelligent fighters. The fighters had, of course, to be brave, but intelligence was more important, for the dogs were expected to nip at the victim from behind and spring back from his counter blow rather than to close at final grips.

Thus there were bloodhounds and greyhounds as well as a bulldog in the Yancy pack, together with a few half-breeds. Most of the pack had marked personality. There was Croaker, a small lady hound with a sensitive nose and a miserable little croak for a bay. You could not hear her fifty feet away; but fortunately Big Ben followed her everywhere, and he had a voice like the bell for which he was named. He always stuck close to Croaker and translated her feeble whispers into tones that all the world within a mile or two could understand.

Then there was Old Thunder, a very old, very brave dog, with a fine nose. He was a combination of all good gifts and had been through many fights, but had escaped destruction, thanks to his shrewdness. Though slow and feeble now, he was the acknowledged leader of the pack, respected by dogs and men.

The bulldog is known for his courage rather than for his good judgment; hence the post of "bulldog to the pack" was often open. The last bulldog had been buried with the bones of the last grizzly. But Yancy had secured a new one, a wonder. He was the perfect product of a long line of fighting bulldogs, kept by a famous breeder in another state. When the new leader arrived, it was a large event to all the hunters. He was no disappointment; broad of head and chest, massive in the upper arm, and hard in the flank—a perfect beast of the largest size. The hunters at Yancy's knew at once that they had a fighting treasure in the Terrible Turk, who was even more surly and savage than most bulldogs.

It was with some distrust that he was turned loose on the ranch, because he was so unpleasant in his manner. There was a lack of dogginess about him in the gentle sense, and never did one of his race display a greater haughtiness. He did not try to hide his sense of superiority, and the pack seemed to accept him at his own value. Clearly they were afraid of him. He was given the right of way—avoided, indeed—by his future comrades. Only Silly Billy went bounding in hilarious friendliness to meet the great one, and a moment later flew howling with pain to hide in the arms of his little mistress.

In the next two weeks that passed about the ranch the Terrible Turk had quarreled with nearly every hound in the pack. There was only one that he had not actually injured, and that was Old Thunder. Even they met once or twice when Thunder was gnawing a bone, but each time he stood his ground and showed his teeth. There was a certain dignity about Thunder that even a dog will feel, and in this case the Terrible Turk retired.

In October word came that Old Reelfoot, a famous cattle-killing grizzly, had reappeared in the Arrow-Bell Cattle Range, and was up to his old tricks of destroying livestock. A big reward was offered for his destruction, several times as much as for an ordinary bear.

Bob Yancy was ablaze with hunter's fire when he heard the news. His only dread was that some rival might get ahead of him. It was a spirited procession that left the Yancy claim that morning, headed for the Arrow-Bell Ranch, the pack straggling along or forging ahead till ordered back in line by the huntsman. There was the venerable Thunder trotting by the heels of his old friend Midnight, Yancy's coal-black mare; and just before was the Terrible Turk with his red-rimmed eyes upturned at times to measure his nearness to the powerful, black mare's hoofs. Big Ben was near Croaker, of course. Next was a pack horse loaded with a huge steel bear trap on each side, followed by pack horses with the camping outfit, and other hunters, the cook, and the writer of this story.

Everything was in fine shape for the hunt, and we were well started when trouble tumbled in among us. With many a yap of glee, there, bounding, came the foolish bull terrier, Silly Billy. Like a June bug among honeybees, like a crazy schoolboy in a council room, he rollicked and yapped, eager to be first, to be last, to take liberties with Thunder, to chase rabbits, ready for anything but what was wanted of him—to stay at home and mind his own business.

Bob might yell "Go home!" till he was hoarse. Silly Billy would only go off a little way and look hurt, then make up his mind that the boss was "only fooling" and didn't mean a word of it, and start in louder than ever.

No one wished him to come, but there was no way of stopping

him; so Silly Billy came to have a place in the first bear hunt of the season.

That afternoon they arrived at the Arrow-Bell Ranch, and the expert bearman was shown the latest kill, a fine heifer barely touched. The grizzly would surely come back for his next meal. Yes, an ordinary grizzly would, but Reelfoot was an extraordinary animal. Just because it was the bear fashion to come again soon, he might not return for a week. Yancy set a huge trap by this kill; but he also found the kill of a week gone by, five miles away, and by that set another trap. Then all retired to the ranch house.

Who that knows the grizzly will be surprised to hear that the night brought the hunters nothing, and that the next was blank? But the third morning showed that the huge brute had come to his older kill.

I shall not forget the thrills of that time. We passed the recent carcass near the ranch. It lay untouched and little changed. We rode on the five miles to the next. And before we were near, we felt there was something unusual in the air, for the dogs seemed excited. I could see nothing; but, while yet a hundred yards away, Bob was exclaiming, "A catch this time, sure enough."

Dogs and horses were all inspired. The Terrible Turk breasted his way to the front, and the rumbling in his chest was grand as an organ. Ahead, behind, and all around him was Silly Billy, yapping and tumbling.

There was the carcass still untouched. The place of the trap was vacant; log and all were gone; and all around were signs of an upset, many large tracks, so many that scarcely any were clear; but farther on we got the sign most sought, the thirteen-inch track of a monster grizzly, and the bunch on the right paw stamped it as Reelfoot's trail.

I had seen the joy blaze in Yancy's eyes before, but never as now. He glowed with the hunter's heat, and let the dogs run free, and urged them on with whoops and yells of "Sic him, boys! Ho, boys! sic him!" Not much urging was needed; the dogs were possessed of the spirit of the day. This way and that they circled, each for himself. The bear had walked around awhile before going off. It was Croaker that first had the real trail. Big Ben was there to let the whole world know; then Thunder indorsed the statement. Had it been Plunger that spoke, the rest would have paid no heed; but all the pack knew Thunder's voice, and his judgment was not open to question. They left their different tracks and flocked behind the leader, baying deep and strong at every bound, while Turk came hurrying after, and Silly Billy tried to make up in noise for all he lacked in judgment.

Away we went, with the bawling pack as guides. The country was a wilderness of rocky gullies, dense thickets, and down timber, where fire and storm had piled the mountain slope with dead forest. But we kept on, and before an hour the dinning of the pack announced the bear at bay.

Creeping from trunk to trunk we went forward. The thought flashed up, "Which of us will come back alive!" What a din those dogs were making! Every one of them was in the chorus. They were yapping and baying, high and low, swaying this way and that; this meant that the bear was charging back and forth and still had some freedom.

"Look out now! Don't get too close!" said Yancy. "Log and all, he can cover fifty feet while you make ten, and I tell you he won't bother about the dogs if he gets a chance at the men. He knows his game."

There were more thrills in the woods than the mere sounds accounted for. My hand trembled as I scrambled over the down timber. It was a moment of fierce excitement as I lifted the branches and got my first view. But it was a disappointment. There was the pack, bounding, seething, yelling, and back of the brush was some brown fur; that was all. Suddenly the brushwood swayed and a shaggy mountain of flesh rushed forth, a tremendous grizzly (I never knew one could look so big), and charged his tormentors. They scattered like flies when one strikes at a swarm of them. But the log on the trap caught on a stump and held him, the dogs surged around, and now my view was clear.

This is the moment of all in the hunt. This is the time when you size up your hounds. This is the fiery furnace in which the metals all are tried. There was Old Thunder baying, tempting the bear to charge, but ever with an eye to the safe retreat; there was Croaker doing her duty; there were the greyhounds, yapping and nipping at his rear; there in the background, wisely waiting, saving his power for the right time, was the Terrible Turk; and here and there, bounding and yapping, was Silly Billy, dashing into the very jaws of death again and again, but saved by his restless activity, and proud of the bunch of bear's wool in his teeth.

Round and round they went, as Reelfoot made his short, furious charges, and Turk still kept in the background, baying hoarsely, biding his time for the favorable moment. And whichever side Old Thunder took, there Turk went too. Yancy rejoiced at this, for it meant that the fighting dog had good judgment.

The fighting and the baying swung behind a little bush. I wanted to see it all and tried to get near, but Yancy shouted out "Keep back!" He knew the habits of the bear and the danger of coming into range. But his shouting attracted the notice of the bear, and he charged straight for Bob.

Many a time before had Yancy faced a bear. This time he had his gun, but, perched on a small and shaky rotten log, he had no chance to shoot. As he swung for a clearer view he raised his rifle with a jerk, but the rotten log crashed under him, and Bob fell sprawling among the tumbled logs. The grizzly now had him in his power, and we were struck with horror. We had no power to stop that certain death; we dared not fire—the dogs and the man himself were right in line. The pack closed in. Their din was deafening; they sprang on the huge, haired flanks; they nipped the soggy heels; they hauled and held, and did their best; but they were as flies on a badger or as rats on a landslide. They held him not an instant. The small logs cracked as he rushed forward, and Bob would in a moment more be smashed with that huge paw, for now no human help was possible. Good Old Thunder saw the only way. It meant sure death for him, but it was the only way.

He ceased all halfway dashing at the flank or heel and leaped at the bear's throat. One swift sweep of that great paw sent him reeling back, bruised and shaken. Still he rallied, rushed as though he knew it all must turn on him; when Turk, the mighty warrior, the hope and valor of the pack, who long had held back, sprang forward now and gripped with all his strength—on the bear? NO! shame of shames!—how shall I say the truth?—on *poor Old Thunder*, wounded, battered, winded, downed, seeking to save his master! On him the bulldog fastened with a grip of hate. This was what he had waited for; this was the time of times that he took to vent his pent-up jealous rage. He sprang from behind, dragged Thunder down, and held him, gasping, in the brushwood. The bear had freedom now to take revenge, for his only foe was gone; what could prevent him? But from the reeling, yapping pack there sprang a small white dog, not for the monster's heel, not for his flank, nor even for his massive shoulder, but for his face—the only place where a dog could count in such a sudden attack. He seized with an iron grip above the monster's eye, and the huge head jerking back made that small dog go flapping like a rag; however, the dog hung on. The bear reared up to claw, and we realized for the first time that the small white dog was Silly Billy, none else, hanging on with all his might and weight.

Bob scrambled to his feet, escaped! The huge brute seized the small white body in his great paws, which looked like stumps of trees, just as a cat might seize a mouse. He wrenched him, quivering, and hurled him like a bundle far to one side, and wheeling for a moment paused to seek the greater foe, the man. The pack drew back. Four rifles rang, a long, deep snort, and Reelfoot's huge bulk sank limp on the storm-tossed logs. Then Turk, the traitor Turk, with chesty gurgle as a war cry, closed bravely on the dead brute's haunch and tore out the hair, while the pack sat lolling back, the battle done.

Bob Yancy's face was set. He had seen nearly all the fight, and we supplied the rest. Billy was wagging his tail, shaking and shivering with excitement. There were some red-stained slashes on his ribs. Bob greeted him affectionately, "You dandy. It's the finish that shows up the stuff a bear-dog is made of, and I tell you there isn't anything too good on Yancy's ranch for you. Good Old Thunder has saved my life before, but this is a new one. I never thought you'd show up this way.

"And you," he said to Turk, "I've just two words for you. Come here!" He took off his belt, put it through the collar of the Terrible Turk, and led him to one side. I turned my head away. A rifle cracked, and the big, strong bulldog was no more. He had been tried in the fire and found wanting—a bully, a coward, a thing not fit to live.

In the triumphal procession heading homeward, on the front of Yancy's saddle was Billy, the hero of the day, his white coat stained with red. His body was stiff and sore, but his spirits were not lessened. He probably did not fully understand the feelings he had aroused in others; but he did know that he was having a glorious time, and that at last the world was returning the love he had so bounteously given to it. Old Thunder was riding on a pack horse. It was weeks before he got over the mauling he had had from the bear and the bulldog, and he was soon afterward put into honorable retirement on account of his age.

Billy was all right again in a month. A half year later he had shed his puppy ways, and his good dog sense came forth in strength. He had proved himself brave as a lion, full of energy, affectionate, true as steel. Within two years he was leader of the pack. They do not call him "Silly" now, but "Billy, the dog that made good."

WHITEY'S SUNDAY HORSE

by Glen Rounds

Uncle Torwal and Whitey were out to see how their range stock was getting along. Torwal was a slow-speaking fellow with a droopy red mustache, and a good many of the horses running in the Badlands belonged to him. Whitey, who was probably ten years old or thereabouts, had lived with him on the ranch for several years, almost since he could remember. He wore a cast-off Stetson hat of Torwal's and high-heeled riding boots from the same source. They lived alone like any two old sourdoughs and were a familiar sight at all the round-ups and in town of a Saturday, Torwal on a crop-eared black and Whitey on a pot-bellied old pinto named Spot. Torwal usually spoke of Whitey as his "sawed-off" foreman.

On this day, as they rode along, they came on something that interested them both. In a grassy hollow at the head of a dry coulee they saw a little brown mustang mare and a brand new colt. The colt was an awkward-looking scamp as he stood with his trembling legs braced wide apart, catching his breath after the effort of getting up. His body was close knit and compact, and his back was strong and flat, but his legs were so long and slender he appeared to be walking on stilts.

The mare whirled to face them, keeping the colt behind her. With her teeth bared and her ears laid back, she looked half wolf for sure.

"Spunky critter, that mare," Whitey said to Torwal as they rode carefully around, trying to get a good look at the colt.

"She's a wolf, all right," Torwal agreed. "Better not crowd her. She'd just as soon paste you outa your saddle as not, the way she's feeling now."

They sat on their horses and admired the colt. "Do you reckon we better take him home," asked Whitey, "so the wolves won't get him?"

"Don't reckon we'll take him anywhere," Torwal said. "Looks like I'm a-going to have to shoot him!"

"Shoot him! Why?" squalled Whitey. "Why he's the purtiest colt on the ranch!"

"Better look him over closer, Bub," said Torwal. "See if you notice anything outa the way about him."

"I don't see anything wrong, myself," Whitey told him, after he'd walked Spot in a circle around the mare and colt again. "He looks to me just like the kind of critter I'd like to have for a 'Sunday' horse."

"Look at his eyes! They're white," Torwal growled. "That colt's blind as a bat!"

"Aw, they're just china eyes, Uncle Torwal," Whitey said. "Lots of horses have china eyes. Even Old Spot has one."

"They're not china eyes, not by a long shot," said Torwal. "If you look close you'll see that they're pure white. He's blind, and we gotta shoot him. Otherwise he'll fall in a hole somewhere or get wolf et."

"Well, even if he is blind do we *hafta* shoot him?" Whitey asked. "Couldn't I take him home and keep him at the ranch?"

"All he'd be is a mess of trouble even if you got him home, and I doubt that he'd get that far," Torwal told him.

"Well, anyway, do we hafta shoot him?" Whitey said. "Couldn't we just let him loose?"

"Now quit your squalling," Torwal told him patiently. "I don't like it any more than you do, but if we leave him he'll either fall in a hole and starve or else he'll get wolf et."

While Whitey sat with his lip hanging down almost to his collar, Torwal took another chew from his plug and got his rifle out of his saddle scabbard. But whenever he tried to get near the colt the little mare was there, lashing out with her heels and baring her teeth to bite either man or horse that got too near.

After this had gone on a little while, Whitey spoke up again. "Listen, Uncle Torwal," he said, "I don't believe any wolf could get to that colt, the way the mare uses her heels. If you'll let him go, I'll watch mighty close to see if he falls in anything. I'll ride out every day to see that he's all right. And if he does fall in I—I—I'll shoot him myself!"

Uncle Torwal thought the matter over a while. "You want that colt mighty bad, don't you?" he said at last.

"I sure do! He's the purtiest thing I've ever seen!" said Whitey. "I don't think anything will happen to him, really, Uncle Torwal! He's too smart!"

"Well," Torwal said doubtfully, "since you feel like that about it, we'll let him go this time. We'll be riding over here every day for a while, so we can always shoot him later.

"But don't go getting your hopes up," he added. "The chances are he won't last a week."

"Nothing is going to happen to him," Whitey exclaimed. "You'll see."

"Maybe," said Uncle Torwal, but Whitey could see that he was glad to have an excuse for not shooting the colt. They sat watching a while, then rode off.

The little mare stood guard until they were out of sight. When she could no longer hear them, she started down the trail toward the place where she'd left the mustang band, with the blind colt following close against her flank.

Off and on all summer and fall, Whitey saw the mustangs and the blind colt with them. He seemed to have learned how to take care of himself as well as the colts that could see. Then late in the winter—March it was—there came a great blizzard, and one morning Whitey went out to the horse pasture and saw the blind colt in the open-faced shed with the saddle horses. He could only guess what had happened. Probably the blind colt had been separated from the wild horses as they drifted ahead of the storm and had stumbled on until he found shelter. Ordinarily, the ranch horses would have chased him out because he was strange to them, but old pot-bellied Spot took a fancy to the lost and lonely youngster, as old horses will sometimes do, and let him have a place between him and the wall of the shed.

The next morning, when Whitey came wading across the pasture, he found the horses standing around the stockyard fence waiting for him to throw them some hay.

Whitey's excitement can be imagined, when he saw Spot come trotting up with the blind colt following a safe distance behind, snorting softly and cocking his ears forward and back. The boy rubbed Spot's head and talked softly to the colt which stood some distance off. Spot seemed to be as proud of the colt as if he'd foaled it himself. Confusion, the dog, sat on the snow with his tongue hanging out and didn't express an opinion.

Whitey didn't mean to let Uncle Torwal find out that the blind colt was there if he could help it. He might start talking about shooting the poor blind critter.

Whitey thought the matter over as he threw hay over the fence and scattered it out on the snow. Now that the horses were out in the open again, they remembered the colt was a stranger and chased him away from the hay when they could. But always he came back to where Old Spot was and when he learned to keep his distance from the others he had little trouble.

After he'd thrown the hay out, Whitey hung around as long as he dared, admiring the colt and trying to think of a way he could keep him without Uncle Torwal finding out about it. But after a while he had to leave for fear Torwal would get to wondering what had happened to him and come out to look.

That afternoon he came back again. He still didn't have a plan, but he brought a pan of oats. When he rattled them in the pan, Spot threw up his head and came trotting up. He knew what the sound meant. The colt followed at a distance as he had in the morning. Tolling Spot along with the pan of oats, Whitey walked away from the rest of the horses. When he'd gotten him off by himself he scattered some of the oats on the snow and walked off some distance and stood still.

Spot got busy right away eating the oats while the colt listened to find what Whitey was doing. Not hearing anything, he moved cautiously forward a few steps at a time, snorting and bowing his neck. By the time he got to where Spot was, most of the oats were gone, but he did manage to get a taste.

When Spot finished, Whitey rattled the pan again, and poured out some more oats on the snow where he stood. Spot trotted to him while the colt whirled away, only to come slowly back as Whitey stood still. He repeated the performance several times that afternoon and the first thing next morning he was back again. He was trying to teach the colt to come to the rattle of the oats pan.

Gradually the colt lost some of his fear, and after a time he would come up within a few feet and eat the spilled oats greedily. But before he got so he'd let Whitey touch him, the snow was gone and something had to be done about him if Uncle Torwal wasn't to find out.

So one afternoon Whitey brought the oats and a hackamore and caught Old Spot and climbed up on his back. Then he rattled the oats pan and rode slowly off towards the far end of the pasture. He'd remembered a little box canyon over in the far corner that had a small unused corral.

The colt was somewhat puzzled by this business, but by now he had begun to lose his fear of Whitey, and the oats rattling in the pan sounded mighty good, so he followed cautiously along.

When they came to the corral Whitey rode on in to the farther side. Getting down on the ground he stayed quiet except for rattling the oats pan now and then while the colt came up and carefully investigated the corral gate. Seeing that the colt was not minded to come any nearer as long as he was there, Whitey poured out part of the oats on the ground and climbed carefully over the fence and walked away.

At his first move the colt had whirled away, but after a little he ventured back up to the gate and snorted around until he was convinced that Old Spot was alone inside. After that he walked carefully up to get his share of the oats, and while he was busy with them Whitey moved around and shut the gate.

Then he pushed his second-hand Stetson to the back of his head and looked through the bars of the corral at his new horse. The colt was his now, and he was so full of pride that his chest hurt him considerably. He felt as though he might swell and burst any minute.

Now all he had to do was keep Uncle Torwal from finding out anything until he had the colt gentled and perhaps taught him some tricks. He figured that once he got him trained, Uncle Torwal would see what a smart horse he was and wouldn't say anything more about turning him loose.

Whitey stayed around the corral a long time that day, talking softly to the colt and thinking about the stir he'd cause when he went riding into town on his new horse. And folks that had never noticed him to speak of, when he'd ridden Old Spot around, would point him out as being the only fellow in the country who had a blind horse for a Sunday horse.

It took plenty of patience to gentle that wild colt but finally Whitey had him so he would come and eat out of his hand. Then, gradually, the colt lost his fear of the boy and would let himself be curried all over, have his feet picked up, and would even lead. Next Whitey taught him to come to his whistle.

One afternoon Whitey was sitting on top of the old corral fence thinking how lucky he was that Uncle Torwal hadn't found out what he was doing.

He was just in the middle of deciding that he'd show the blind colt at the county fair in the fall, and was all wrapped up in listening to the crowds in the grandstand hollering with excitement at seeing the blind colt jump through a flaming hoop, when he was interrupted by Uncle Torwal's voice below him.

"What's that little 'Crow-bait' doing here, Bub?"

Whitey nearly fell off the fence, he was so surprised. Uncle Torwal had ridden up from the other side, and Whitey had been so busy with his county fair imaginings that he hadn't heard him.

"Oh, he's just grazing with Old Spot," Whitey said after he had pulled himself together. "Isn't he a purty scamp, though?"

Uncle Torwal got off his horse and climbed up on the fence beside Whitey before he answered. Then he took his jackknife out of his pocket and settled down to whittling as if he were going to spend the afternoon horse trading or something.

"He is a right likely looking piece of horseflesh, for a fact," he said after a while. "Too bad he's blind."

"You bet he's purty!" Whitey said, and he wondered what he should say next. He knew that the time had come for a showdown, but he also knew that Uncle Torwal had his horse-trading humor on and that there was no use coming straight out and asking him anything. So he decided to horse trade too, and he took out his jackknife and waited for Uncle Torwal to make the next move.

"Him and Old Spot act like they was old friends. Kinda looks like the colt musta been in here some time," Torwal said after a while.

"Yessir, it does kinda look that way for a fact," Whitey agreed, and whittled busily.

"Wouldn't be surprised if maybe he drifted in during the blizzard," Uncle Torwal went on after a time.

Whitey knew that all this had nothing to do with whether he could keep the colt or not. Uncle Torwal was just playing cat and mouse with him and he'd have a lot better chance for keeping the colt if he could keep on acting like a horse trader. So he tipped his old hat further back on his head and whittled some more.

"Yessir, that's probably just about what happened," Whitey said, as if he weren't worried at all.

"Now that he's made up to Old Spot the way he has, it's kinda too bad we gotta shag him out on the range again," Uncle Torwal said.

"Yeah, it does seem kinda too bad," said Whitey.

"Of course, if he was gentle and knowed anything, it'd be different," Torwal went on. "But you take a critter raised wild like he was, and being blind too, I doubt that a feller would ever be able to do anything with him."

"But you figure that if he could be gentled, he might make a good Sunday horse?" Whitey asked, grinning to himself.

"Well, I dunno," Torwal said. "But when I was a kid I had a blind saddle mare and she was a dandy. Sure-footed as a goat, she was. But she was extra smart," he added.

"This colt is mighty smart, just like I always said!" Whitey exclaimed.

"Well, he did manage not to get wolf et," Torwal agreed, "But that was probably just luck. It doesn't mean he could learn anything else."

Whitey saw that now was the time to get busy if he wanted to keep the colt. So he slid down off the fence.

"Watch this, Uncle Torwal," he said and whistled shrilly.

The colt stopped grazing and came trotting up. When he got close he smelled Torwal and snorted and stopped. Whitey called him and the colt came on, keeping his ears pointed at Torwal, however, and snorting a little.

Whitey fed the colt a handful of oats and put the hackamore on him and rubbed his hands all over him and picked up his feet, one by one, to show that he was gentle. He'd seen horse traders do that. Then Whitey called Confusion and the dog came running and jumped up on the blind colt's back.

"How do you like this, Uncle Torwal?" Whitey asked as he led the colt up with Confusion still on his back.

"Well, now!" Torwal exclaimed. "Don't know as I've ever seen anything like it, before."

"Oh, he's a smart feller all right," Whitey said, grinning fit to split his face.

"Hmm," Torwal said, cautiously. "Can he do anything else?"

Whitey had hoped Uncle Torwal would ask that, because he had spent a lot of time teaching the colt a special trick.

He turned to the colt. "Do you think you could learn to be a fancy saddle horse?" he asked him, and scratched him lightly between the forelegs. The colt nodded his head up and down.

"You're never going to be any trouble to anybody, are you?" he asked again, and at the same time he scratched the colt's shoulder. The colt nodded his head sidewise.

"See that, Uncle Torwal!" Whitey said. "He can even talk!"

Torwal grinned. "Reckon he's smarter than I figured!"

"Yessir!" said Whitey. "And he'll learn to do a lot of other things, too!"

Uncle Torwal climbed down off the fence and walked over to his horse.

"Well, you better bring him home and put him in the calf pasture if you figure on keeping him," he said as he climbed into the saddle.

"Yessir! I'll bring him right over!" Whitey said.

HI GUY—THE CINDERELLA HORSE

by Paul Brown

His name was Robin, but nobody knew that and he couldn't tell them.

Wearily he cocked an ear and turned his head to see if anyone was coming to the stable. It was many hours since the man who owned him had put a foot in his stall. He needed food and water, and the filth on the slanting bottom of his stall was soggy and wet and foul-smelling, and it was not a good thing for his feet.

With a stiff motion he shifted his weight to try to find an easier position. It had never been like this at any of his other homes or at the clean, comfortable stables of the Lairds where he had lived for so many happy years. He thought of the broad acres there, and of the meadow with its streams where he and the other horses were turned out to eat and drink their fill or doze in the shade of the trees.

When misfortune had come to the Lairds it came to their animals, too. Some found good homes where they lived for a time, others like Robin soon started down hill. He was now at the bottom of the grade and his home was a drafty, leaky shack.

Where would it all end? He was startled out of his dream by a rat which ran across the moldy, sodden hay in his packing-box manger.

The fact of the matter was that his owner and his family had moved out leaving a cat and Robin behind, because it was the easiest way to get rid of them.

As the day drew to its close, a dog chased the cat up onto the shed roof and a stranger, chasing the dog, discovered the pitiful state of Robin. The dog's owner called the police, who led Robin from the mess in which he stood. Poor fellow, he was so stiff that he could hardly move and a loose shoe clanked, all skew-gee, on one foot as he stepped awkwardly out into the yard.

He drank deeply from a pail of water but could scarcely eat food that was offered, because of the condition of his teeth. The police were stumped and they borrowed a horse van and removed him to the village pound, where it was decided to put the poor, trembling fellow out of his misery.

"Let's give him a last meal of oats," said one of the officers, and while Robin was eating as best he could, a new arrival, whom everyone called Barney, came upon the sad scene behind the barn.

From every angle he surveyed the scarecrow, as it sought eagerly for every last oat in the measure on the ground. "Let's see your mouth," he said to Robin, and interrupted the horse's eager searching long enough to look at his teeth.

"Uh, huh," Barney said, and took another turn around the scrawny creature.

"Come on, Barney, let's get on with the job," spoke up one of the officers as he spun the chambers of his service revolver.

"Give you five dollars for him as is," answered Barney. It was a new low price in Robin's career. "Put a blanket on him and put him back in the van. I'll meet you over at my place." And with that Barney left and phoned Dr. Cheshire the "vet" to meet him at his stables.

At the barn Robin found himself surrounded by a welcoming committee of two dogs, a cat, Mr. and Mrs. Barnett, Althea who was eight years old, Alan two years older, and Doc Cheshire.

With one movement Barney whisked off the blanket.

"Whew! What a mess!" Althea said, as she ran her hand over the dirt caked hard in Robin's hair.

"Boy! You sure unveiled something from the Wizard of Oz," commented the veterinarian.

"Put the scarecrow out in the fields and you'll scare the crows so bad they'll bring back the corn they stole last year," said Alan.

"Aw, you heard that on the radio!" Althea said.

"The poor, poor dear," was all Mrs. Barney could say, and she hurried away.

"Maybe I bought something and maybe I didn't," said Barney defensively. "I don't think he's ready to be fed to the hounds—and who knows, maybe he's a Cinderella."

"Some Cinderella!" mumbled Doc Cheshire, as he started his examination.

Before he was through, poor old Robin had his nose buried deep in a bucket of soft, warm bran mash which Althea and her mother had produced. My, but it was good! It was the first decent food, other than the small measure of oats, that he'd had in months, and the first that he'd been able to eat with comfort for a long, long time. As he ate hungrily he rolled his eye at Mrs. Barnett and seemed to say, "Gee, you are swell people!"

"Give him this," said the vet, as he handed Barney a prescription. "I'll be over to fix his teeth in the morning."

With that, six hands went to work with curry-combs and

brushes. The dirt flew, and after a while Barney said, "That'll do for tonight. Put his 'pajamas' on and I'll make his bed."

Alan got a clean blanket and tossed it up onto Robin's back, and he and Althea tugged it straight and buckled it in place. By that time Barney was waiting to lead the horse into a single stall into which he had forked dry straw, which lay knee-deep on the level floor.

The whole Barnett family, including Mother, who had returned to herd the children to bed, said good night to Robin, turned out the stable light, and went to the house.

Poor Robin! He was very happy and he felt clean and secure for the first time in a great while. He took a look around the comfortable stable, stood deep in thought for a while and then, with a sigh, he lay down in the sweet-smelling straw and went to sleep.

Early the next morning the children came into the stable and went right to Robin. "Hi, Guy!" they greeted him as they crowded into his stall, with complete confidence that it would be safe. They treated him as though he had been there for months, and after a few minutes they went their way to see that all was well with their old friends in the barn. It was "Hi, Guy!" here and "Hi, Guy!" there, as they went from stall to stall.

For the next few weeks Robin did nothing but rest and eat and get acquainted with the people and animals of the Riding Academy. At first he was a curiosity, but in no time at all his thin neck began to fill out, his "hat rack" hips and his "washboard" ribs disappeared, and his coat showed a rich brown mahogany color.

Then one day Barney said, "I'm going to try the ex-scarecrow tomorrow and see how he goes."

The tryout was a great disappointment, for the years between the shafts of carts, putting his weight into a collar had changed Robin's gait and had stiffened his shoulders. "Like riding four pogo sticks," was the way Barney described Robin's action, and after a week of tryouts, he announced, "Sorry, but he just won't do around here. He'll have to go."

And so the horse, just as he had become attached to surroundings and people, was to be wrenched up and transplanted, and there was nothing that he could do about it.

But Robin's luck had changed, for the following Saturday a group of boys and girls were going on a horseback picnic and every horse that Barney could get would be needed.

"I can't put anyone up on such a bone-jarring thing as you've turned out to be," he said to Robin, who was poking hopefully at Barney's pockets, looking for sugar. Again Barney counted noses, but still there weren't horses enough. "I can just do it if —if I ride you. Me—I'll have to spend the day on you—and then go to the osteopath."

The gorgeous day, soft bridle paths and many horses brought memories of other days at Lairds' to Robin's mind. Thoughts of men in pink coats, and the excitement of jumping fences to stay with hounds, caused Robin to give Barney a great surprise.

When it came time to canter, the man gritted his teeth. "Well, here we go—bone-crusher," he murmured, but, to his amazement, after a couple of strides, he found that Robin without thinking had started to "roll" his shoulders as of old. Barney could hardly believe the feel that Robin gave him. "Why, you old devil, you!" he exclaimed, and revelled in the change which had come over the horse.

Later in the day, when some of the party were playing around over some very small jumps, it seemed to the rider that Robin was acting queerly; he bobbed his head and champed on his bit and pawed the ground.

"What's eating you, crow-bait?" he muttered, and then, pretending not to notice it, he allowed his mount to sidle into the file of riders who were waiting to jump. "Can it be *you* want to take a hand at this sport?" he thought.

To his surprise Robin fairly leaped forward when it was his turn to go, and not once but several times Barney let the old horse flit over the little fences. Then, just to see what would happen, he had a couple of the youngsters put a rail up to three feet.

"Now let's see!" The result was the same. Robin went over the fence every time without the slightest hesitation, and he and Barney were in "seventh heaven" on the way home. At the stable Althea and Alan were waiting to help unsaddle and cool out horses, and they were surprised to see the wide grin on their father's face. "Gee, I thought he'd be dismal," said Alan, "after the way he started out on the scarecrow."

Later they learned why their Dad threw his right leg over the saddle and slid off to the ground so lightly and said, "Here—forget the rest of 'em. Give this fellow the best the 'hotel de horse' has to offer."

"Moves true as a die, no stiffness. Boy! Was I afraid of what I'd see," said Barney the next morning after watching Alan trot Robin back and forth. "Come on. Let's get to church and then try him over a few of the home fences. I think you'll see something."

And "see something" they did. Barney put Robin over some jumps and then came the inevitable, "Can I try him?" That was settled by the flip of a coin and Althea rode first.

Around the ringside they cantered for her to get the feel of Robin. They took the first fence easily and turned toward the second. Then things happened quickly.

A horse led by a groom suddenly bucked and kicked and then reared. He moved backward to keep his balance. His hind feet hit some rails lying in the grass by the wing of the fence, and he came down with a crash, taking the wing and the fence with him. The wreckage fell right under Robin's nose and before he could help himself he had thrust a leg through the boards of the wing, and Althea went over his head. A little foot somehow caught in a loop of rein and she was suspended head down under Robin's nose above the horse thrashing on the ground. There she dangled, hanging by her foot and her grip on the reins.

The groom and Barney stood petrified, then leaped forward,

but they were too late. Robin reared slowly, deliberately withdrawing his foot from the wreckage. He turned on his hind feet and stood stock still.

Quickly Barney and the groom set Althea on the ground.

"Well—I guess that's that," sighed Barney with relief. "That's what?" asked Althea; "I want my ride," and away she went again. Alan was next, and then Robin was unsaddled and turned out for a day of rest, while the other horses in the Academy carried the regular Sunday customers over the countryside.

As they turned Robin out into the paddock, Althea said, "It's funny, we don't know what to call him. He's got to have a name."

"Well, we always say, Hi, Guy! to him, and look at the way he jumps! Let's call him Hi Guy," said Alan. So from that day on Robin was Guy for short.

Hi Guy's common sense and lovable qualities completely won over the Barnetts. Now he belonged to Althea and Alan, though once in a while Barney threw a leg over his back.

Alan spent his time on Hi Guy in the ring under the watchful eye of his Dad. "Relax, relax, keep those hands down, heels down too," rang in his ears, for he was far behind Althea in his riding. This was not due to any failing on his part, but to an illness which had made any such physical activity as riding an unwise thing. He was now coming along apace, and a whole new world was opening up before him. But it was a world of embarrassment because he wasn't as advanced in active sports as other boys of his age, and he couldn't match strides with them.

As for Althea, all the help she wanted was assistance in saddling her beloved Hi Guy. Once that was done, he followed her like a big dog to a post and rail fence. There she'd lead him against it and climb into the saddle. But once in a while Hi Guy'd have *his* fun. He'd stand just far enough away so that she couldn't get aboard.

She'd huff and puff and scold and push with her little hands against the under side of his belly until he good-naturedly gave in and moved over. But Althea solved that problem by accident.

She found a place on his side where he was ticklish. From that time on all she had to do was wiggle a finger at the spot and a funny scared look would come into Hi Guy's eye and he would move over—quick.

At first dismounting was a problem, but she solved that, too, by lying on her tummy on the saddle and grasping the stirrup leather with her hands. She slid down it and then dropped to the ground and, without a word of direction, Hi Guy would follow her into the stable to the place where she always left a carrot or two.

The horse-show placards and circulars, which began to appear as summer came on, intrigued the Barneys and they decided to enter Hi Guy in the three-foot class in the local show. When Hi Guy's number was announced people looked at their programs and read, *Hi Guy, Br. G., 15.2 Aged—, Althea and Alan Barnett.* Then they looked at the entry which had come into the ring, and more than one person said, or thought, "He's not much to look at." But he carried off the blue ribbon. When he left the ring poor Alan, who was riding and who had had a terrific case of stage fright, was greeted by Althea, who said, "What a help to Hi Guy you turned out to be! You rode like a stiff poker. The only thing you didn't do was fall off."

The next week-end it was Althea's turn to ride, and again it was the blue for the old horse. So it went throughout the summer. They went to bigger and better shows and met stiffer competition, and Hi Guy carried off far more than his share of the ribbons, and a few championships.

"Did you know that Cinderella's prize money has more than paid for all his keep?" said Barney to Doc Cheshire.

"And we're going to put a show case in the stable to hold his ribbons," added Althea.

When the last show of the season's campaign was over Barney said to Hi Guy, "Now you go to a new home. From here on, you get the big box-stall next to the office." So it was, and the case for the ribbons and Hi Guy's name was placed on the wall of the box.

The next year it was the same story all over again. Barney studied the show dates carefully and planned for the least amount of travel, to save Hi Guy. He divided the season's work so that their one-horse show team could have some rest periods. "Because, if he does well I'm sending him to 'the National' at 'the Garden'," announced Barney.

Long before the time of the National, Alan's pleasant experiences in the show rings had done him a world of good. Thanks to Hi Guy, he had lost his fear of crowds, but the thought of the Garden—well, that was "a horse of a different color."

"Come on, snap out of it. This is just like any other show. Never mind the big names and the decorations. You just go in there and give Hi Guy a good ride," encouraged Barney, who had been watching Alan closely and had noted the growing signs of nervousness.

All too quickly, so far as Alan was concerned, he found himself sitting on Hi Guy, looking through the big entrance gates into Madison Square Garden Arena. They were next! The gates swung toward them. The time was *now*. Automatically Hi Guy started forward, out into the bright lights of the ring. The announcer saw their number, spoke into the loudspeaker, and "Number 49" echoed through the Garden as the gates closed behind the pair.

This was it! This was the National. Alan gulped. Vaguely he saw the array of fences and potted shrubs, the orange and black streamers, uniformed attendants, judges, and the boxes full of people. Behind them were more people, people everywhere, all with their eyes on him. He felt the steady movement of Hi Guy between his knees and it gave him confidence. He swallowed hard. It helped to clear his mind, and he remembered his Dad's instructions. He stopped Hi Guy and pretended to adjust a stirrup-leather. This gave the old horse a chance to get used to the light and take a look around the arena. Then, very calmly and deliberately, Alan walked Hi Guy slowly around the all-important preparatory circle. Now completely at ease, he leaned forward just a bit and the horse broke into a canter and started for the first fence. It was made of evergreens, and Hi Guy brushed through the top of it and went on to the Eighth Avenue end of the Garden. Back across it on a diagonal he came, working easily, surely, with clocklike precision. "He certainly makes it look easy," said someone, as Alan went over the course with its crossed bars, triple bar and oxer. Hi Guy was no stranger to many in the vast audience, and when he finished with a clean performance, a fine round of applause burst forth. The jump off of a tie was a bit too much for him, and a couple of minor mistakes gave him third place and the yellow ribbon.

"Oh, Guy, Guy," said Althea proudly. "A ribbon in your first class at the National! Any ribbon here is a real honor."

The next afternoon it was her turn to be up, and the little minx saw to it that Hi Guy was one of the first horses to show in the class. "Come on, open those gates and let's go!" bubbled out of her as the entry in the ring finished his turn over the jumps. In her exuberance she was Hi Guy's undoing, for, momentarily, she forgot the course they were to travel. She realized her mistake just in time and turned Number 49 back onto the proper one, but her error put him into an awkward position for the next fence and, even though he leaped cleverly, he couldn't help taking down a rail. Althea bit her lip, but try as she would she couldn't stop the tears, and by the time she reached the exit gate they were pouring down her face.

"Oh, Guy, it's all my fault," she sobbed, as she lay forward and buried her face in his mane. Her father comforted her as they waited for the rest of the horses to jump. One after another they had knock-downs or refusals marked against their names. "Only five more to jump," said Alan. "And if two of them will only knock down one rail apiece, you'll be in there in a three-horse tie for fourth place."

The suspense could have been drawn out, but it wasn't. The next horse would have none of the first easy fence and the second, third and fourth all made bad mistakes, while the fifth jumped cleanly to take the blue.

"Numbers 49, 52 and 78 to jump off," came over the loudspeaker. With her jaw set tight, Althea sent Hi Guy on his way. "Come on, boy—steady—attaboy—come on, fella. Once more, watch it now," she said in a quiet, encouraging voice as Hi Guy went about his work. At last the final fence was behind the old horse and the young rider. It was a convincing, clean performance, and the crowd rose as one to applaud the game demonstration, for they realized that the previous little mistake had possibly robbed this pair of first place. Number 52 knocked down a rail at the second, and that did for him so far as Hi Guy was concerned. Next was Number 78. He had always been a horse that gave Hi Guy tough competition, but this was not his day, and the Barneys all breathed a sigh of relief when he hit the third fence. "It's the red for you and Guy," laughed Barney, as he gathered Althea in his arms.

There was one more class, two days later, for Hi Guy. Alan was up in the saddle when the old horse faced the bright lights again. The boy wasn't bothered by stage-fright this time and the pair went right to work, but at the fourth fence things went wrong. Somehow Alan lost a stirrup, quickly he reached to adjust the "iron" but, as it thrashed about, it cracked him on the wrist, and his whole arm went numb. The Garden swam before his eyes and the next jump was hazy as it loomed before him. Automatically Alan kept in the saddle and guided the horse with his right hand as he bent over and hugged his left arm against his stomach. By this time Hi Guy knew his way around because they were competing over the same course he'd jumped so many times before, and he went unerringly from fence to fence.

"He knew what to do!" gasped Alan when telling his folks about it a few seconds later. "Oh, my arm—even my fingers are numb!"—and he shook his hand. "Guy knew something was wrong and he didn't let the flapping 'iron' or anything bother him."

When all the horses had jumped, the Barneys found themselves in another tie. This time for the blue, with two other horses. This was Hi Guy's big chance, and Alan, sportsman that he was, shut his mouth tightly and nodded yes when Barney put his hand on his shoulder and asked him to let Althea carry on and give the old horse every possible chance. "Sure, he's the one that counts," said the boy, as he clenched his teeth and hugged his still numb left arm to his body.

"Change of rider for Number 49 because of injury," was announced to the spectators as Althea, who had no time to get her cap or jacket, rode Hi Guy into the ring.

With the deliberation of a veteran, who was out to jump for her life, she settled herself in the saddle and let Hi Guy go to it. Over the brush with a swish of the evergreens they went. The slanting posts and rails of the second fence were a snap. She let the wise old horse set his own pace as they turned the end of the arena. Three white rails of the third fence flashed under Hi Guy and Althea, and the little wall that was next was cleanly jumped also. By this time applause rang out louder as each fence was cleared.

"Atta girl—ride 'em!" came from someone in the stands as she turned Hi Guy, but she never relaxed long enough to throw a glance of appreciation toward the voice.

"Steady, boy—steady—we're gonna win it," she said, as they rose to the fifth fence and landed beyond it. With the sixth only a few feet ahead, Hi Guy put in one stride and jumped again.

"Atta boy—only two to go—come on, fella—steady now, C-A-R-E-FUL," she gulped, as up and over the last jump but one they went, and the Garden rocked with applause and then became deathly silent as the pair went for the last fence. "Keep it up—one more—just one more—it's *got* to be clean."

The old horse set himself perfectly and took off to go over the broad white boards. It seemed that he was well over, but there was a rap against the top board.

Althea's heart sank. Seven fences clean and then . . . As Hi

Guy landed she turned in the saddle to see what damage had been done. The top board was still *there* in place. That was a help. She flashed a white, frightened, inquiring look at the judge nearest the fence. With a gesture he signalled, CLEAN, to the other judges and to her he called, with a smile, "He kicked up a stone and it hit the fence—you're O.K." He said the O.K. in a manner that showed his pleasure at being able to make the decision, and the groan from the people in the stands gave way to a crash of applause as they realized that the performance was clean.

In the next few minutes, that seemed as long as an age to the Barnetts, each of the other two horses made mistakes, and the blue belonged to Hi Guy.

Quickly the result of the class was written on a piece of paper and handed to an attendant with a "walkie-talkie." He relayed the winning numbers to the man at the loudspeaker and "Winner of Class 62, Hi Guy, Number 49; second, Carefree," was announced, but the rest was unimportant to the Barneys. The entrance gates opened and Alan, grinning from ear to ear, trotted into the ring, leading Hi Guy with his good hand, to receive the blue; while Althea, not to be denied her place in the limelight, was there to carry off Hi Guy's silver trophy.

That ended the show work for the year. When, once again at the Academy, Hi Guy held open house in the stable, one of those who came early and stayed late was Althea's friend, the judge from the National. As he left he said, "Know what? You ought to change the old fellow's name. I've been thinking of where you found him and of his fine qualities. You ought to call him 'Pound Sterling.'"

But Hi Guy remained Hi Guy. He went on collecting ribbons and cups for several seasons, and today he is turned out in clover. His show days are over, and he is ridden only for exercise by the members of his family. Alan, now a Naval aviator, sometimes tries his wings on horseback, and Althea taunts the old horse by threatening to tickle that spot in his ribs to make him move around to be saddled so that she can go for a ride.

BALTO'S RACE AGAINST DEATH

by Irma H. Taylor

The pale face of Dr. Curtis Welch grew very serious as he looked about the hospital room. He knew that he faced a hard fight—and all alone! He was the only doctor in the little town of Nome, Alaska, that bitter, cold winter in 1925.

Already three people were dead.

On the hospital beds lay twenty-five sick people. They had diphtheria, a terrible throat disease. If it should get out of control, it would sweep like wildfire over hundreds of square miles. Eleven thousand Eskimos and white people were in danger!

"We've got to have help," Dr. Welch said in a worried voice. "I mean help from the outside!"

"Yes, it's getting away from us," agreed a nurse. "Maybe some town can send us more doctors. If we were only on the railroad, or if the sea weren't frozen! This load is too much for you alone."

"It is not doctors or nurses we need," said Dr. Welch. "It is medicine. I have hardly five shots of antitoxin left, and that is six years old. Maybe it is no good." He clasped his thin fingers. If he could shoot fresh antitoxin into the arms of the people who were well, they probably would not get sick.

The nurse spoke eagerly, "Can't you radio to the United States for antitoxin?"

"Yes, but it will take six weeks to get here. By that time we may have one of the worst disasters in history."

"But, Doctor, couldn't they reach us sooner with airplanes?" broke in the nurse.

"Not through this weather. No pilot could make it, and it is fifty degrees below zero." The doctor looked very grave. "Our only hope is to get antitoxin from some place closer. Take care of that Eskimo woman's throat while I call the radio station."

A few minutes later the cry for help was flashing across the snows. As people heard the bad news, they were much alarmed. Nome was up in the Arctic Circle, four hundred miles from the nearest railroad and frozen in by the sea. Yet help must be sent at once.

A doctor in southern Alaska heard the message. He happened to have a good supply of antitoxin, and immediately wired Dr. Welch: "I am sending antitoxin to Nenana on today's train." Nenana was the town closest to Nome on the railroad.

So the precious twenty-pound package was started on its journey. After the three hundred miles by train, it must be carried six hundred and fifty miles over the cruel snowbound trail stretching between Nenana and Nome.

Only dogs could make it!

Again the radio sent out a call—this time for drivers of dog teams. These drivers are known as mushers and their dogs as huskies, the right name for what are sometimes called Eskimo dogs. At once brave mushers picked out their strongest dogs, hitched them to their sleds, and hurried to the trail. The six-hundred-and-fifty-mile trail had never been covered in less than nine days. But this was a race against death, with eleven thousand lives at stake!

At eleven o'clock on Tuesday evening, January 27, the package on which so many lives depended was taken off the train. The first musher, waiting with his dog team, took it eagerly and set out on the trail.

The great relay race had begun. Each musher would struggle on until he reached the next man, twenty-five to one hundred miles away.

We do not know much about the first heroes who carried the medicine. We know their names and the route they took. But the greatest honor has been paid to the two mushers who bore the most dangerous part of the journey. Of course, their skill and daring would not have been enough. The others had to do their part also, but to these two fell the greatest tests of heroism. Their courage and that of the huskies who led their teams would have been hard to equal.

Shannon was the first musher. Every inch of the trail was familiar to him as he hurried down a frozen stream bed toward the Yukon River. Even in the dark he recognized which Indian dwelling he was passing. He knew he was making good time—more than five miles an hour.

Wednesday noon Shannon, tired but happy, turned the package over to the second musher. It was time for Shannon to stop, because his dogs were worn out. Losing no time, the second stout team plunged down the trail. By seven o'clock in the evening they had reached the Yukon River.

One hundred and fifty miles in twenty hours!

If the next teams could only keep up the pace! Just twenty-four hours later the antitoxin was three hundred and fifty miles on its way.

Friday afternoon it was placed in the hands of Leonard Seppala, known far and wide as "the king of dog-team drivers." This daring musher had come out from Nome to meet the medicine. He had covered two hundred miles of difficult trail in four days. Now, with no chance to rest his picked team of Siberian dogs turned back on the trail.

Seppala hoped to carry the antitoxin all the way back to Nome so that it would get there Saturday afternoon. This would mean covering those two hundred miles in one day! Even in the fresh fallen snow! And with the temperature down below zero.

His team soon came to the edge of the ice-covered Norton Bay. Anxiously he looked out over the frozen surface, for the direct route to Nome lay across this bay. It would be safer to take the land route around it, but that would add almost another hundred miles. If he followed the land, maybe the antitoxin would arrive too late. Seppala decided quickly. It would be the short, dangerous way.

"Gee, Togo!" he cried, and the beautiful forty-eight-pound husky dog headed over the ice.

The musher watched the sixteen-year-old dog with a thrill of pride. Togo was a natural leader. He was a wonder at picking up the trail, and the other dogs knew they must obey him.

It was now dark. The condition of the ice worried Seppala. Any minute it might break up and drift out to sea. Sometimes before they realized that the ice was free, travelers have been carried for miles on a loose ice cake. Some have been blown out into Bering Sea and drowned.

Horrible thoughts crowded into Seppala's mind. "Suppose the bay ice should suddenly crack up. We would be carried to open water and drift helplessly all night. Nobody could rescue us. My dogs would freeze to death—and so would I—if we did not drown first. And the antitoxin would be lost, somewhere on the bottom of the sea. They trusted it to me, and I must get through."

Speed—there lay his safety. Togo picked his way carefully as the team raced along. Each husky seemed to know that Seppala was depending upon him. They loved this master who never struck with a whip.

Midnight came. Seppala wondered whether they were halfway across. How cold it was! Didn't he hear a cracking noise? His heart stood still! Togo raced on as if he knew the danger.

At last the sky turned gray. The musher looked eagerly for signs of land. Ahead lay only an icy stretch.

No, wasn't that a shadowy coast line a bit to the right? A few minutes later he was sure. Another mile slipped by. They would make it safely—the ice would hold!

"My good dogs!" he cried proudly. "Gee, Togo!"

Togo led the team up on the snowy bank, and the treacherous bay ice was left behind. Seppala hummed a little song. Now if this team he loved could only go the rest of the way.

Suddenly, as he rounded a turn, he saw a dog team and musher waiting on the trail. Much as he would have liked to press on himself, he knew it would be wiser to let this fresh team of dogs take over.

"Hello, Olson," he called, stopping his sled beside the new

team. "Here is the antitoxin." He smiled cheerfully as he handed over the package to the musher.

"Things are worse in Nome . . . another death!" said Olson. His fingers were busy tying the package to his sled. "You made wonderful time, Seppala."

Olson and his seven dogs were off. Before their twenty-five-mile run was over, these dogs were almost frozen.

With great relief Olson handed the antitoxin to the last musher. Gunnar Kasson, who lived in Nome, had been waiting in an empty cabin for two days and nights. He had not even lain down, because he was afraid he might fall asleep and then miss Olson. Thirteen stouthearted dogs made up his team.

He said to Olson, "I am going to take the antitoxin into the cabin for a few minutes. The terrible wind may have frozen it."

Although the men waited inside the cabin for two hours, the weather kept getting colder. It was thirty degrees below. Snow began to fall. Every time they looked outside, the flakes were pelting down all the faster. A snowstorm meant dangerous going, Kasson knew. But he said, "There is no use waiting any longer."

Stepping outside, he called his lead dog, "Hey, Balto!"

Thirteen balls of fur scrambled out of their warm nests in the snow.

"Here, Balto. Here, boy!"

A handsome husky with a glossy coat ran to his place at the head of the traces. As Kasson fastened the dog into the harness, he said, "Tonight we'll have a hard pull. We have to make it through, boy!"

The dog pricked up his ears and raised intelligent eyes as if he understood.

Thirty-four miles away lay the next town, a little place called Safety. They must reach it before snowbanks could pile up and block the trail.

"Mush!" cried Kasson.

The dogs headed out bravely on the trail following the coast. It was terribly hard pulling. Although animals and sled sank into the heavy snow, the team struggled on.

"Whew, I never felt a colder wind!" thought Kasson, trying to pull his long reindeer coat closer around him. Sealskin boots reached to his hips, and over these he wore sealskin trousers. His head was protected by a reindeer hood. But the fierce eighty-mile gale whipped right through the skins.

Their way led straight into the wind. How could he or the dogs face it? He feared they would all freeze to death. Even though they kept going, how long could they stay on the trail?

Something else made Kasson very uneasy. The ice under his feet was in constant motion from ocean ground swells. He turned the dogs in closer to the shore line. Now he was crossing the mouth of a frozen river.

Suddenly he realized that Balto was in trouble.

The lead dog had stepped into a pool of water, an overflow that had run up on the ice. Unless Balto's feet could be dried off immediately, the skin would stick to the ice and be torn off. Then he would have to drop out—and he was the only lead dog in the team. It was a bad moment. Just then Kasson saw the one thing which could save Balto's feet—a snowdrift a few yards away.

"Gee, Balto!" he shouted, and the dog turned sharply to the right.

When Balto felt the soft snow, he knew just what to do. He worked his paws in the snow until they were dry. Now the skin was safe. Kasson breathed a sigh of relief.

Starting off again, he headed the team up a six-hundred-foot hill. Here there was nothing to stop the fury of the wind howling in off the sea. Kasson's lips set tightly. This hill was the spot he feared more than any other. Near the top he discovered that his right cheek had no feeling. It was frozen. He grabbed some snow and rubbed the cheek until it felt alive again.

He was glad to leave the hill behind. Next came a flat stretch six miles long. He wondered whether they would ever get across it, for the wind was picking up masses of snow and hurling them.

Kasson was choked and blinded. He strained to catch sight of the dogs. The dog nearest the sled was not even a blur. He held up his hand—no use, he could not see it!

His heart sank. Lost—he was hopelessly lost. The antitoxin would never reach Nome.

Yet the sled was moving steadily on. There was one hope left—that the dogs could keep the trail themselves. Kasson thought, "Balto will not fail me!"

The heroic lead dog never hesitated. Hurrying straight ahead, he scented the trail on the glaring, wind-swept ice. For two hours the musher held to the sled and trusted everything blindly to Balto.

They entered the tiny village of Solomon. Kasson did not even see the cabins. In this village a message was waiting for him: "Stop in Solomon until the storm clears. Then go on to Safety. Ed Rohn is there with a fresh team. Let him finish the race."

Kasson sped on through the storm, not knowing that he had passed Solomon—not dreaming he had missed an important message.

If anything, the wind grew more bitter in the next twelve miles. Kasson was filled with joy when finally he caught sight of an old log store. He was in the village of Safety. His wonderful Balto had followed the trail!

Kasson saw that all the houses were dark. Not knowing that another musher was waiting here, he thought, "Shall I stop for help? It would mean a long delay. There may not be any dogs in town strong enough to mush through the storm. Balto knows the trail; there is no other dog like him."

Speeding past the dark hotel, the team soon left Safety behind. Just twenty-one miles to go. The trail followed the shore of Bering Sea.

An angry wind whipped in from the sea. "I will tear you off the sled!" it seemed to cry. Kasson clung the tighter.

He was growing very tired. The dogs too, were slowing up, almost worn out by the long, cruel grind. Deep drifts made the pulling terribly hard. Yet they struggled bravely on. They would reach the goal—or die in the traces!

Kasson was thinking of many things; the rosy flames of a warm fire, how wonderful it would feel when he got to Nome. Would all his dogs make it through? Too bad to lose even one—it must not be Balto! What wouldn't he give for a drink of steaming hot coffee? How far away was Nome? Fifteen miles? Twelve miles? How many more sick people had died? He must hurry—hurry—

Just then Kasson felt the sled pitch roughly. The next instant he was flung into the snow. As the sled overturned in a great drift, Balto slowed down and stopped the team. The dogs began to bark and fight, tangling up their harness.

Kasson jumped up and put the sled back on both runners. Then, lashing his whip, he quieted the dogs. It took him some time to straighten their harness in the dark. When they were ready to start again, he reached down to see whether the antitoxin was securely fastened.

What a horrible moment—the antitoxin was gone!

Crawling on his hands and knees, he hunted frantically in the snow. The sled had turned over on the right. Surely he would find the metal can there—if he had not lost it miles back on the trail. Could that have happened?

No, thank heaven, here it was!

His heart began to beat again. This time he tied the package very securely.

As they set out, the snowfall seemed lighter. At times he could see a bit of trail ahead. Then in the half-light he saw that two dogs were suffering—the two that had been frozen a few weeks before. The poor creatures were limping stiffly. Stopping the team, he fastened rabbitskin covers over these two dogs; but it didn't help much, for the cold went right through. If they should die, he would leave them and press on. If all the dogs should die, he would still go on, carrying the antitoxin in his arms. Nome—he must get to Nome!

He wished for morning as the hours dragged by. Now he was

running behind the sled, for the team was staggering. "Keep going, Balto!" he cried. "We're almost there!" It seemed that the team could not last another mile.

He was straining his eyes looking for the lumber mill at the edge of Nome.

At last it appeared out of the falling snow. Thank God, they had made it—they had made it to Nome! It was 5:36 in the morning of Monday, February 2—just five and a half days after the start at Nenana.

The dogs seemed to know that the end of the great race was here. They hurried past the mill, past a row of wooden houses. Kasson heard people shouting, knew they were running after him. He turned to the left—there was the hospital. The next thing he knew, Dr. Welch was wringing his hand. "You got here in time!" said the doctor joyfully. The crowd shouted.

Half frozen and almost blinded Kasson dropped down into the snow. With tears in his eyes he started to pull ice splinters out of Balto's paws.

"Balto!" he cried. "Wonderful dog! You brought us through!"

THE HORSE THAT CAME FROM HEAVEN

by Catherine C. Coblentz

The Black Horse hoped something important was going to happen to him. There was expectation in each high-stepping foot, in the way he arched his neck, in the tilt of his nose.

Proudly and happily he led all the other Spanish horses. Forgotten was the ocean journey of several weeks from the Island of Cuba to Mexico. Forgotten, too, were the battles with the Indians when he had carried first one master and then another on his back.

Now his rider was Cortez himself, that Spanish Conquistador who had conquered the Aztecs and all Mexico for Spain. The Black Horse had heard him say that he was going southward next to Honduras.

It didn't matter much to the Black where they went. He liked to glimpse from the corners of his slanting eyes that black silken banner with a scarlet cross in its centre waving over the Spanish soldiers. He liked to hear the bugle playing, and didn't mind at all the high shrill shrieks from the herd of pigs taken along to provide food for the soldiers in case game should be scarce.

But gradually the pace of the Black slowed a little. Cortez was not a light person to carry, and besides he was dressed in heavy armor. The Black remembered that he had no idea how long the way might be to Honduras.

He was glad later that he had saved his strength. He had never dreamed there would be such high chains of mountains to be crossed, such rivers that must be conquered. Sometimes he swam across them. Sometimes he was carried across by Indians in canoes.

Good grass was often scarce. Flies settled on the Black's coat by day and mosquitoes by night, even though he switched his tail or twitched his skin constantly to shake them off.

Sometimes in the dusk horrible bats would descend upon him and plague him almost as much as did the insects and flies, and the bats were not so easily dislodged.

Day after day went by, and the Black still led the way southward. After all, he once thought, this was probably the most important thing that could happen to him.

One morning he came to a wide river. It flowed fast in places, but along the shores it seemed hardly to move at all, and it was filled with alligators. The Black had heard it said that alligators were fond of eating horses. So he waited eagerly for the bridle rein to tighten. If Cortez urged him into the water, he knew he would obey.

But after he had cantered up and down the river-bank for a little, Cortez patted his neck and said, "No, my Black, that river is not for *you* to swim." And the man slipped from the horse's back and led him over to the shadow of some ceiba trees.

There for four days the horse of Cortez rested with the other horses, watching while the Spaniards cut down trees and built a narrow bridge. When it was done Cortez led the Black across the bridge, while the other Spaniards followed, leading their steeds. The Black switched his tail triumphantly at the hungry alligators. Surely now the worst of his troubles were over.

Even as that idea passed through his mind his left fore foot sank under him. Quickly he placed the other front foot on what appeared to be solid ground. It, too, sank out of sight.

Then the third and fourth foot plunged into black mud and ooze. All the horses that had followed after him were sinking also. He could hear their frightened breathing; somewhere one of them screamed. What had looked like solid earth was a terrible marsh.

He glimpsed Cortez jumping from grassy hummock to grassy hummock. Then he heard the voice of his master calling his horse to follow him.

Vainly the Black tried to obey. But the more he struggled the deeper he sank into the muck. His two front legs were in the mire to his knees, his hind quarters to his body.

Desperately he lunged, and succeeded in raising his front feet for a moment on what seemed to be firm ground. But as he attempted to free his hind quarters even this ground failed him, and the front feet sank down once more, until he felt the mire along his whole body. The morass was filled with struggling, snorting, and neighing horses.

Taking another quick glimpse, the Black saw that all the *men* had crossed, and he was glad of that. He heard Cortez shout an order and caught the answering voices of the men, who were coming back again toward their horses. They had picked up anything on which they could lay their hands, and brought armfuls of long reed-like grasses and fallen tree branches, and threw them down in front of the animals, urging them to attempt to use even this frail support. Some of the horses succeeded in partially raising themselves in this way.

But the Black, after getting one foot upon the armful of stuff Cortez thrust before him, saw both foot and the green grass disappear again in the dark slipperiness.

Deeper and deeper he sank. The mud was cool against his sides, but he did not appreciate the coolness. He was afraid, desperately afraid.

Then the mud closed over his spine with a sucking sound. He flung his head up and back as far as he could. But it seemed useless. The black stuff drew him down, down. Now it was at his mouth, his nostrils. Taking one last, long breath of air, he sank out of sight. Only his ears were to be seen, little points above the black mud.

And then, "Swim, my Black One, swim," came the voice of his master. "Swim, swim! I tell you, *you can swim*. Black One, come, *come! Swim!*"

Was the master out of his mind? What horse could swim in *mud?* But the horse of Cortez obeyed the voice. He thrust his feet out in the swimming motion. And he moved. Slowly but surely he moved forward.

The sucking mire seemed to leave his nose. He felt men's hands pushing down through the mud to his hind quarters, propelling him forward. He heard the voice of Cortez calling, coaxing. Valiantly he struggled.

Suddenly he was freed. He was swimming quite easily. He shook the mud from his eyes and opened them. A few feet ahead of him some Spaniards were standing and calling. Others were jumping frantically from grass spot to grass spot at one side of the horses. Horses were swimming to the right and to the left of the Black. Ahead of him he saw one scrambling out of the mire and standing erect with four feet securely on firm ground. The Black made for that spot.

Afterward as he lay panting on the ground he listened to the men explaining how the struggling of the many horses in the mud had caused a middle lane of water to gather, and by this narrow waterway the steeds had finally been able to swim to safety.

The Black looked around him happily. He was a ridiculous sight, covered from his eyes to the end of his tail with drying mud. But he did not mind. The sky had never seemed so blue, or the trees so green.

He struggled to his knees. Suddenly Cortez was beside him and all the Spaniards likewise fell on their knees. There in the sunlight, under the gray moss that swayed from dead tree branches, the men gave thanks for the saving of their horses.

The Black, too, felt very thankful.

PURE-BRED PULLS THROUGH

by Montgomery Atwater

It was January. Far away in Kentucky, his birthplace, Kentucky Roamer's brothers and sisters and cousins were all blanketed and kept in heated stalls. Tuckee might have laughed if he had seen them. He wore no blanket, and the stable of his master, the forest ranger, did not have a furnace.

Burning heat or bitter cold are all one to an Arab horse, and Tuckee was an Arab. His desert ancestors had needed no coddling and neither did he, though their stout-hearted heritage came to him through generations of delicate race horses.

His red coat was as long and thick as a bear rug. January, the month of blizzards, bothered him no more than it did the two mountain horses who were his companions. But he did wish for summer, for now there were no long rides through the hills with the gray-green man on his back. The trails he knew so well were choked with three feet of snow, and when the forest ranger went out it was with queer, clumsy things—skis or snowshoes—tied to his feet.

Once a month, at the most, the gray-green man rode Tuckee the few miles to town, leading one of the other horses to bring back a load of supplies. Most horses would have thought that hard work enough, in winter, but to Tuckee it was nothing at all.

Only yesterday they had made such a trip, and for Tony, in the next stall, it had certainly been hard enough. He had fallen down on a hidden patch of ice, wise veteran though he was, and strained one shoulder. He was feeling very sorry for himself and very disgusted, for he was known as the best snow-horse in that part of the Rockies. He munched his hay dejectedly, and only flattened his ears when Tuckee put his head over the side of the stall and made a playful nip at him.

Kentucky Roamer turned back to his own well-filled manger. Nothing to do for another month. Really it was discouraging, when a horse's legs were fairly aching for some real exercise. Tuckee did not dream that before the close of the short winter day he was to have all the exercise he wanted, and possibly a good deal more.

In his office not far from the stable, Kentucky Roamer's master was looking at the barometer. Down three points since the evening before! With one finger he tapped it lightly and the needle dropped another half point. That meant a storm coming. Yes, the sky told him the same thing. At first glance it seemed clear, but a second look discovered a faint haziness. No doubt a blizzard straight from the Arctic Circle was getting close. It was about time for one.

The forest ranger went outside to look at the thermometer; the red column stood at fifteen degrees below. With his hand on the office door he paused at the sound of a faint droning overhead, and his keen eyes soon located the source: an airplane flying past several miles to the west. It was a little early for the mail plane to be going over, he thought, but perhaps the pilot was worried about the storm.

The plane disappeared behind a near-by mountain and its buzzing was heard no more. But still the forest ranger lingered, in spite of the cold. At the very last moment before it passed from sight the plane had seemed to drop into a dive. Now why should he have thought that? He shrugged finally, and went inside. His eyes must have played him a trick.

A few minutes later the telephone rang. He took up the receiver and recognized the voice of his chief: "Did you see a plane go over your way a little while ago?"

"Why, yes," he answered, "just a few minutes ago. Why?"

"Reported by radio that they were making a forced landing. A Captain Craig, of our Air Service, and Wolfe-Arnold, the English Air Minister making a tour of inspection in this country, are in that plane. It must be the one you saw. They're probably done for, but if there's any chance at all it depends on you to make it good."

"You bet," answered the ranger. "I'll do all I can."

"Just a second," came the voice. "What's the weather like out there?"

"Barometer says a storm's coming up."

"I just wanted to be sure you knew. The Weather Bureau predicts a blizzard in less than twelve hours, so you haven't much time. Good luck!"

The gray-green man dropped the receiver on its hook and went to work. "Poor devils," he thought as he laced up his moccasins, "They're certainly up against it, but there's still time."

With the speed of long practice he assembled the things a man must take when he goes out against the wilderness in winter. A belt around his waist supported pistol, knife, and hatchet. Binoculars hung from a strap about his neck. For the aviators, in case they had managed to make a safe landing, he took two pairs of snowshoes. To the snowshoes he tied a bundle containing a first-aid kit, food, and a thermos bottle full of hot coffee.

As an afterthought he added to the bundle two pairs of heavy socks and mittens. If they were using a cabin plane the men would not be wearing the right kind of clothes for a snowshoe trip in fifteen-below weather. One hand, plunged into his pocket, made sure of his waterproof match-safe and the stub of candle which the woodsman always carries when a quick fire may mean the difference between life and death.

Outside the office he adjusted the fastenings of his skis, strapped the pack to his shoulders, and started off. The snow lay deep and soft, but the polished wooden runners carried him easily and swiftly over the surface. His course was up the side of the mountain which towered over his cabin. From its bald summit he hoped with the aid of his binoculars to locate the wrecked airplane. From there, in fact, he *must* locate it, if the flyers were to be saved. Without shelter, without proper clothes, injured perhaps, they could live only a few hours in the bitter cold; and there was the blizzard to reckon with.

An hour of unceasing labor brought him to the mountain-top, where he slipped his pack and took the binoculars out of their case. Above him in the sky the storm haze was now unmistakable. Below him was spread the endless confusion of the wilderness, cañon after cañon, mountain beyond mountain. On Tuckee he had ridden the length of every one of those cañons. He knew the name of the farthest mountain—and he knew, also, how inhospitable that wilderness could be to anyone caught helpless and unprepared in the midst of its vast expanse.

The ranger lifted his glasses and began patiently to search each meadow, clearing, and mountain park. A razor-keen wind bit through his heavy jacket, but he ignored it. If the aviators had managed to land in some open space he could search them out with his ten-mile eyes. If they had crashed among the trees or into a cañon, it would make little difference to them when they were discovered.

Little by little the binoculars swept the horizon; halfway around and still no sign of the plane. Suddenly the ranger's nerves tingled. There was no chance of a mistake. In a clearing only a short distance away was the airplane. The powerful glasses showed every detail. The machine lay on its side, with one wing crumpled, but it did not seem badly smashed. The ranger fired into the air three times and then watched for some indication that his signal had been heard; but there was none.

Finally he put the glasses back in their case, picked out several landmarks to guide him, and began the descent from the mountain. Downhill on skis is swift traveling. In a few minutes, with a hiss of dry snow under his runners, the gray-green man emerged from the timber and skidded to a halt beside the plane.

Anxiously he looked into the cabin. The men were there. One lay on the floor as though dead, wrapped in an overcoat; the other huddled in his seat, apparently only half conscious. He had heard neither the shots nor the sounds of the ranger's arrival.

The gray-green man jerked open the door of the cabin and cried: "How about it? Anyone on deck?"

It was a wonderful thing to see the light of hope in the eyes turned toward him. The huddled figure in the seat stirred and then said, in the unmistakable voice of an Englishman, "I say, how in the world did you get here?"

The ranger had unslung his pack and was working at the knots. "Never mind that," he said cheerfully. "Let this drive the cold out of your bones," and he extended the thermos bottle.

The Englishman stretched out one cold-stiffened hand, then dropped it. "Give the other chap some first. He's unconscious."

In a moment the ranger had lifted the flyer's head and was pouring the hot fluid down his throat, a little at a time. The man choked, gasped, and took a deep breath. Only then did the Englishman take his turn. "That makes a chap feel different!" he exclaimed after a few swallows. "Y'know, you got here just in time. It's so beastly cold—"

The ranger kindled a fire, using the fabric and framework of the broken wing. To its warmth he dragged the unconscious pilot and laid him on the snowshoes, to keep him from sinking into the snow. "How about you?" he asked the Englishman. "Need some help to get over here?"

England's Minister of the Air smiled ruefully. "I'm afraid I do," he replied. "My leg is broken."

The ranger's heart sank. The extra snowshoes were of no use. Less than six miles away was his cabin, and safety, but it might as well have been six hundred. He thought swiftly. The day was still young; could he go back and telephone for help? A glance at the sky warned him—the thickening haze showed plainly that the blizzard was not far off.

He explained rapidly to the Englishman: "I'm going for horses. My cabin is only six miles or so from here, but there's a blizzard coming. We must hurry."

"Righto," answered the Englishman. "But just a moment. A blizzard's pretty bad business. You really mustn't take any risks for our sakes, old chap."

"Don't worry about that," said the ranger. "Just keep that fire going. We've got plenty of time before the blizzard gets here." But he turned away so that the Englishman might not read the truth in his face.

The gray-green man drove himself to the limit over the homeward miles, but once inside the stable, he paused with a feeling of dismay. In his excitement he had been counting all along on Tony. There was a horse, born and brought up in a deep-snow country, who would get through if any horse could. And until this moment he had forgotten Tony's wrenched shoulder. It was out of the question to use him. There were left only gallant, inexperienced Kentucky Roamer, and Brownie, too old for work like this.

Tuckee saw his master standing as though he did not know

what to do next, and nickered inquiringly. At this the gray-green man seemed to make up his mind, and hurriedly saddled Tuckee and Brownie.

The red horse was surprised when his master turned him toward the mountains. He had expected nothing more than another gallop to town. Not for months had they gone in this direction. He snorted as his legs sank into the snow. The chilly white stuff came up to his broad chest. This wasn't going to be much fun, but it was up to his master. Before there had always been Tony to break the trail on trips like this. Only long training, added to unusual courage, can overcome a horse's instinctive fear of deep snow, and Tuckee had only the courage. Brownie held back on the lead rope. Did something warn him?

The forest ranger chose the path with care, going through the thickest timber, where the snow would not be quite so deep. But presently they came to a drift, where the snow was deep and crusted. The ranger dismounted, and Tuckee saw him sink to his waist, and farther, as he broke a way through. No skis or snowshoes for him now. He must use his strength to save that of the horses.

Twice he went back and forth, then with a tug at the reins he urged Tuckee to try it. Obediently the red horse stepped forward. Now his feet no longer touched the ground. He trembled and stopped. There are not many things a horse fears more than to lose the feel of solid ground. But his master urged, "Come on, boy, let's go."

Kentucky Roamer gathered himself together and made a bound. Once, and again, and again. The sweat broke out all over him, but at last he was through. It was easier for Brownie now, though he balked and the ranger had to lash him.

So they pressed forward, stopping to rest only when forced to do so by sheer exhaustion. The ranger put one horse and then the other in the lead. As much as he could, he broke the trail himself. It is heart-breaking toil to walk in deep snow. It is like having a stone tied to each leg. The white flakes that seem so soft and light are like a million hands holding back.

More and more the ranger began to doubt the success of his desperate venture. Tuckee was bearing up splendidly, but Brownie was already nearly tired out. Only the thought of the helpless flyers drove the man on.

The distance the ranger had covered in an hour on skis took three times as long now, but finally they reached the goal. The fire was blazing cheerfully, and the American aviator had regained consciousness. He was even able to smile when the Englishman greeted the gray-green man with: "Forgive our bad manners, old chap, if we don't rise," adding as his eyes fell on Tuckee: "I say, that's a magnificent horse you have there—a true Arab, or I never saw one."

Tuckee was wringing wet with perspiration, and panting, but he could still prick his ears and arch his neck at the two strangers. Perhaps he wondered what in the world they were doing out here in the snow. For the airplane he had a snort of surprise. But there was no time to waste.

The haze had become a curtain that made half twilight of early afternoon. Already his master was helping one of the strangers into the saddle. What a queer way to ride, he thought, as the American slumped forward weakly. The other stranger was boosted into Brownie's saddle.

The trail was broken now, and the going was better, but Tuckee slipped and floundered. Why did the gray-green man keep urging him on, faster and faster? He would have liked to balk and shake the stranger off. It was hard enough to push his weary legs through that clinging, freezing blanket without a dead weight on his back to make it worse. But no, his master had put the stranger there and he must carry him, although his legs ached and his breath came in gasps.

He could see, too, that the gray-green man was very tired, stumbling on ahead, tramping down the snow to make it a little easier. He no longer turned his head to speak to Tuckee or the two airmen. Just behind him, Tuckee could hear Brownie laboring more and more painfully.

It was just after they had struggled through the deepest drift that the first catastrophe overtook them. Brownie was staggering now. Suddenly, without warning, he collapsed. The ranger had just time to pull the Englishman free. Tuckee looked around curiously at his friend lying half buried, with the air rattling in his lungs. Brownie could not get up. The snow had beaten him.

There was only one thing to do, and the ranger did it with his mouth set in a grim line. The pistol shot was short and harsh in the cold air. Just once he stroked Brownie's head. "Tough luck, old sport," he murmured. "All over now."

"I'll stay here," said the Englishman. "You've done all you can."

The ranger only shook his head, and with a shrug the English flyer allowed himself to be boosted up behind the American. Tuckee braced himself against the double load. What was the matter here, anyhow? These people should have their own horses. His master spoke quietly to him and rubbed his nose for a moment. Then they started forward again.

Tuckee was dazed with fatigue. His legs wanted to crumple under him, as Brownie's had. The red horse kept his eyes on his master, plodding, stumbling, sometimes crawling, doggedly ahead. They were nearing safety, however. "Careful here, old man," croaked Tuckee's master.

They were going along the edge of a deep, narrow gully. The horse trod cautiously. A little farther and he would be past the dangerous place. But all at once he set his foot on a smooth log buried under the snow. He slipped sideways toward the ravine, and his weary muscles could not save him. At the last moment the gray-green man seized the riders and pulled them back. Then, with a crash, Tuckee went over and tumbled down.

He came to rest on his back at the very bottom, all four feet in the air. Desperately he struggled to turn, but the steep banks held him as in a vise. "Easy, boy," came the voice of his master, and

Tuckee lay still. The gray-green man would fix it; the Arab horse was sure of that, and he fought down his fear.

Who could measure or describe the bitter hopelessness of the ranger? He himself could drag the two aviators to the cabin, now less than half a mile away. But what of Kentucky Roamer? Must he lie there helpless, so close to home, until the blizzard finished him? No, there was a quicker way than that. Once more his fingers closed on the butt of his pistol.

He felt a hand touch him, and turned to look into the eyes of England's Air Minister. "Too bad," said the aviator, "I wouldn't care so much—if it weren't for the plucky horses."

"I can get you two in now," groaned the ranger. "It's only a little way. But I can't leave Tuckee like that." He drew the pistol.

The Englishman raised his head. "Only a little way? Why, then we must save him! All of us or none, I say."

"It's no use. I can't turn him over alone."

"Drag me over to that tree," ordered the Air Minister. "I can't walk, but I can pull."

In their frantic haste they left the pilot as he had fallen, face down, in the snow. The ranger dragged the Englishman to a tree above the horse. Then he brought the lead rope and the two braced themselves.

Tuckee felt them tighten the rope. It pulled his head up and over his chest. Next his shoulders came away from the earth and rocks and snow of the ravine. He wanted to struggle; every fiber revolted against lying still in that helpless strained position. But the voice of his master held him quiet. He heard the sobbing breath of the two men as inch by inch they drew him up.

It must have been a grotesque and terrible scene there in the forest; the horse with legs pointing stiffly up and neck stretched out over his chest, the weary men braced against the tree, pulling with gritted teeth. A sharp gust of wind, first herald of the blizzard, powdered them all with tiny ice crystals.

At last they could do no more. Numbed fingers could no longer hold the rope; exhausted muscles could not pull another ounce.

As the ranger tied the rope to the tree the Englishman suddenly fell back, his face as white as the snow.

The horse now lay partly on his back and partly on his haunches, a sort of half-sitting position, with his head pulled down between his forelegs. "He'll have to do the rest," said the ranger. "If the rope holds, and he doesn't crack his neck, he can make it."

He spoke to the horse: "Try it, Tuckee! Try it, boy!"

Kentucky Roamer was not so tired now. While the men had been working, he had been resting, if only for a few minutes. For an Arab, a few minutes are enough. The muscles along his back tightened and the rope rasped against the tree. That rope gave the red horse a purchase, something to work against. With a surge he straightened the curve of his back and neck. Now his forefeet could touch the sides of the gully. In another moment he had clawed his way over, and stood up.

It was easy work to scramble out of the ravine, but then there was a long struggle to get the two flyers upon his back again. Both were unconscious now, and as the ranger pressed against Tuckee's shoulder, lifting them into position, the horse could feel that his master was trembling like one who makes his final effort. When they were safely up, he slapped Tuckee's haunches and said, "All right, boy, go on home."

Tuckee went forward ten feet. Then he stopped, for his master was not coming. He looked around and saw the ranger on his knees in the snow. What in the world was the matter now? He snorted impatiently. Again his master ordered him forward; but he would not go.

With the wail of a demon, a wind, sharp, cutting, and laden with ice particles, drove through the trees. The blizzard! Kentucky Roamer hung his head and stood. Then, through the uproar of the storm, he heard a faint dragging and scraping. The frightful cold that accompanied the wind must have roused the ranger, for he was coming at last.

The gray-green man dragged himself along until he reached the horse, pulled himself upright by means of the stirrup leathers, and his hands joined those of the Englishman on the saddle horn. Tuckee needed no order now. He started forward slowly, sidling a little to avoid stepping on his master's dragging feet.

And so he brought all three of them home.

THE DOG OF POMPEII

by Louis Untermeyer

Tito and his dog Bimbo lived (if you could call it living) under the city wall where it joined the inner gate. They really didn't live there; they just slept there. They lived anywhere. Pompeii was one of the gayest of the old Roman towns, but although Tito was never an unhappy boy, he was not exactly a merry one. The streets were always lively with shining chariots and bright red trappings; the open-air theaters rocked with laughing crowds; sham battles and athletic sports were free for the asking in the great stadium. Once a year the emperor visited the pleasure city, and the fireworks and other forms of entertainment lasted for days.

But Tito saw none of these things, for he was blind—had been blind from birth. He was known to everyone in the poorer quarters. But no one could say how old he was; no one remembered his parents; no one could tell where he came from. Bimbo was another mystery. As long as people could remember seeing Tito—several years at least—they had seen Bimbo. The dog never left his side. He was not only a watchdog, but mother and father to Tito.

Did I say Bimbo never left his master? (Perhaps I had better say "comrade," for if anyone was the master, it was Bimbo.) I was wrong. Bimbo did trust Tito alone exactly three times a day. It was a custom understood between boy and dog since the beginning of their friendship, and the way it worked was this:

Early in the morning, shortly after dawn, while Tito was still dreaming, Bimbo would disappear. When Tito awoke, Bimbo would be sitting quietly at his side, his ears cocked, his stump of a tail tapping the ground, and a fresh-baked loaf of bread—more like a large round roll—at his feet. Tito would stretch himself, Bimbo would yawn, and they would breakfast.

At noon, no matter where they happened to be, Bimbo would put his paw on Tito's knee, and the two of them would return to the inner gate. Tito would curl up in the corner (almost like a dog) and go to sleep, while Bimbo, looking quite important (almost like a boy), would disappear again. In a half-hour he would be back with their lunch. Sometimes it would be a piece of fruit or a scrap of meat; often it was nothing but a dry crust. But sometimes there would be one of those flat, rich cakes, sprinkled with raisins and sugar, that Tito liked so much.

At suppertime the same thing happened, although there was a little less of everything, for things were hard to snatch in the evening with the streets full of people.

But whether there was much or little, hot or cold, fresh or dry, food was always there. Tito never asked where it came from, and Bimbo never told him. There was plenty of rain water in the hollows of soft stones; the old egg-woman at the corner sometimes gave him a cupful of strong goat's milk; in the grape season the fat wine-maker let him have drippings of the mild juice. So there was no danger of going hungry or thirsty. There was plenty of everything in Pompeii if you knew where to find it—and if you had a dog like Bimbo.

As I said before, Tito was not the merriest boy in Pompeii. He could not romp with the other youngsters or play hare-and-hounds and I-spy and follow-your-master and ball-against-the-building and jackstone and kings-and-robbers with them. But that did not make him sorry for himself. If he could not see the sights that delighted the lads of Pompeii, he could hear and smell things they never noticed. When he and Bimbo went out walking, he knew just where they were going and exactly what was happening.

As they passed a handsome villa, he'd sniff and say, "Ah, Glaucus Pansa is giving a grand dinner here tonight. They're going to have three kinds of bread and roast pigling and stuffed goose and a great stew—I think bear stew—and a fig pie." And Bimbo would note that this would be a good place to visit to-morrow.

Or "H'm," Tito would murmur, half through his lips, half through his nostrils. "The wife of Marcus Lucretius is expecting her mother. She's airing all the linens; she's going to use the best clothes, the ones she's been keeping in pine needles and camphor, and she's got an extra servant cleaning the kitchen. Come, Bimbo, let's get out of the dust!"

Or, as they neared the forum, "Mm'm! What good things they have in the market place today! Dates from Africa and salt oysters from sea caves and cuttle-fish and new honey and sweet onions and—ugh!—water-buffalo steaks. Come let's see what's what in the forum." And Bimbo, just as curious as his comrade, hurried on. Being a dog, he, too, trusted his ears and nose more than his eyes, and so the two of them entered the center of Pompeii.

The forum was the part of the town to which everybody came at least once during each day. Everything happened there. There were no private houses; all was public—the chief temples, the gold and red bazaars, the silk shops, the town hall, the booths belonging to the weavers and the jewel merchants, the wealthy woolen market. Everything gleamed brightly here; the buildings looked new. The earthquake of twelve years ago had brought down all the old structures; and since the citizens of Pompeii were ambitious to rival Naples and even Rome, they had seized the opportunity to rebuild the whole town. Hence there was scarcely a building that was older than Tito.

Tito had heard a great deal about the earthquake, although,

since he was only about a year old at the time, he could hardly remember it. This particular quake had been a light one, as earthquakes go. The crude houses had been shaken down, and parts of the outworn wall had been wrecked, but there had been little loss of life. No one knew what caused these earthquakes. Records showed they had happened in the neighborhood since the beginning of time. Sailors said that it was to teach the lazy cityfolk a lesson and make them appreciate those who risked the dangers of the sea to bring them luxuries and to protect their town from invaders. The priests said that the gods took this way of showing their anger to those who refused to worship properly or failed to bring enough sacrifices to the altars. The tradesmen said that the foreign merchants had corrupted the ground and it was no longer safe to traffic in imported goods that came from strange places and carried a curse upon them. Everyone had a different explanation, and everyone's explanation was louder and sillier than his neighbor's.

People were talking about it this afternoon as Tito and Bimbo came out of the side street into the public square. The forum was crowded. Tito's ears, as well as his nose, guided them to the place where the talk was loudest.

"I tell you," rumbled a voice which Tito recognized as that of bathmaster Rufus, "there won't be another earthquake in my lifetime or yours. There may be a tremble or two, but earthquakes, like lightning, never strike twice in the same place."

"Don't they?" asked a thin voice Tito had never heard before. It had a high, sharp ring to it, and Tito knew it as the accent of a stranger. "How about the two towns in Sicily that have been ruined three times within fifteen years by the eruptions of Mount Etna? And were they not warned? And does that column of smoke above Vesuvius mean nothing?"

"That?" Tito could hear the grunt with which one question answered another. "That's always there. We use it for our weather guide. When the smoke stands up straight, we know we'll have fair weather, when it flattens out, it's sure to be foggy; when it drifts to the east——"

"Very well, my confident friend," cut in the thin voice, which now sounded curiously flat. "We have a proverb: 'Those who will not listen to man must be taught by the gods.' I say no more. But I leave a last warning. Remember the holy ones. Look to your temples. And when the smoke tree above Vesuvius grows to the shape of an umbrella pine, look to your lives!"

Tito could hear the air whistle as the speaker drew his toga about him, and the quick shuffle of feet told him that the stranger had gone.

"Now what," said Attilio, the cameo-cutter, "did he mean by that?"

"I wonder," grunted Rufus. "I wonder."

Tito wondered, too. And Bimbo, his head at a thoughtful angle, looked as if he were doing a heavy bit of pondering. By nightfall the argument had been forgotten. If the smoke had increased, no one saw it in the dark. Besides, it was Caesar's birthday, and the town was in a holiday mood. Tito and Bimbo were among the merrymakers, dodging the charioteers, who shouted at them. But Tito never missed his footing. He was thankful for his keen ears and quick instinct—most thankful of all for Bimbo.

They visited the open-air theater; then went to the city walls, where the people of Pompeii watched a sham naval battle in which the city, attacked from the sea, was saved after thousands of flaming arrows had been burned. Though the thrill of flaring ships and lighted skies was lost to Tito, the shouts and cheers excited him as much as anyone.

The next morning there were two of the beloved raisin cakes for his breakfast. Bimbo was unusually active and thumped his bit of a tail until Tito was afraid he would wear it out. Tito couldn't imagine whether Bimbo was urging him to some sort of game or was trying to tell him something. After a while he ceased to notice Bimbo. He felt drowsy. Last night's late hours had tired him. Besides, there was a heavy mist in the air—no, a thick fog rather than a mist—a fog that got into his throat and made him cough. He walked as far as the marine gate to get a breath of the sea. But even the salt air seemed smoky.

Tito went to bed before dusk, but he did not sleep well. . . . He awoke early. Or rather, he was pulled awake, Bimbo doing the pulling. The dog had dragged Tito to his feet and was urging the boy along. Where, Tito did not know. His feet stumbled uncertainly; he was still half asleep. For a while he noticed nothing except the fact that it was hard to breathe. The air was hot and heavy, so heavy that he could taste it. The air, it seemed, had turned to powder, a warm powder that stung his nostrils and burned his sightless eyes.

Then he began to hear sounds, peculiar sounds. Like animals under the earth. Hissings and groanings and muffled cries. There was no doubt of it now. The noises came from underneath. He not only heard them—he could feel them. The earth twitched; the twitching changed to an uneven shrugging of the soil. Then, as Bimbo half pulled, half coaxed him along, the ground jerked away from his feet and he was thrown against a stone fountain.

The water—hot water!—splashing in his face revived him. He got to his feet, Bimbo steadying him, helping him on again. The noises grew louder; they came closer. The cries were even more animal-like than before, but now they came from human throats. A few people began to rush by; a family or two, then a group, then, it seemed, the whole city of people. Tito, bewildered though he was, could recognize Rufus' voice as he bellowed like a water buffalo gone mad.

It was then the crashing began. First a sharp crackling, like a monstrous snapping of twigs; then an explosion that tore earth and sky. The heavens, though Tito could not see them, were shot through with continual flickerings of fire. Lightnings above were answered by thunders beneath. A house fell. Then another. By a miracle the two companions had escaped the dangerous side streets and were in a more open space. It was the forum. They rested here awhile; how long the boy did not know.

Tito had no idea of the time of day. He could *feel* it was black—an unnatural blackness. Something inside, perhaps the lack of breakfast and lunch, told him it was past noon. But it didn't matter. Nothing seemed to matter. He was getting drowsy, too drowsy to walk. But walk he must. He knew it. And Bimbo knew it; the sharp tugs told him so. Nor was it a moment too soon. The sacred ground of the forum was safe no longer. It began to rock, then to pitch, then to split. As they stumbled out of the square, the earth wriggled like a caught snake, and all the columns of the Temple of Jupiter came down. It was the end of the world, or so it seemed.

To walk was not enough now. They must run. Tito, too frightened to know what to do or where to go, had lost all sense of direction. He started to go back to the inner gate; but Bimbo, straining his back to the last inch, almost pulled his clothes from him. What did the dog want? Had he gone mad?

Then suddenly he understood. Bimbo was telling him the way out. The sea gate, of course. The sea gate—and then the sea, far from falling buildings, heaving ground. He turned, Bimbo guiding him across open pits and dangerous pools of bubbling mud, away from buildings that had caught fire and were dropping their burning beams.

New dangers threatened. All Pompeii seemed to be thronging toward the marine gate, and there was the chance of being trampled to death. But the chance had to be taken. It was growing harder and harder to breathe. What air there was choked him. It was all dust now, dust and pebbles as large as beans. They fell on his head, his hands—pumice stones from the black heart of Vesuvius! The mountain was turning itself inside out. Tito remembered what the stranger had said in the forum two days ago: "Those who will not listen to men must be taught by the gods." The people of Pompeii had refused to heed the warnings; they were being taught now, if it was not too late.

Suddenly it seemed too late for Tito. The red-hot ashes blistered his skin; the stinging vapors tore his throat. He could not go on. He staggered toward a small tree at the side of the road and fell. In a moment Bimbo was beside him. He coaxed, but there was no answer. He licked Tito's hands, his feet, his face. The boy did not stir. Then Bimbo did the thing he least wanted to do. He bit his comrade, bit him deep in the arm. With a cry of pain, Tito jumped to his feet, Bimbo after him. Tito was in despair, but Bimbo was determined. He drove the boy on, snapping at his heels, worrying his way through the crowd, barking, baring his teeth, heedless of kicks or falling stones.

Sick with hunger, half dead with fear and sulphur fumes, Tito plodded on, pursued by Bimbo. How long he never knew. At last he staggered through the marine gate and felt soft sand under him. Then Tito fainted.

Someone was dashing sea water over him. Someone was carrying him toward a boat.

"Bimbo!" he called. And then louder, "Bimbo!" But Bimbo had disappeared.

Voices jarred against each other. "Hurry! Hurry!" "To the boats!" "Can't you see the child's frightened and starving?" "He keeps calling for someone!" "Poor child, he's out of his mind." "Here, boy, take this!"

They tucked him in among them. The oarlocks creaked; the oars splashed; the boat rode over the toppling waves. Tito was safe. But he wept continually. "Bimbo!" he wailed. "Bimbo! Bimbo!"

He could not be comforted.

Eighteen hundred years passed. Scientists were restoring the ancient city; excavators were working their way through the stones and trash that had buried the entire town. Much had already been brought to light—statues, bronze instruments, bright mosaics, household articles, even delicate paintings which had been preserved by the ashes that had taken over two thousand lives. Columns were dug up, and the forum was beginning to emerge.

It was at a place where the ruins lay deepest that the director paused.

"Come here," he called to his assistant. "I think we've discovered the remains of a building in good shape. Here are four huge millstones that were most likely turned by slaves or mules, and here is a whole wall standing, with shelves inside it. Why, it must have been a bakery! And here is a curious thing—the skeleton of a dog!"

"Amazing!" gasped his assistant. "You'd think a dog would have had sense enough to run away at that time. What is that flat thing he's holding between his teeth? It can't be a stone."

"No. It must have come from this bakery. Do you know, it looks to me like some sort of cake, hardened with the years. And bless me, if those little black pebbles aren't raisins! A raisin cake almost two thousand years old! I wonder what made him want it at such a moment?"

"I wonder," murmured his assistant.

COMANCHE

by Alice Gall and Fleming Crew

The first rays of the morning sun touched the tops of the cottonwood trees along the river bank, and from the parade ground at the army post came the clear call of a bugle. Down in the cavalry shed Comanche pawed the wooden floor of his stall impatiently. It was time for his oats and he was hungry.

The days always began like this at Fort Lincoln. First the notes of the bugle, then the voices of the men at the troopers' quarters and a stamping and nickering of the horses in the cavalry shed. Comanche had been with the regiment for eight years now, and he knew all these sounds well.

He knew that soon the man would come to feed him, the man who walked with a limp and who always had a pat and a friendly word for him. Putting his ears forward, Comanche listened. Some soldiers were coming toward the cavalry shed, and in a moment he heard the low half-door at the back of his stall swing open. Turning his head he whinnied softly. The man had come at last.

"I'm giving you double rations today, Comanche," the man said, "double rations to remember me by when you're out in the plains country fighting Indians."

Limping over to the feed box the old soldier poured a pail of oats into it and then stood looking at the horse approvingly. "Not so handsome as some," he said presently. "Body too stocky, neck too thick, legs too short and heavy for speed. But you've got plenty of strength and endurance," he added, giving Comanche a friendly slap on the rump.

This man was Trooper Briggs. He had served under General Custer back in Civil War days, and it was in one of the last battles of this war that he had received the wound which made him lame.

These were stirring days out in the Indian country. The long struggle between the red men and the white men had been going on for more than two centuries, and it was not yet finished. In the land of the warlike Sioux and Cheyenne Indians there were still powerful tribes who dared to take the warpath and fight the white man. And so the United States Government built forts and army posts, and sent soldiers to subdue these last unconquered tribes. For the white man needed even these far lands.

To one of these posts, Fort Lincoln, Comanche had been sent when he was a young horse five years old, and he had been assigned to the famous Seventh Cavalry commanded by General Custer, the greatest Indian fighter of them all. Many times since then Comanche had gone into battle, ridden by Captain Miles Keough, whose favorite mount he was, and always he and his rider had come through safely.

For several weeks scouts had been bringing to Fort Lincoln alarming reports from the western plains. Sitting Bull was on the warpath again. And so on this fine spring morning, the regiment moved out of Fort Lincoln, on its way to the Sioux country. The Seventh Cavalry went first, led by General Custer. He was a striking figure, sitting very straight in his saddle, his long yellow hair falling to his shoulders under his wide brimmed hat. Behind him rode Captain Miles Keough mounted on Comanche, and following the cavalry came the marching soldiers. Bands were playing, banners were flying. It was a splendid procession.

It was late in June when the regiment reached the land of the Sioux Indians in the Black Hills country. Here it divided into detachments of several companies each, and each detachment followed the line of march assigned to it. General Custer, with four companies, proceeded cautiously toward the Little Big Horn River, on whose banks it was thought the Indians would make their stand. At the head of one of these companies rode Captain Miles Keough on Comanche.

General Custer was not familiar with this country, but the red men knew the region well, for it was their home and the home of their fathers. On every hillside the Sioux chiefs had stationed keen-eyed watchers, and scouts slipped among the trees. Slowly a net of red warriors was drawn round the white men. And then one day, outnumbered ten to one, General Custer and his men rode into the deadly trap prepared for them.

Just exactly what happened that day no one will ever know. A rifle cracked, then another and another, and the air was suddenly filled with the dreadful war whoops of the Indians. It was quickly over. The shouting ceased, the firing died away, and all was quiet again. A great battle had been fought—the battle of the Little Big Horn.

It was not until two days later that General Terry arrived with his command. He had reached the river on the day agreed upon beforehand, but he had come too late. As he and his men came over the brow of the hill and looked down into the valley, a worried frown appeared on General Terry's face.

"I don't like the look of this," he said.

On every hand there were signs that many Indians had passed that way, but now there were none to be seen. A moment later a scout came hurrying toward him. "I bring bad news, General," he said. "Custer and his men have been defeated; the loss is heavy, sir."

"How many are dead?" asked General Terry.

"Many," said the scout. "It was a terrible disaster, sir."

"And what of Custer?" General Terry asked anxiously.

The scout shook his head. "Dead, sir," he answered.

For a moment General Terry could not trust himself to speak. "The wounded must be cared for without delay," he said. "You may report back to your captain now."

But the scout did not move. "There are no wounded, sir," he said slowly.

General Terry looked at him in horror. "You mean—"

The scout nodded sadly. "All are dead, sir," he said. "It was a gallant stand. There was no retreat. Custer's men fought until the last trooper had given his life."

The scout turned to go but faced about again and addressed the General. "There is one horse that still lives, sir," he said, "the only life left on the field. You may know him—he's been with the regiment a long time. It's Comanche, the horse that Captain Keough always rode. The horse is wounded, but the men are doing what they can to make him comfortable."

And so it happened that the small river steamboat, *Far West*, which had arrived with additional supplies and ammunition and had started back again to Fort Lincoln, had aboard her one wounded horse, the only survivor of the battle of the Little Big Horn.

On a night in July Old Briggs sat by the river smoking thoughtfully. It had been more than a month since General Custer and his men had left Fort Lincoln to fight the Indians. Presently he heard a sound up the river that brought him to his feet with a start. It was the whistle of a steamboat. He emptied his pipe and, going to the very edge of the water, stood looking up stream.

It's the *Far West*, he thought. I know her whistle. She will be bringing us news of the regiment.

To Old Briggs that night seemed, ever after, like a dream: the dim gray shape of the steamboat coming out of the dark; the sparks from her funnels floating high in the air; the steady throb of her engine; and the swish of water thrown up by the paddle wheel.

A number of troopers, wakened by the steamboat's whistle, came hurrying across the parade ground toward the river. For many days they had been eagerly awaiting the arrival of the *Far West*. Old Briggs joined them, and they climbed into two small boats, and started across the river. No one spoke. Each man was wondering what news they would hear.

They put their little boat ashore just below the wharf and went aboard the *Far West* at once. Captain Marsh, her commander, stood on deck talking to a group of people gathered round him. "Three hundred men killed," he was saying. "Four companies of the famous Seventh Cavalry, the flower of the regiment, and not a man left alive. They died as troopers should die, with their rifles at their shoulders."

For a moment Old Briggs could not believe he had heard these words. Not a man left alive of the three hundred who rode away with General Custer on that memorable day! Slowly he turned away. He did not want to hear more just then.

The old trooper's shoulders drooped as he went down to the lower deck and he felt, all at once, very tired and alone. General Custer gone, Captain Keough gone, and Captain Keough's mount, Comanche. But suddenly he straightened up with a jerk. He had heard the low nicker of a horse; a nicker he had learned to know from all others.

Hurrying along the deck Old Briggs came upon a deck hand dozing in a chair. "Have you got a horse here?" he asked excitedly.

"Yes sir," answered the deck hand, rubbing his eyes. "There's a horse on board but he's pretty badly done for. The Indians got him with half a dozen bullets, in the big battle when Custer and his men were killed. Comanche, they call him, and they found him wandering around the battlefield alone. He's back yonder in a stall we fixed up for him."

But Old Briggs was already gone. "I'm coming, Comanche!" he shouted. "It's your old friend Briggs, Comanche! It's your old friend Briggs!"

Back home once more came Comanche, the Indian-fighting horse. When the little steamboat carried him across the river to Fort Lincoln next morning, the men and officers of the fort welcomed him as a hero. Old Briggs scarcely left him, day or night, until Comanche's wounds were healed.

One day this order went out from Army Headquarters:

Headquarters Seventh U. S. Cavalry
Fort A. Lincoln, D. T.
April 10, 1878

GENERAL ORDERS No. 7

1. The horse known as "Comanche" being the only living representative of the bloody tragedy of the Little Big Horn, his kind treatment and comfort shall be a matter of special pride and solicitude on the part of every member of the Seventh Cavalry to the end that his life shall be preserved to the utmost limit. Wounded and scarred as he is, his very existence speaks in terms more eloquent than words, of the desperate struggle against overwhelming numbers, of the hopeless conflict, and the heroic manner in which all went down on that fatal day.

2. The commanding officer of Company I will see that a special and comfortable stall is fitted up for him, and he will not again be ridden by any person whatsoever, under any circumstances, nor will he ever be put to any kind of work.

3. Hereafter, upon all occasions of ceremony of mounted regimental formation, Comanche, saddled and bridled and draped in mourning, and led by a mounted trooper of Company I will be paraded with the regiment.

By command of Colonel Sturgis.

E. A. GARLINGTON
First Lieutenant and Adjt. Seventh Cavalry

Comanche's fighting days were over. He had earned a rest and now he was to have it. There was a meadow not far from the army post where the grass was soft and green. This was now Comanche's own field, and here he spent his days nibbling the tender grass and listening to the familiar sounds that came to him from the fort. He had his own shed, too, and his own comfortable stall to stay in when the weather was cold and stormy. And, always, he had his good friend Briggs, the trooper, to look after him. Here Comanche lived for many years. Each day Old Briggs limped over to carry him some dainty or other.

"You haven't changed much, old fellow," Briggs said to him one morning as he opened the gate to Comanche's field. "You haven't changed much, old soldier, in spite of all the hard fighting you have seen."

Comanche whinnied softly and began to eat the corn husks Briggs had brought. When he had finished he rested his muzzle on the top of the gate and blinked drowsily while the old trooper stroked his neck and talked to him.

Suddenly, over on the parade ground, the army band began to play, and Comanche raised his head quickly. Mounted troopers were riding out. Pack horses and ammunition wagons were being brought up. "They are off for the Indian country again," Old Briggs said half to himself. "But you and I are not going, Comanche. Our fighting days are done."

They stood there together, the old trooper and the old horse, and watched another splendid procession march away from the army post, with banners flying, rifles glistening in the sunshine, and the big ammunition wagons rumbling along the river trail. After a time Old Briggs picked up his basket. "Well, I must be getting back to quarters," he said and limped away.

Comanche looked after him for a moment and then glanced once more at the marching regiment. It had been a fine exciting life, fighting Indians out on the wide plains, and he had enjoyed it. But here in this meadow the grass was fresh and tender. Comanche lowered his head and began to browse.

8

From Myths and Fables to Legend and History

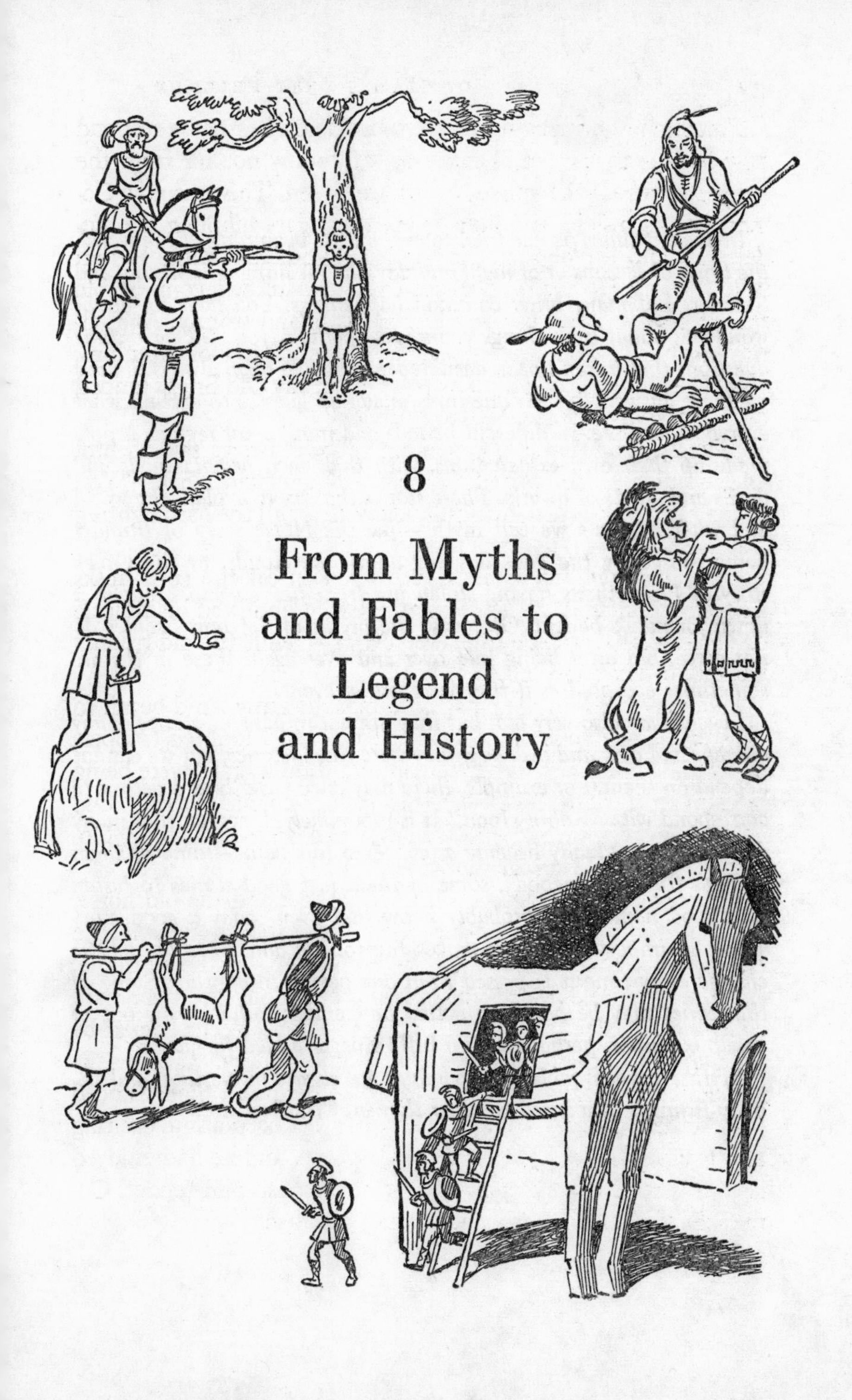

In ancient times people tried to explain the beginning of the world, the cause of seasons or of night and day, the meaning of lightning and thunder, and many other common happenings. You have no doubt wondered about such things yourselves—perhaps you still have some questions that haven't been answered yet. People seem always to have made up answers to such questions, made up guesses to explain what everybody can see. In different periods and in different regions people made up their own explanations, with their own peculiar gods and devils and giants or dwarfs. These stories that try to explain the world and what happens we call myths—*like the Norse story of thunder being caused by the gods bowling above the clouds, or the Greek story of Prometheus having stolen fire from heaven and brought it down for man's benefit. Of course the myths of different peoples do not agree; but after being told over and over again these myths are sometimes accepted as if they were actual events.*

Legends are also very old, but they are not impossible stories. They are repeated over and over as if they were true histories, but we cannot depend on them. For example, there may once have lived a person to correspond with "Robin Hood." It is more likely, however, that many good stories gradually became attached to this name—some of them perhaps true of somebody, some of them just good stories to fasten to a good name. You probably know that even today a good story about an important person makes the rounds and takes on a little change every time it is passed from one person to another. Some of the stories may be based on actual happenings; others grow out of gossip or rumor, perhaps with a little vinegar added for flavor.

Myths, legends, fables and parables are always interesting, and nobody is much concerned whether they are "true" or not.

WILLIAM TELL

by Horace Elisha Scudder

Switzerland is a republic, like the United States, and the men who live among its mountains are a brave, free people. But long ago the Emperor of Austria claimed the land as a part of his empire, and sent a man named Gessler to rule the people in his stead.

Gessler was a tyrant. He wished to stand well with his master, the emperor, and he ruled the bold Swiss with a rod of iron. He had soldiers at his command, and he seemed able to do whatever he wished, but there was one thing he could not do: he could not make the proud people bow down to him when he came among them.

He was angry enough at this, and he cast about for some new ways in which to make them feel his power. In those days, as now, every town had a public square called a market-place. Here the people flocked to buy and sell of each other. The men and women came down from the mountains with game and cheese and butter; they sold these things in the market, and bought goods which they could not make or grow in their mountain homes.

In the market-place of Altorf, a Swiss town, Gessler set up a tall pole, like a liberty pole. But on the top of this pole he placed his hat, and, just as in the city a gilt crown on some high point was the sign of the emperor's power, so this hat was to be the sign of Gessler's power. He bade that every Swiss man, woman, or child who passed by the pole should bow to the hat. In this way they were to show their respect for him.

From one of the mountain homes near Altorf there came into the market-place one day a tall, strong man named William Tell. He was a famous archer, for it was in the days before the mountaineers carried guns, and he was wont to shoot bears and wild goats and wolves with his bow and arrows.

He had with him his little son, and they walked across the market-place. But when they passed the pole, Tell never bent his head; he stood as straight as a mountain pine.

There were servants and spies of Gessler in the market-place, and they at once told the tyrant how Tell had defied him. Gessler commanded the Swiss to be brought before him, and he came, leading by the hand his little son.

"They tell me you shoot well," said the tyrant. "You shall not be punished. Instead you shall give me a sign of your skill. Your boy is no doubt made of the same stuff you are. Let him stand yonder a hundred paces off. Place an apple on his head, and do you stand here and pierce the apple with an arrow from your quiver."

All the people about turned pale with fear, and fathers who had their sons with them held them fast, as if Gessler meant to take them from them. But Tell looked Gessler full in the face, and drew two arrows from his quiver.

"Go yonder," he said to the lad, and he saw him led away by two servants of Gessler, who paced a hundred steps, and then placed an apple on the boy's head. They had some pity for Tell in their hearts, and so they had made the boy stand with his back to his father.

"Face this way," rang out Tell's clear voice, and the boy, quick to obey, turned and stood facing his father. He stood erect, his arms hanging straight by his side, his head held up, and the apple poised on it. He saw Tell string his bow, bend it, to try if it were true, fit the notch of the arrow into the taut cord, bring the bow slowly into place. He could see no more. He shut his eyes.

The next moment a great shout rose from the crowd. The arrow had split the apple in two and had sped beyond. The people were overjoyed, but Gessler said in a surly tone to Tell:

"You were not so very sure of your first shot. I saw you place a second arrow in your belt."

"That was for thee, tyrant, had I missed my first shot," said Tell.

"Seize him!" cried the enraged tyrant, and his soldiers rushed forward, but the people also threw themselves upon the soldiers, and Tell, now drawing his bow again, shot the tyrant through the heart, and in the confusion that followed, taking his boy by the hand, fled quickly to the lake near by, and, loosing a boat, rowed to the other shore, and so escaped to the mountain fastness.

THE WOODEN HORSE

by Bella Koral

About four thousand years ago, a great city stood on the shores of the Aegean Sea, near the mouth of the Hellespont. That great city is entirely gone and people in our time have found relics of it by digging deep into the ground. And the name Hellespont, like the name of the city—Troy—is part of ancient legends and writings. The actual waterway still exists and is called The Dardanelles, which you can find on the map; but Troy is no more.

The walls of this great city were so high that no enemy could climb over them. And they were so thick and strong that no enemy could break through them or batter them down. And the gates of the city were well defended by its ablest and bravest soldiers.

Yet, proud and glorious though its history had been, and confident as the Trojans were that their city would live forever, Troy at last fell upon evil days. This was because Paris, a prince of Troy, stole Helen, the most beautiful woman in the world, away from her husband Me ne la′us, a king of the Greeks.

To avenge this great wrong, Menelaus called together all the heroes and great warriors of his country, among them the wise and courageous Ulysses. In two years of preparation, the Greeks assembled a tremendous army. They set sail for Troy in a fleet of a thousand ships. They landed on the beaches of the coastal plain before the city, and there the heroes made camp. The Trojans, too, were well prepared for battle, and their old king, Priam, gathered many brave fighters and chieftains about him. The Greeks defied the Trojans to engage in battle.

For nine long years the Greeks laid siege to Troy. Many fierce battles were fought outside the gates, and many were the noble heroes who were slain on both sides, for the chief warriors would engage in single combat as their armies stood by, and the old people and children of Troy would come out to watch the contests from the city's walls. On both sides, the warriors were equally valiant, so that the Trojans could not rid their beaches of the invaders, nor could the Greeks force their way into the city. Both sides suffered and struggled and the weary siege dragged on and on. Finally the Greeks began to despair of ever conquering Troy in outright battle.

"For nine years we have been laying siege to Troy. Our bravest comrades are dead. Still the city is not ours, and Menelaus has not been avenged for the theft of Helen," the Greek soldiers grumbled.

"To fight any longer is useless. Let us give up this hopeless struggle! Our wives and children will learn to forget their husbands and fathers. We long to see our homes once more," they whispered at night among themselves.

Ag a mem′non, chief of the Greek army, came to Ulysses. "Surely you, with your great cleverness and wisdom, can find a way to subdue the Trojans and save us," he urged.

After long consideration, Ulysses thought of a plan which the Greek chieftains decided to carry out.

Ulysses ordered his men, with the aid of a Greek sculptor, to build a colossal horse of wood. It was so huge and spacious that it could hold a hundred armed men within its hollow body. It was fitted with a door so skillfully concealed, that no one could possibly notice it. One night, under the cloak of darkness, Ulysses, Menelaus, Agamemnon, and others of the Greek heroes, fully armed, crept into the wooden figure. The door was shut upon them, and the rest of the Greek army broke up camp and set sail, leaving the enormous wooden horse on the beach.

The Greeks pretended they were abandoning the siege and were sailing for home. But once out of sight of Troy, they anchored behind a somewhat distant neighboring island, where they were well hidden from their enemies.

When the sun rose the next morning, there was not a Greek ship to be seen on the shore, and not a single tent on the plain. Only the huge wooden horse remained. Like wildfire, the exciting news spread throughout the city. "The Greeks have fled! The Greeks have fled! They have left at last!" cried the people. Hundreds of eager men, women, and children ran toward the city's walls, and gazed with happy, straining eyes toward the last straggling ship as it disappeared around the bend of the distant island.

Then the Trojans went wild with delight. The long years of siege were over, they thought. Everywhere there were embraces, kisses and joyous shouts of laughter.

The newly found peace and liberty were wonderful to a people long besieged. They surged forward to the city gates which were soon flung wide open and quickly the crowds streamed over the site of the deserted enemy camp.

Now they saw the great wooden figure of the horse, resting on a wide platform of wood. Slowly they drew near it. Gazing and wondering, they walked round and round the colossal image. Touching it curiously, as little children will a strange object, they marveled at its tremendous height and girth.

"Perhaps it is a peace offering from the Greeks to the goddess, Athene," said one Trojan to another. A few cautious ones continued to be afraid of the strange wooden creature, but others, becoming bolder, thought it should be carried back into the city as a war trophy.

At this, La o co′ön, priest of Neptune, god of the sea, came forward. "Trojans," warned the old man, "put no trust in this horse. Have you so soon forgotten the sad years of siege and suffering? Whatever this is, I fear the Greeks, even when they bear gifts," he cried.

Suddenly a great uproar was heard, the priest's warning was drowned in the hubbub that followed. "It's a Greek! A Greek!" A poor wretched fellow wearing Greek garments, was dragged forward, his hands tightly bound. The ragged, badly beaten captive had been found by some shepherds hiding among the reeds along the shore.

The captured Greek in reality was Sinon, a trusted friend of the crafty Ulysses, and he had been left behind by his companions to deceive the Trojans into taking the wooden horse within their gates.

"Do not kill me," he begged his Trojan captors. "It is true that I am a Greek, but I escaped from my cruel countrymen when they were about to sacrifice me to the gods."

Sinon was brought before the Trojan chiefs, who promised to spare his life if he would tell them the truth about the wooden horse. "The Wooden Horse," he told them, "was built by my countrymen as an offering to appease the goddess, Athene. It was made so large so that you would be unable to take it within your walls. For," he went on lying craftily, "those who own this wooden horse will gain the favor and protection of Athene. If once the horse stands within the walls of Troy, the city can never be captured!"

At first the Trojans doubted the spy's story, but after a while Sinon convinced them that if they took the sacred object the Greeks had left behind them into their city, they would have happiness and prosperity forever.

Soon they devised a scheme for taking the huge figure into the city. Putting rollers under the wooden platform on which the horse stood, they fastened long ropes about its legs and began dragging the immense image across the plain toward the walls of Troy.

Again, out of the crowd, came the voice of the aged priest, Laocoön. "Men of Troy," he cried, "beware, beware of the treacherous Greeks. Cast the horse into the sea, or burn it, for it will bring you only misery and ruin!" As he spoke, he hurled his spear against the side of the horse, and it resounded with a hollow clang of armor.

While some people were again persuaded to doubt, and were standing about discussing the priest's warning, an event occurred before their very eyes which seemed an omen direct from the gods. Out of the sea rose two immense serpents. With rearing heads, their eyes and tongues flashing flames before them, they swiftly glided through the terrified, panic-stricken crowd and made straight for Laocoön and his two sons.

Before they could escape, the two serpents entwined their coiling, slimy bodies about the three unfortunate men, and crushed them to death. The monsters then slipped away again into the sea, as quickly and silently as they had come.

The Trojans, frozen with horror at this dreadful scene, were sure that this punishment had come to Laocoön for his words against the wooden horse. "He has been doomed for his sacrilege against this gift," they cried. "We will offer thanks to our protector Athene and bring the sacred image into our city."

Amid great acclaim, many willing hands dragged and pushed the great horse on its rolling platform over the plain, and little by little it approached the gate. When it was reached, they found that the opening was too narrow to admit the horse. So they pulled down part of the wall and made a breach to allow the wooden horse to be brought into the city. "Now," said the Trojans, "our city is safe from every enemy," and they draped wreaths and garlands of flowers around the horse.

That night they had a great feast of wild merrymaking to celebrate the end of nine years of anxious watching and suffering. For the first time in nine years, no one was on guard on the walls of Troy. On that night all went to sleep, secure in the belief that the gods were on their side.

When the noises of the city had died down, and the streets were quiet and empty, Sinon, as had been planned, opened the cunningly concealed trap door in the side of the wooden horse. Out of it came the hero Ulysses, Menelaus, and the many other hidden Greeks. They set up a beacon light as a signal to the Greek army, for during the night the ships that had anchored behind the island had sailed back again toward the Trojan shore.

Soon, thousands of Greek soldiers swarmed through the streets of a proud city sunken in darkness and sleep. It was to the sounds of battle that the Trojans awoke from their dreams of peace. So the prophecy of Laocoön was fulfilled.

Priam, the king, and his noblest warriors were killed. Greek soldiers robbed the palaces and plundered the city of all its wealth and treasure. Helpless, the Trojans watched as their glorious city, set to the torch, burned to its very foundations.

Then the Greeks set sail for their own country taking with them many Trojan captives. With them they took also the fair Helen, for whose sake the dreadful war had been waged. At last she had awakened from the spell that the goddess Venus had cast upon her, and she was eager to behold again her native land.

But the glory of Troy was gone forever. Nothing but smouldering ruins and the everlasting renown of its valiant heroes remained of the wondrous, rich city on the shores of the Aegean.

KING ARTHUR*

by Mary Macleod

The Marvel of the Sword

When Uther Pendragon, King of England, died, the country for a long while stood in great danger, for every lord that was mighty gathered his forces, and many wished to be King. For King Uther's own son, Prince Arthur, who should have succeeded him, was but a child, and Merlin, the mighty magician, had hidden him away.

Now a strange thing had happened at Arthur's birth, and this was how it was.

Some time before, Merlin had done Uther a great service, on condition that the King should grant him whatever he wished for. This the King swore a solemn oath to do. Then Merlin made him promise that when his child was born it should be delivered to Merlin to bring up as he chose, for this would be to the child's own great advantage. The King had given his promise so he was obliged to agree. Then Merlin said he knew a very true and faithful man, one of King Uther's lords, by name Sir Ector, who had large possessions in many parts of England and Wales, and that the child should be given to him to bring up.

On the night the baby was born, while it was still unchristened, King Uther commanded two knights and two ladies to take it, wrapped in a cloth of gold, and deliver it to a poor man whom they would find waiting at the postern gate of the Castle. This poor man was Merlin in disguise, although they did not know it. So the child was delivered unto Merlin and he carried him to Sir

* Reprinted by permission of the publisher from *Book of King Arthur and His Noble Knights,* by Mary Macleod. Copyright, J. B. Lippincott Company.

Ector, and made a holy man christen him, and named him Arthur; and Sir Ector's wife cherished him as her own child.

Within two years King Uther fell sick of a great malady, and for three days and three nights he was speechless. All the Barons were in much sorrow, and asked Merlin what was best to be done.

"There is no remedy," said Merlin, "God will have His Will. But look ye all, Barons, come before King Uther to-morrow, and God will make him speak."

So the next day Merlin and all the Barons came before the King, and Merlin said aloud to King Uther:

"Sir, after your days shall your son Arthur be King of this realm and all that belongs to it?"

Then Uther Pendragon turned to him and said in hearing of them all:

"I give my son Arthur God's blessing and mine, and bid him pray for my soul, and righteously and honourably claim the Crown, on forfeiture of my blessing."

And with that, King Uther died.

But Arthur was still only a baby, not two years old, and Merlin knew it would be no use yet to proclaim him King. For there were many powerful nobles in England in those days, who were all trying to get the kingdom for themselves, and perhaps they would kill the little Prince. So there was much strife and debate in the land for a long time.

When several years had passed, Merlin went to the Archbishop of Canterbury and counselled him to send for all the lords of the realm, and all the gentlemen of arms, that they should come to London at Christmas, and for this cause—that a miracle would show who should be rightly King of the realm. So all the lords and gentlemen made themselves ready, and came to London, and long before dawn on Christmas Day they were all gathered in the great church of St. Paul's to pray.

When the first service was over, there was seen in the churchyard a large stone, four-square, like marble, and in the midst of it was like an anvil of steel, a foot high. In this was stuck by the point a beautiful sword, with naked blade, and there were letters written in gold about the sword, which said thus:

> *"Whoso pulleth this sword out of this stone and anvil is rightly King of all England."*

Then the people marvelled, and told it to the Archbishop.

"I command," said the Archbishop, "that you keep within the church, and pray unto God still; and that no man touch the sword till the service is over."

So when the prayers in church were over, all the lords went to behold the stone and the sword; and when they read the writing some of them—such as wished to be King—tried to pull the sword out of the anvil. But not one could make it stir.

"The man is not here, that shall achieve the sword," said the Archbishop, "but doubt not God will make him known. But let us provide ten knights, men of good fame, to keep guard over the sword."

So, it was ordained, and proclamation was made that every one who wished might try to win the sword. And upon New Year's Day the Barons arranged to have a great tournament, in which all knights who would joust or tourney might take a part. This was ordained to keep together the Lords and Commons, for the Archbishop trusted that it would be made known who should win the sword.

How Arthur Was Crowned King

On New Year's Day, after church, the Barons rode to the field, some to joust, and some to tourney, and so it happened that Sir Ector, who had large estates near London, came also to the tournament; and with him rode Sir Kay, his son, with young Arthur, his foster brother.

As they rode, Sir Kay found he had lost his sword, for he had left it at his father's lodging, so he begged young Arthur to go and fetch it for him.

"That will I, gladly," said Arthur, and he rode fast away.

But when he came to the house, he found no one at home to give him the sword, for every one had gone to see the jousting. Then Arthur was angry and said to himself:

"I will ride to the churchyard, and take the sword with me that sticketh in the stone, for my brother, Sir Kay, shall not be without a sword this day."

When he came to the churchyard he alighted, and tied his horse to the stile, and went to the tent. But he found there no knights, who should have been guarding the sword, for they were all away at the joust. Seizing the sword by the handle he lightly and fiercely pulled it out of the stone, then took his horse and rode his way, till he came to Sir Kay his brother, to whom he delivered the sword.

As soon as Sir Kay saw it, he knew well it was the sword of the Stone, so he rode to his father Sir Ector, and said:

"Sir, lo, here is the sword of the Stone, wherefore I must be King of this land."

When Sir Ector saw the sword he turned back, and came to the church, and there they all three alighted and went into the church, and he made his son swear truly how he got the sword.

"By my brother Arthur," said Sir Kay, "for he brought it to me."

"How did you get this sword?" said Sir Ector to Arthur.

And the boy told him.

"Now," said Sir Ector, "I understand you must be King of this land."

"Wherefore I?" said Arthur; "and for what cause?"

"Sir," said Ector, "because God will have it so; for never man could draw out this sword but he that shall rightly be King. Now let me see whether you can put the sword there as it was, and pull it out again."

"There is no difficulty," said Arthur, and he put it back into the stone.

Then Sir Ector tried to pull out the sword, and failed; and Sir Kay also pulled with all his might, but it would not move.

"Now you shall try," said Sir Ector to Arthur.

"I will, well," said Arthur, and pulled the sword out easily. At this Sir Ector and Sir Kay knelt down on the ground before him.

"Alas," said Arthur, "mine own dear father and brother, why do you kneel to me?"

"Nay, nay, my lord Arthur, it is not so; I was never your father, nor of your blood; but I know well you are of higher blood than I thought you were."

Then Sir Ector told him all, how he had taken him to bring up, and by whose command; and how he had received him from Merlin. And when he understood that Ector was not his father, Arthur was deeply grieved.

"Will you be my good, gracious lord, when you are King?" asked the knight.

"If not, I should be to blame," said Arthur, "for you are the man in the world to whom I am the most beholden, and my good lady and mother your wife, who has fostered and kept me as well as her own children. And if ever it be God's will that I be King, as you say, you shall desire of me what I shall do, and I shall not fail you; God forbid I should fail you."

"Sir," said Sir Ector, "I will ask no more of you but that you will make my son, your foster brother Sir Kay, seneschal of all your lands."

"That shall be done," said Arthur, "and by my faith, never man but he shall have that office while he and I live."

Then they went to the Archbishop and told him how the sword was achieved, and by whom.

On Twelfth Day all the Barons came to the Stone in the churchyard, so that any who wished might try to win the sword. But not one of them all could take it out, except Arthur. Many of them therefore were very angry, and said it was a great shame to them and to the country to be governed by a boy not of high blood, for as yet none of them knew that he was the son of King Uther Pendragon. So they agreed to delay the decision till Candlemas, which is the second day of February.

But when Candlemas came, and Arthur once more was the only one who could pull out the sword, they put it off till Easter; and when Easter came, and Arthur again prevailed in presence of them all, they put it off till the Feast of Pentecost.

Then by Merlin's advice the Archbishop summoned some of the best knights that were to be got—such knights as in his own day King Uther Pendragon had best loved, and trusted most—and these were appointed to attend young Arthur, and never to leave him night or day till the Feast of Pentecost.

When the great day came, all manner of men once more made the attempt, and once more not one of them all could prevail but Arthur. Before all the Lords and Commons there assembled he pulled out the sword, whereupon all the Commons cried out at once:

"We will have Arthur for our King! We will put him no more in delay, for we all see that it is God's will that he shall be our King, and he who holdeth against it, we will slay him."

And therewith they knelt down all at once, both rich and poor, and besought pardon of Arthur, because they had delayed him so long.

And Arthur forgave them, and took the sword in both his hands, and offered it on the altar where the Archbishop was, and so he was made knight by the best man there.

After that, he was crowned at once, and there he swore to his Lords and Commons to be a true King, and to govern with true justice from thenceforth all the days of his life.

THOR LOSES HIS HAMMER AND FINDS IT AGAIN*

by Katherine Pyle

Thor's hammer was the protection of the gods. The giants, who were the Asas' bitter enemies, feared it as they feared nothing else, and always Thor kept it where he could catch it up at any moment. But on a certain morning he awoke to find his hammer gone. Someone had stolen it in the night. At once he suspected Loki; for Loki was a mischief-maker. Nothing pleased him more than giving others trouble or distress.

In haste Thor sent for Loki; but he soon found the mischief-maker knew no more about the loss than he himself. Loki, indeed, was sore afraid when he heard Thor's hammer had been stolen. "If the giants learn of this," he said, "it may prove a dangerous thing for the Asas. They might even take courage to come here to Asgard and attack us." He then told Thor to keep the loss as secret as he could.

"But how shall we win the hammer back?" asked Thor.

"Let me think for a moment's time," said Loki; then presently —"First of all we will go to Freya. From her I will borrow her falcon dress, and put it on. Then as a falcon I will fly about the world until I find the hammer. After that it will be for thee to win it back. But we will tell none but Freya of all this."

The plan pleased Thor, and at once the two Asas went to Freya's palace. There Thor told her of his loss, and asked if she would lend her falcon dress to Loki so that he might fly forth in search of Miölner.

Freya cried, "If it were of silver he should have it, Thor, and if

* Reprinted by permission of the publisher from *Heroic Tales from the Norse*, by Katherine Pyle. Copyright, 1930, by J. B. Lippincott Company.

it were of gold still I would lend it to him," and at once she fetched the dress. Loki put it on, and became a falcon. He said farewell to Freya and to Thor, and spreading wide his wings, away he sped—down to Midgard.

There a fearful storm was raging, rain and hail and wind; the lightning flashed and thunder rolled across the heavens. Loki needed no more than that to tell him who had Thor's hammer. The giant Thrym had the power to send out storms, but never before had he been able to make thunder and lightning; only with Thor's hammer could he do that. Loki waited until the storm was over; then winged his way to Jötunheim and to Thrym's palace.

Thrym gave him greeting. "How goes it with the Asas upon Asgard's heights?" he asked.

"It goes but ill with them," Loki answered. "Thor is in a rage because thou hast stolen his hammer. Where hast thou hidden it, Thrym?"

Thrym answered, "Where thou wilt never find it, Loki. It is hidden eight miles down below the mountains of Jötunheim."

Loki asked, "Wilt thou sell it back to us?"

"Yes, for a price," Thrym answered. "Let the Asas give me Freya for a wife and Thor shall have his hammer back."

Loki said, "That is a price that will never be paid. Of all the goddesses there is not one as fair as Freya. The gods would never let her go from Asgard. Moreover she is Odur's wife; he would never give her up. Ask for some other thing, oh Thrym."

Thrym answered, "There is nothing else that I desire. My treasure house is full of treasures; servants obey my word; I have steeds for pleasure and cows with golden horns. Unless I can have Freya as the price, I will keep Thor's hammer."

Loki said, "I will carry that message back to Asgard, but I fear the gods will never agree to give thee Freya."

At once he put on his falcon dress again, and returned to Asgard. There he told Thor he had learned where the hammer was—that Thrym had stolen it; told him, too, all the giant had said.

Thor cried, "Let us at once seek Freya. She must go to Thrym, for until I have my hammer back the Asas are not safe—no not even here in Asgard."

Loki said, "Be not hasty Thor. Let us first call a meeting of the gods and we will all talk this matter over. Freya too shall come to our meeting."

To this Thor after some talk agreed, though most unwillingly. The gods were bidden to Gladsheim, the great council hall, and Freya too was told to come.

After they had all assembled there Thor rose and told them how his hammer had been stolen; told them, too, who had taken it. Pale grew the Asas when they heard. Thor told, as well, how Loki had gone to bargain for the hammer, and of the price Thrym asked for the return of it. Then turning to where Freya sat he said, "Now make thyself ready as quickly as thou canst, Freya. I myself will ride with thee to Jötunheim and deliver thee to Thrym. Then I can bring my hammer back with me."

Then Freya was filled with such wrath, her necklace Brisingamen burst apart and fell down clashing on the floor. "Shall I, who am the wife of Odur, go like a lovesick maid to Jötunheim to be the wife of Thrym?" she cried. "That shall never be. Better death than that."

Odur, too, was filled with fury, and others of the gods as well, though some thought Thor spoke wisely. But the white Heimdall rose and called for silence. Wise was he beyond most others, and the gods fell silent to listen to him.

"There is no need for Freya to go to Jötunheim," he said. "There is another way of winning back the hammer. Thor shall dress as a bride in women's robes and ornaments; he shall wear Freya's necklace on his breast, and draw a veil across his face, and go to Thrym, and in some way win back his Miölner."

Then Thor's eyes flashed fire. Sparks flew from his beard. "Never will I consent to this," he cried. "The mighty Thor will never act the bride and make himself a laughingstock for gods and men."

But Loki cried sharply, "Silence, Thor! This thing must be, for Freya will not go, and only so canst thou win back thy hammer; only so can we be safe, and our homes and wives as well. I will myself dress as thy serving maid, and ride with thee to Thrymheim."

Then Thor at last gave way, though sullenly. They dressed him as a bride with shining robes, and bracelets on his arms, and fastened Brisingamen about his neck. They braided his hair right cunningly so that it appeared as a woman's, and last of all they drew a veil across his face.

Loki, too, made ready, and presently the two set out riding high in Thor's chariot. Thor's wrath and shame were still so great that as they journeyed on the mountain smoked, and flames rose from the earth.

Thrym was watching for his guests. As they drew near he hastened out to meet them. He would have drawn aside Thor's veil and kissed the pretended bride, but Thor leaped back with such a furious bound that all who saw it wondered. Loki cried in haste, "Thy bride is shy, and she is strange in Jötunheim. Let her alone and she will soon grow used to it."

Then Thrym took Thor's hand and led him into the palace hall. Thor hung his head and would not speak, and once again Loki said, "She is too shy; she will talk presently." So Thrym was satisfied.

A great wedding feast had been prepared, and presently they all sat round the board with Thor at Thrym's right hand. Thor arranged his veil so his mouth was free to eat and drink. Brisingamen, Freya's necklace, glittered on his breast so that Thrym's eyes were dazzled by it. Scarce could he see aught else.

Greatly the giants ate, but Thor ate even more. Whole oxen he devoured, and sheep and salmon, fruit and cakes; all that had been prepared for the women he ate himself, and he drank greatly, too.

Thrym was amazed. He said, "Methinks my bride hath a mighty hunger, and a mighty thirst."

Loki said, "For eight days she hath eaten nothing, and no drop hath passed her lips, so greatly hath she longed for thee and Jötunheim."

Then for the third time Thrym was satisfied.

When the feast was ended Thrym's old sister came to ask for a marriage present from the bride. She begged for jewels from Thor's breast, or for the rings from his fingers, but he gave her nothing then, though later he gave her that for which she neither asked nor wished.

Thrym cried, "Now shall our wedding joy be sealed by a bride-gift"; and he brought Thor's hammer to him in his hands. At sight of it Thor's eyes flashed fire so that they seemed to burn even through his veil, and Thrym said, "How sharp are the bride's eyes!"

Loki said, "They burn with love for thee!"

And now Thrym laid the hammer across the knees of the pretended bride.

At once Thor seized it in his hand and rose; he tore aside his veil, he tore aside his woman's robes, and swung the hammer high, and Thrym and all giants cried aloud with fear, seeing who it was, and knowing they had been tricked. Then they would have fled away, but Thor threw his hammer first of all at Thrym, and he fell, and afterward at the others, and always when it was thrown a giant fell, and always the hammer at once returned to Thor's hand again. Many were the Jotuns who were slain that day, and to Thrym's sister Thor gave smacks instead of jewels, and blows instead of rings. After that Thor and Loki burned Thrym's castle down and left it a heap of ruins. So they returned triumphantly to Asgard and there were great rejoicings there, for now Thor had his hammer once again and the gods could dwell in peace and safety in their glittering houses on Asgard's heights.

HOW ROBIN HOOD BECAME AN OUTLAW

by Howard Pyle

In merry England in the time of old, when good King Henry the Second ruled the land, there lived within the green glades of Sherwood Forest, near Nottingham Town, a famous outlaw whose name was Robin Hood. No archer ever lived that could speed a gray goose shaft with such skill and cunning as his, nor were there ever such yeomen as the seven-score merry men that roamed with him through the greenwood shades. Right merrily they dwelt within the depths of Sherwood Forest, suffering neither care nor want, but passing the time in merry games of archery or bouts of cudgel play, living upon the King's venison, washed down with draughts from crystal fountains.

Not only Robin himself but all the band were outlaws and dwelt apart from other men, yet they were beloved by the country people round about, for no one ever came to jolly Robin for help in time of need and went away again with an empty fist.

And now I will tell how it first came about that Robin Hood fell afoul of the law.

When Robin was a youth of eighteen, stout of sinew and bold of heart, the Sheriff of Nottingham proclaimed a shooting-match and offered a prize of forty marks to whomsoever should shoot the best shaft in Nottinghamshire. "Now," quoth Robin, "will I go too, for fain would I draw a string for the bright eyes of my lass, for so goodly a prize as that." So up he got and took his good stout yew bow and a score or more of broad cloth-yard arrows, and started off from Locksley Town through Sherwood Forest to Nottingham.

As he walked along with a brisk step and a merry whistle, he came suddenly upon some foresters seated beneath a great oak tree; fifteen in all, making themselves merry around a huge pasty. Each man was clad in Lincoln green, and a fine show they made, seated upon the sward beneath that fair, spreading tree. Then one of them, with his mouth full, called out to Robin,—

"Hulloa, where goest thou, little lad, with thy one penny bow and thy farthing shafts?"

Then Robin grew angry, for he was mightily proud of his skill at archery.

"Now," quoth he, "my bow and eke mine arrows are as good as thine; and I'll hold the best of you twenty marks that I hit the clout at three-score rods."

At this all laughed aloud, whereat Robin grew right mad. "Hark ye," said he; "yonder, at the glade's end, I see a herd of deer, even more than threescore rods distant. I'll hold you twenty marks that I cause the best hart among them to die."

"Then I will take thy wager," cried one of the foresters, "and will hold thee twenty marks that thou causest no hart to die." Robin took his good yew bow in his hand, and drew the gray goose-feather to his ear; the next moment the bow-string rang and the arrow sped down the glade. High leaped the noblest hart of all the herd, only to fall dead, reddening the green path with his heart's blood.

"Ha!" cried Robin. "How likest thou that shot, good fellow?"

Then all the foresters were filled with rage, and he who had wagered the twenty marks was more angry than all. "Get thee gone, straightway," cried he, "or, by all the saints of heaven, I'll baste thy sides until thou wilt ne'er be able to walk again. Thou hast killed the King's deer, and, by the laws of our gracious lord and sovereign, King Harry, thine ears should be shaven close to thy head."

Never a word said Robin Hood, but he looked at the foresters with a grim face; then, turning on his heel, strode away from them down the forest glade. But his heart was bitterly angry, for his blood was hot and youthful and prone to boil.

Now, well would it have been for him who had wagered had he left Robin Hood alone; but his anger was hot. Of a sudden, and without any warning, he sprang to his feet, seized upon his bow and fitting to it a shaft, sent the arrow whistling after Robin.

It was well for Robin Hood that that same forester's fingers slipped the string a little, or else he would never have taken another step; as it was, the arrow whistled within three inches of his head. Then he turned around and quickly drew his own bow, and sent an arrow back in return.

"Ye said I was no archer," cried he aloud, "but say so now again!"

The shaft flew straight; the forester fell forward with a cry, and lay on his face upon the ground, his arrows rattling about him from out of his quiver, the gray goose shaft wet with his heart's blood. Then, before the others could gather their wits about them, Robin Hood was gone into the depths of the greenwood. Some started after him, but not with much heart, for each feared to suffer the death of his fellow; so presently they all came and lifted the dead man up and bore him away to Nottingham Town.

So Robin Hood became outlawed and so he came to dwell in the greenwood that was to be his home for many a year to come. Two hundred pounds were set upon his head as a reward for whoever would bring him to the court of justice.

But Robin Hood lay hidden in Sherwood Forest for one year, and in that time there gathered around him many others like himself, outlawed for this cause and for that.

So, in all that year, fivescore or more good stout yeomen joined themselves to him, and chose him to be their leader and chief. Then they vowed that even as they themselves had been despoiled they would despoil their oppressors, whether baron, abbot, knight, or squire, and that from each they would take that which had been wrung from the poor by unjust taxes, or land rents, or in wrongful fines; but to the poor folk they would give a helping hand in need and trouble, and would return to them that which had been unjustly taken from them. Besides this, they swore never to harm a child nor to wrong a woman, be she maid, wife, or widow; so that, after a while, when the people began to find that no harm was meant to them, but that money or food came in time of want to many a poor family, they came to praise Robin and his merry men, and to tell many tales of him and of his doings in Sherwood Forest, for they felt him to be one of themselves.

Up rose Robin Hood one merry morn when all the birds were singing blithely among the leaves. "For fourteen days," said he, "we have seen no sport, so now I will go abroad to seek adventures forthwith. But tarry ye, my merry men, all, here in the greenwood; only see that ye mind well my call. Three blasts upon the bugle horn I will blow in my hour of need; then come quickly, for I shall want your aid."

So saying, he strode away through the leafy forest glades until he had come to the verge of Sherwood. There he wandered for a long time, through highway and byway, through dingly dell and forest skirts. At last he took a bypath that dipped toward a broad, pebbly stream spanned by a narrow bridge made of a log of wood. As he drew nigh this bridge he saw a tall stranger coming from the other side. Thereupon Robin quickened his pace, as did the stranger likewise; each thinking to cross first.

"Now stand thou back," quoth Robin, "and let the better man cross first."

"Nay," answered the stranger, "then stand back thine own self, for the better man I wot, am I."

"That shall we presently see," quoth Robin, "meantime bide thou here a little while till I come again." So saying he stepped quickly to the coverside and cut a good staff of ground oak, straight, without flaw, and six feet in length. "Lo, here is a good staff, lusty and tough," quoth he. "Now we will fight until one or the other of us tumble into the stream by dint of blows."

"Marry, that meeteth my whole heart!" cried the stranger, twirling his staff above his head, betwixt his fingers and thumb, until it whistled again.

Then followed a great and mighty battle betwixt these two

stout yeomen. Never did the Knights of Arthur's Round Table meet in a stouter fight than did these two. Each stood in his place, neither moving a finger's breadth back, for one good hour, and many blows were given and received by each in that time, till here and there were sore bones and bumps, yet neither thought of crying "Enough," or seemed likely to fall from off the bridge. At last Robin gave the stranger a blow upon the ribs that made his jacket smoke like a damp straw thatch in the sun. So shrewd was the stroke that the stranger came within a hair's breadth of falling off the bridge; but he regained himself right quickly, and, by a dexterous blow, gave Robin a crack on the crown so fairly that he fell heels over head into the water, as the queen pin falls in a game of bowls.

"And where art thou now, good lad?" shouted the stranger, roaring with laughter.

"Oh, in the flood and floating adown with the tide," cried Robin; nor could he forbear laughing himself at his sorry plight. Then, gaining his feet, he waded to the bank, the little fish speeding hither and thither, all frightened at his splashing.

"Give me thy hand," cried he, when he had reached the bank. "I must needs own thou art a brave and a sturdy soul, and, withal, a good stout stroke with the cudgels. By this and by that, my head hummeth like to a hive of bees on a hot June day."

Then he clapped his horn to his lips, and winded a blast that went echoing sweetly down the forest paths. Soon the distant twigs and branches rustled with the coming of men, and suddenly a score or two of good stout yeomen, all clad in Lincoln green, burst from out the covert, with merry Will Stutely at their head.

"Good master," cried Will, "how is this? Truly thou art all wet from head to foot, and that to the very skin."

"Why, marry," answered jolly Robin, "yon stout fellow hath tumbled me neck and crop into the water, and hath given me a drubbing besides."

"Then shall he not go without a ducking and eke a drubbing himself!" cried Will Stutely. "Have at him, lads!"

"Nay, forbear!" cried Robin; "he is a right good man and true, and no harm shall befall him. Now hark ye, good youth, wilt thou stay with me and be one of my band? Three suits of Lincoln green shalt thou have each year, besides forty marks in fee, and share with us whatsoever good shall befall us. Thou shalt eat sweet venison and quaff from crystal springs, and mine own good right-hand man shalt thou be for never did I see such a cudgel-player in all my life before. Speak! wilt thou be one of my good merry men?"

"Ay, that will I," answered the other joyfully, "for well I love the greenwood glade and well I love stout sport with such as thou, good master."

"Then I have gained a right good man this day," quoth jolly Robin. "But tell me, what name goest thou by, good fellow?"

"Men call me John Little whence I came," answered the stranger.

Then Will Stutely, who loved a good jest spoke up. "Nay, fair little stranger," said he, "I like not thy name and fain would I have it otherwise. Little art thou indeed, and small of bone and sinew, therefore shalt thou be christened Little John, and I will be thy godfather."

Then Robin Hood and all his band laughed aloud.

"So be it, good friend," said Robin Hood. "Little John shall it be. So come, my merry men, and we will go and prepare a christening feast for this fair infant."

So turning their backs upon the stream, they plunged into the forest once more, through which they traced their steps till they reached the spot where they dwelt in the depths of the woodland. There had they built huts of bark and branches of trees, and made couches of sweet rushes spread over with skins of fallow deer. Here stood a great oak-tree with branches spreading broadly around, beneath which was a seat of green moss where Robin Hood was wont to sit at feast and at merry-making with his stout men about him. Here they found the rest of the band, some of whom had come in with a brace of fat does. Then they built great fires, and after the feast was ready they all sat down, but Robin Hood placed Little John at his right hand, for he was henceforth to be the second in the band.

Thus it was that Robin Hood became outlawed; thus a band of merry companions gathered about him, and thus he gained his right-hand man, Little John.

DAMOCLES AND THE SWORD

by Frederick S. Hoppin

Syracuse is a beautiful city on the island of Sicily in the Mediterranean Sea. In olden times it was not only a great city but it was also the capital of a large and prosperous country. The ruler of Syracuse was certain to become a very rich and powerful man, and so a great many people wanted to be ruler of the city. After a good deal of fighting and struggling a man named Dionysius gained so much power there that he could do exactly as he wished. He was called the Tyrant of Syracuse, and was one of the most famous and powerful men in the whole world.

Dionysius was very proud of his power and riches, but he knew that a great many people envied him because of them and that many others hated him for things that he had done while he was getting control of the city. He did not trust any of the people around him. He was always in fear of their plotting against his life and trying to take away his power.

The men at his court, who wanted presents and favours from him, spent their time saying what they thought would please him most.

One day, when one of these men named Damocles had been

saying to Dionysius how wonderful it must be to have such power as he had and to live in such a magnificent way and how happy he must be and what a splendid time he must have, Dionysius said to him:

"Damocles, would you like to see how it feels to be Tyrant of Syracuse for one evening?"

Damocles answered that nothing in the world could possibly be more wonderful and glorious, and that he would like it above all things.

"Very well then," said Dionysius. "Tomorrow evening you shall come to a grand feast at the palace and take my place at the table, and every one shall treat you exactly as if you were Dionysius himself."

Damocles was overjoyed at this. The next evening he put on his very finest robes and went to the palace.

At the palace door he was met by a great crowd of men all in their gayest clothes. Flower girls strewed roses before him, and musicians played while they led him in much state into the banquet hall.

There stood a table loaded down with every kind of costly and delicious thing to eat and drink. The whole hall was hung around with beautiful and brightly coloured stuffs, and brilliantly lighted with thousands of candles in golden candlesticks.

Damocles was led to a magnificent couch on a platform at the head of the table. There he proudly took his place. The musicians played their gayest and everyone cheered and applauded.

A slave, superbly dressed, approached and, kneeling before him, held out a golden platter. On it was some delicious fruit, the very sight of which made Damocles' mouth water. He took some in his hand and started to raise it to his mouth. As he did so he happened to glance up and, to his amazement and horror, there, hanging just over his head and apparently held up in the air only by a thread, was a tremendous sword whose sharp blade gleamed in the light of the candles.

He wanted to spring up and get out of the way, but he did not dare to move too quickly for fear of shaking the sword down and, suddenly, the men on either side of him seized him and held him down, just beneath the sword which seemed to Damocles to swing to and fro a little, as if it might break loose and fall at any instant.

As he sat there, trembling and staring up at the bright edge of the blade, Dionysius came forward from the crowd where he had been watching what was going on.

He laughed at Damocles' terror.

"Why do you tremble, Damocles?" he said. "You wanted to be in the place of Dionysius for one evening and there you are. Did you not know that there is always a sword hanging over the head of anyone who is great or powerful, and whom many people envy and hate and are only waiting for a chance to harm?"

"I understand that now," faltered Damocles. "Never again will I envy anyone who is rich or powerful. Let me go before the sword falls, and take the place again yourself. You are more used to it than I am and it may not seem so terrible to you."

So they let Damocles come down from the high seat. Dionysius took his place as usual on the couch at the head of the table and the banquet went on. But Damocles, with the greatest relief, sat down once more at the lower end of the banquet hall and ate and drank whatever was given to him, happily and with contentment.

THE LABORS OF HERCULES

Anonymous

Juno hated Her′cu les, and feared him too, even before he was born.

She hated him because he was the son of her husband Jupiter

and her rival Alc men′e, a mortal woman. And she feared him because Jupiter had once declared that the first grandson of Per seus′, would become the ruler of his people—and Hercules would have been that first grandson.

Juno therefore used her wiles to delay the birth of Hercules and to hasten the birth of another grandson of Perseus, Eu rys′theus. Eventually, then, Eurystheus became king of the Argives, instead of his cousin Hercules.

Even while Hercules was in his cradle, Juno tried to destroy him by sending two serpents to strangle him. But this prodigious infant grasped one of the snakes in each hand and choked it to death. That caused a great sensation, naturally. And it made Juno decide to proceed more cautiously in her efforts to get Hercules out of the world.

When Eurystheus became king, Juno arranged to have him send Hercules on very difficult missions, in the hope that these tasks would bring about his end. Hercules, who knew he was the son of Jupiter, disliked taking orders from his cousin, but even Jupiter was unable to help him out of this pass, since he had to keep his promise about the first-born grandson of Perseus. He advised Hercules to finish the assignments and count on getting his reward later.

The First Task

In the valley of Ne me′a, a monstrous lion was killing cattle, and men too. He was the terror of the whole countryside and none could devise any way to overcome him. Eurystheus thought that going forth to slay this lion would surely lead to the undoing of Hercules. He therefore demanded of Hercules that he bring him the skin of the animal.

Hercules set out alone with his club and located the lion's cavern. He stood outside and shouted to the monster, and so drew him out into the open. Hercules struck at him with his club, but his powerful blows made no impression on the tough animal. Hercules then dropped his club and strangled the lion with his bare hands, just as he had strangled the serpents in his cradle. Instead of skinning the lion, he raised the animal on his shoulders and brought it to Eurystheus. But when the king saw the huge, hideous beast and realized the tremendous strength of Hercules, he told him that the next time he brought him the fruits of his achievements, he better leave them outside the town.

Second, the Many-headed Hydra

Near a sacred spring in Argos, which once had saved the inhabitants after a serious drouth, a strange, many-headed monster had settled down and had become a menace to all, besides polluting the waters of the spring. Eurystheus ordered Hercules to kill this monster. But that took more than strength. For one of the Hydra's nine heads was immortal; and each of the other eight, while it might be knocked off, was immediately replaced by two new ones.

Hercules went out with his servant, a nephew of his, and swung his club lustily. Against all the odds of multiplying heads, the task could never end. At last Hercules changed his tactics. With the help of I o la′us, he tied the beast down. Then, as he knocked each head off they seared the stump with a flaming tree, so that it could grow no more. The last head, which was indestructible, he buried in a deep hole and placed over it a great rock.

Eurystheus was angered by his cousin's success and set him at what would seem an impossible task.

The Augean Stables

Au ge′us, the king of Elis, owned three thousand oxen. For thirty years, the stables in which he kept these animals had not been cleaned. You can hardly imagine the mounts of filth and rubbish that had piled up in and around the stables. And all this Hercules was required to clean out before sunset.

As Hercules looked about him, he couldn't conceive himself shoveling fast enough to accomplish much in one day. Instead of digging his shovel into the manure he decided to dig detours for two rivers nearby, the Alpheus and the Peneus. By turning these rivers into new channels running through the stables, Hercules got the waters from the hills to do his work for him and by night the stables were all clean and in order.

The Queen's Girdle

The daughter of King Eurystheus had set her heart on having the famous girdle of Hip pol′y ta, queen of the Amazons; and the king ordered Hercules to go and fetch it. Now the Amazons were a tribe of fierce women warriors who had driven out any men who ever attempted to get into their country. Sailing with some young men who volunteered to go with him, Hercules at last arrived at the shores of the Amazon country. He told the queen what he wanted, and she received him and his companions graciously, and she even agreed to give Hercules her girdle.

Juno was angered, that Hercules should so lightly come by his goal. She disguised herself as an Amazon and, mingling with the others, started the rumor that Hercules was plotting to carry their queen away. The women took up arms and swarmed down to the ship. Hercules, seeing them come down threateningly, thought that Hip pol′y ta had betrayed him and he killed her. He took her girdle and with his men sailed home.

The Oxen of Geryon

Far to the west lived a great giant who had three bodies and who ruled over very powerful warriors. Geryon had a herd of beautiful brown oxen which Eurystheus wanted Hercules to get for him. The long journey to that far country was beset with hardships and adventures. When Hercules reached the western end of the Mediterranean Sea, where Europe and Africa join, he pulled up the mountain and broke it in two, leaving half on each side. These high rocks are now called the Pillars of Hercules, and the passage between is the Strait of Gibraltar.

Hercules finally located the herd of oxen, but they were in the care of a giant who had a fierce two-headed dog guarding them. The dog scented a stranger when Hercules approached, and ran forward to attack him. Hercules crushed the dog with his club and then killed the giant herdsman. As he was driving the oxen away, Geryon himself appeared and they got into a fight. Here Juno again came to help the enemy of Hercules, but he drove her off by hitting her with one of his arrows, and then he shot Geryon at the point where the three bodies were joined together, and killed him. After many more adventures, he returned to Greece with the oxen.

The Apples of the Hesperides

Eurystheus contrived a more difficult task for Hercules—to bring him the Apples of the Hesperides. These were the golden apples that the Earth goddess had given to Juno on her marriage to Jupiter, and they were in charge of the daughters of Hesperis, the Night. But where were they? Nobody could tell him. He searched for them a long time and had many adventures. It was on this journey that he set Prometheus free from the rock to which the gods had chained him, for stealing fire from heaven and giving it to the mortals. In return, Prometheus gave Hercules some very good advice.

The Golden Apples were guarded by a monster with a hundred heads, who never sleeps. It would be impossible to get past this guard. Prometheus advised Hercules that he persuade Atlas, the father of the Hesperides, to bring him the apples. Atlas, who had to spend all his time bearing the weight of the heavens on his shoulders, could be induced to do this if someone would relieve him of his burden for a while. And indeed, Atlas agreed to do this. Hercules took his load from him and Atlas went into the garden. There he lulled the dragon to sleep, plucked the three golden apples and brought them to Hercules. He did not want to give up his freedom, but he had to hold to his agreement; and Hercules brought the apples back to Eurystheus.

Cerberus

Eurystheus next sent Hercules to fetch Cer'ber us, the watchdog of Hades or Hell, and bring him into daylight. This task took long and very special preparation, deep study of the secret mysteries, and difficult training. For Cerberus was a special kind of monster. He had three heads like dog-heads. The hind part of his body was like that of a dragon's tail. His body was covered, not with hairs or bristles, but with writhing snakes. With the help of Mercury and Minerva, he persuaded Pluto, the lord of Hades, to let him take Cerberus out into the daylight for a time. Pluto made the condition that Hercules should use no weapons. Prepared as he was, Hercules grasped Cerberus and held him firmly while he took him out into the upper regions; and then brought him back again.

Moved by his own hatred for his cousin, and backed by Juno, Eurystheus imposed still more labors on Hercules, twelve in all. At last, however, Hercules was free; and after many journeys and adventures—and some sad misfortunes, too—he destroyed himself on a huge funeral pile which he had built himself. In the fire, his mortal body perished; but the divine part of him was received by the gods and goddesses. For in the end Juno relented and welcomed him to the dwelling of the gods, and gave him in marriage her own daughter, Hebe, the goddess of eternal youth.

EUREKA!

by Frederick S. Hoppin

The King of Syracuse, Hiero, wanted to have a new crown made to wear on great occasions. He took a large lump of gold out of the strong room where he kept all his treasures and gave it to a skilful jeweller, telling him to mould and carve it into a beautiful crown that he could wear comfortably on his head.

The jeweller was a very clever man at his work, but the King did not think that he was very honest and he did not quite trust him. So he had the lump of gold carefully weighed before he gave it to the jeweller so as to be sure that the crown, when it came back to him, would weigh as much as the lump of gold. In that way he felt he could be sure that the jeweller had put all the gold into the crown and had not kept some of it for himself.

After a while the jeweller brought the crown to the King. It was beautifully made and shone like sunlight and was comfortable to wear. When the King weighed the crown it was just as heavy as the lump of gold had been. But Hiero was not altogether satisfied. It was true that the weight of the crown and that of the lump of gold were the same, but Hiero was suspicious lest the craftsman had put into the crown some baser metal and kept some gold out.

Then, like everybody else who was in doubt about anything, the King went to Archimedes, who was a very famous man of science. He found out many things about the world that no one had known before, and invented new ways of lifting heavy weights and of doing other useful things. He was so well known for his knowledge and wisdom that all kinds of people came to him for help when they did not know what to do about something that puzzled them.

Hiero showed Archimedes the crown and told him what had

happened, and asked him if he could find out whether it was made of pure gold and nothing else.

That was a puzzle even for Archimedes.

The King went back to his palace and Archimedes thought over the question for a long time. He could not see any way of finding out the answer. He thought about it for several days without results.

One morning as he was going to his bath, still thinking deeply about the crown, he absent-mindedly stepped into the tub, which the servant had filled to the brim. As Archimedes got into it, the water overflowed and poured out on the floor.

Archimedes watched it pouring out, but he did not think at all about its wetting the room, because an idea had suddenly struck him.

In getting into the full tub he had forced a certain amount of water out of it—just the amount that had filled the place in the tub which his own body took up. A bigger man would have forced out more water than he did and a smaller man less. So it was clear to him that the amount of water forced out of the tub would show the exact size of whatever was put into it.

If the same amount of gold was in the crown that had been in the lump of gold which the King gave the jeweller, then they both would force the same amount of water out of a full bowl. But suppose the jeweller had taken away some of the gold, and had put into the crown instead, a certain amount of some other metal? Since gold is the heaviest of metals, the silver or copper would take up more space than gold. Then the crown could have been made to weigh as much as the lump of gold, but it would take up more space and would force more water out of the bowl than the lump of pure gold would have done.

As this idea grew clear in his mind Archimedes saw in a flash that he had found a new and very interesting way by which he could answer the King's question.

Without waiting a second, he sprang out of the tub crying,

"Eureka! Eureka!" which means in Greek "I have found it! I have found it!"

He dashed out of the house and ran down through the streets of the town to the palace, into the room where the King was sitting, still crying "Eureka! Eureka!" and still dripping with water, just as he had climbed out of his tub.

The King and his courtiers tried the experiment at once of putting, first a lump of gold of just the same weight as the one the King had given to the jeweller and then the crown, into a bowl of water. It turned out exactly as Archimedes had expected. The crown displaced more water from the bowl than the lump of gold.

The jeweller confessed that he had taken some of the gold and put some silver in the crown instead, and he was punished by the King.

Archimedes gained great fame from this discovery which has been of very real use to the world ever since.

THE BARMECIDE FEAST

The Story of the Barber—From the Arabian Nights

by Frances Jenkins Olcott

Now this is the story told by the Barber to the Sultan, about his brother Shacabac; as recorded in the Tales of a Thousand Nights and One Night.

My brother Shacabac had his lips cut off, O Prince of the Faithful. He was extremely poor, possessing nothing. He went forth one day to beg for food, and on his way beheld a handsome house with a wide and lofty porch. At the door stood many servants, and my brother inquired the name of the owner of the house. A servant answered: "He is a son of the Barmecides." On this my brother drew nearer and asked the doorkeeper for some food. "Enter here," replied the doorkeeper, "my master will give thee all thou desirest."

So my brother entered and, passing through the house, which was spacious and magnificently furnished, he came at last to a garden. It was full of flowers of all kinds, and was paved with coloured marbles. At the upper end of the garden he saw a man with a long beard and handsome countenance, who advanced toward my brother and welcoming him said: "What may I do for thee? I am the master of the house." My brother then told him of his extreme need; and hearing this the man rent his clothes, exclaiming: "Alas! Am I in this city, and thou also in it and hungry! Verily I cannot endure such a thing! Thou must stay and partake of my supper." "O my master," replied my brother, "I am so extremely hungry, that I cannot wait long."

Upon this the master of the house called out: "Boy, bring the basin and ewer." And then he said, turning to my brother, "O my guest, advance and wash thy hands." The master then made the motions as though he were washing his hands in a basin and called an attendant to bring a table and spread the feast. Whereupon the slaves began to pass to and fro as though preparing a meal, and after that the master of the house took my brother and sat down with him at an imaginary table, and proceeded to move his hands and lips as though he were eating.

My brother said to himself: "Surely this man loveth a jest," so he also made the same motions as his host, who said: "Eat, O my guest, and observe how white this bread is." "Verily," answered my brother, "in all my life I have never seen bread more beautifully white or of sweeter taste." "It was made by a slave-girl of mine," answered the host, "whom I purchased for five hundred pieces of gold."

He then called out: "Boy, bring the meat," and addressing my brother said: "This meat is more delicious than that served at the

Sultan's table, so eat freely, O my guest, for thou art hungry." Next he called out: "Boy, bring the chickens stuffed with pistachio nuts," and said to my brother: "Eat this for it is more delicious than anything thou hast ever tasted before!"

My brother, whose hunger increased every moment, could scarcely restrain his impatience, but answered: "O my master, verily this dish hath not its equal in flavour!" The host then began to feed my brother imaginary morsels of food, saying: "Taste and enjoy the flavour. Eat and do not be ashamed." "I have had enough meat," answered my brother. Thereupon the host cried: "Boy, bring sweets of every kind, dried fruits and almonds and confections." Then he urged: "Eat more, eat more."

My brother by this time had become indignant at the manner in which the master of the house made a jest of his hunger, and he said to himself: "Verily I will cause him to repent of mocking me after this wise!" Meanwhile the host shouted: "Boy, bring the wine," after which he pretended to fill a cup and hand it to my brother, saying: "Take this wine, it will refresh thee and delight thy soul." My brother made the motion of emptying the cup, and returned it to the master of the house, who thereupon filled another cup and handed it to him. This he did several times, until my brother feigning drunkenness, arose and, lifting his hand, gave the host a ringing blow in the neck.

"What is this thou vile creature!" cried the host. "O my master," answered my brother humbly, "I am thy slave whom thou hast most graciously treated to wine until I have become intoxicated, therefore I have smitten thee. Surely thou wilt not be angry with me seeing the cause!"

At this the master of the house burst into laughter. "Verily," he said: "for a long time I have made game of men, but never before have I met any one who was clever enough to carry out the jest with me, as thou hast done. I pardon thee the blow, and now thou must partake of my hospitality." So he called his slaves and made them prepare a feast, which they did; and the host taking my brother sat down with him, and they spent the evening in eating and drinking and making merry.

After that the master of the house gave my brother a costly dress, and made him his own familiar friend. They continued to dwell together for the period of twenty years, when the man died and the Sultan seized his property and took possession of it.

"Now, O Prince of the Faithful," said the barber, "I have related to thee the adventures of two of my brothers, and thou must see that I am a better man than they."

"Thou hast spoken the truth, O El Samit The Silent," said the Sultan. "Thou verily art a man of few words and devoid of impertinence, but do thou depart at once from this city, and take up thy abode elsewhere." So the Sultan banished me from Bagdad, continued the barber, and I came hither to this city.

YOU CAN'T PLEASE EVERYBODY

after Aesop

A man and his son went to the market one morning. They took along a donkey to bring back whatever they would buy.

As they walked down the road, they met a woman who looked at them with a sour face.

"Are you not ashamed," she called to the father, "to let your little boy walk in the hot sun, when he should be riding on the donkey?"

The father stopped and lifted his boy to the donkey's back. So they went on.

After a little while they met an old man. He began at once to scold the boy. "You ungrateful son!" he shouted. "You let your poor old father walk while you sit there on the donkey like a lazy good-for-nothing!"

When the old man had passed, the father took his frightened son from the donkey and got onto the animal himself.

Further on they met another man, who looked at them angrily. "How can you let your child walk in the dusty road?" he asked. "And you sit up there by yourself!"

The father was troubled, but he reached down and lifted his son up where he could sit on the donkey in front of him.

A little later they met a man and his wife, each of them riding a donkey. The husband called out, "You cruel man! How can you let the poor donkey carry such a heavy load? Get off at once! You are big enough and strong enough to carry the little animal instead of making it carry two of you."

The poor man was now really perplexed. He got off the donkey and took his son off too.

Then he cut down a young tree for a pole and trimmed it. He tied the donkey's four feet to the pole. Then he and his son lifted the pole. They trudged along, carrying the donkey between them.

As they were crossing a bridge over a stream, they met with a crowd of young men. Seeing the donkey being carried on a pole, they started to laugh and shout. Their noise startled the poor donkey who started to kick violently and broke the ropes holding his feet. As he frisked about, he tumbled off the bridge, and was drowned.

The man looked sadly into the stream and shook his head. "My son," he said to the boy, "you cannot please everybody."

B. C. G.

DAMON AND PYTHIAS

by Frederick S. Hoppin

We are told about many pairs of friends in history and in stories, like David and Jonathan in the Old Testament, who were famous for their love and devotion to each other, but when we want to say that two men are the finest and truest of friends we say that they are like Damon and Pythias.

These two boys grew up in the city of Syracuse at a time when it was ruled by the Tyrant Dionysius. He was a very able man who had gained his power by leading the army of Syracuse to victory. At first Dionysius had ruled well and justly, but gradually he became more and more tyrannical. The people murmured so much against him and his harsh laws that he began to be afraid some of them would try to kill him. He lived in constant fear of this, and he did not trust anybody.

At that time Damon and Pythias were about twenty years old. They were both brave and fearless, and Damon had dared to speak openly against one of the Tyrant's laws. Dionysius therefore shut him up in prison and declared that he would have his head cut off on a certain day.

When Damon knew that he was to be killed he asked Dionysius to let him be free for a month first, so that he could go and say goodbye to his father and mother who lived in another town far away from Syracuse. He promised faithfully that, if Dionysius would let him do this, he would come back at the end of the month and have his head cut off.

Dionysius laughed loud and long at this request.

"You would never come back," he said to Damon. "What pledge could you possibly give me that would make me feel sure that you would return here to be killed? No, you will have to stay in prison till the day you are to die."

When Pythias heard of this he did not wait a moment. He went straight to Dionysius and said to him, "I will stay in prison in place of Damon if you will let him go. I know that he will come back on the day he says. If he does not return then you can kill me instead."

Dionysius was filled with astonishment and at first he thought that Pythias was not in earnest. When he was convinced that Pythias meant exactly what he said and was ready to stay in prison while Damon was away, he declared that Damon could go free for the month on condition that he would return and be killed on the day fixed for his execution.

So Pythias went into the prison and waited there patiently while Damon took a ship and sailed away to see his father and mother once more before he died.

The time passed by until it came to the last day before that fixed for Damon's execution. There was no sign of Damon, but Pythias still had perfect confidence in him and felt sure that he would come back as he had promised.

"The winds have been against him," he said, "or he has been held back for some other reason which he could not help. He will keep his word."

The day of the execution dawned. The jailer came to the prison cell to lead Pythias out to die in place of Damon.

Just as they reached the prison door Damon came rushing up. His ship had been held back by a storm, and he had only reached the harbor of Syracuse that morning, just in time.

Dionysius was so struck by the trust of these two friends and their love for each other that he pardoned Damon, and let them both go free.

"I would give all my power," he said, "to know that I had one friend who cared for me as Damon does for Pythias and Pythias for Damon."

THE FIRST CORN

by George Bird Grinnell

A long time ago there lived in a Pawnee village a young man who was a great gambler. Every day he played at sticks, and he was almost always unlucky. Sometimes he would lose everything that he had, and would even lose things belonging to his father. His father had often scolded him about gambling and had told him that he ought to stop it. There were two things that he never staked; these two things were his shield and his lance.

One day he played sticks for a long time, and when he got through he had lost everything that he had except these two things. When he went home at night to his father's lodge he told his relations what he had done, and his father said to him: "My son, for a long time you have been doing this, and I have many times spoken to you about it. Now I have done. I cannot have you here any longer. You cannot live here in my lodge or in this village. You must go away."

The young man thought about it for a little while and then he said: "Well, I will go. It does not make much difference where I am." So he took his shield and his spear and went out of the lodge and started to go away from the village. When he got outside of the village and had gone some distance, he heard behind him a loud rushing sound like a strong wind—the sound kept getting nearer and louder—and all at once it was above him, and then the sound stopped, and something spoke to him and said: "Well, I am here. I have come to find you. I have been sent, and am here on purpose to get you and take you with me." The voice that spoke to him was the Wind.

The Wind took the young man up and carried him away towards the west. They traveled many days, and passed over broad prairies and then across high mountains and then over high, wide plains and over other mountains until they came to the end of the world, where the sky bends down and touches the ground. The last thing the young man saw was the gate through the edge of the sky. A great buffalo bull stands in this gateway and blocks it up. He had to move to one side to let the Wind and the young man pass through. Every year one hair drops from the hide of this bull. When all have fallen the end of the world will come.

After they had passed through this gate they went on, and it seemed as if they were passing over a big water. There was nothing to be seen except the sky and the water. At last they came to a land. Here were many people—great crowds of them. The Wind told the young man: "These are all waiters on the Father."

They went on and at last came to the Father's lodge and went in. When they had sat down the Father spoke to the young man and said to him:

"My son, I have known you for a long time, and have watched you. I wanted to see you, and that is why I gave you bad luck at the sticks, and why I sent my Wind to bring you here. Your people are very hungry now because they can find no buffalo, but I am going to give you something on which you can live, even when the buffalo fail."

Then he gave him three little sacks. The first contained squash seed; the second beans, red and white; and the third corn, white, red, blue and yellow. The Father said:

"Tie these sacks to your shield and do not lose them. When you get back to your people give each one some of the seeds and tell him to put them in the ground; then they will make more. These things are good to eat, but the first year do not let the people eat them; let them put the yield away and the next year again put it in the ground. After that they can eat a part of what grows, but they must always save some for seed. So the people will always have something to eat with their buffalo meat, and something to depend on if the buffalo fail." The Father gave him also a buffalo robe, and said to him:

"When you go back, the next day after you have got there, call all the people together in your lodge, and give them what is in this robe, and tell them all these things. Now you can go back to your people."

The Wind took the young man back. They traveled a long time and at last they came to the Pawnee village. The Wind put the young man down and he went into his father's lodge and said:

"Father, I am here." But his father did not believe him, and said:

"It is not you." He had been gone so long that they had thought him dead. Then he said to his mother:

"Mother, I am here." And his mother knew him and was glad that he had returned. At this time the people had no buffalo. They had scouted far and near and could find none anywhere, and they were all very hungry. The little children cried with hunger. The next day after he got back, the young man sent out an old man to go through the camp and call all the people to come to his father's lodge. When they were there, he opened his robe and spread it out, and it was covered with pieces of fat buffalo meat piled high. The young man gave to each person all he could carry, but while he was handing out the pieces, his father was trying to pull off the robe the hind-quarters of the buffalo and hide them. He was afraid that the young man might give away all the meat, and he wanted to save this for their own lodge. But the young man said:

"Father, do not take this away. Do not touch anything. There is enough."

After he had given them the meat he showed them the sacks of seed and told them what they were for, and explained to them that they must not eat any the first year, but that they must always save some to plant, and the people listened. Then he said to them:

"I hear that you have no buffalo. Come out tomorrow and I will show you where to go for buffalo." The people wondered where this could be, for they had traveled far in all directions looking for buffalo. The next day they went out as he had told them, and the young man sent two boys to the top of a high hill close to camp, and told them to let him know what they saw from it. When the boys got to the top of the hill, they saw down below them in the hollow a big band of buffalo.

When the people learned that the buffalo were there, they all took their arrows and ran out and chased the buffalo and made a big killing, so that there was plenty in the camp and they made much dried meat. Four days after this he again sent out the boys, and they found buffalo. Now that they had plenty of meat they stayed in one place, and when spring came the young man put the seed in the ground. When the people first saw these strange plants growing they wondered at them, for they were new and different from anything that they had ever seen growing on the prairie. They liked the color of the young stalks, and the way they tasseled out, and the way the ears formed. They found that besides being pretty to look at they were good to eat, for when the young man had gathered the crop he gave the people a little to taste, so that they might know the words he had spoken were true. The rest he kept for seed. Next season he gave all the people seed to plant, and after that they always had these things.

Later, this young man became one of the head men, and taught the people many things. He told them that always when they killed buffalo they must bring the fattest and offer them to the Father. He taught them about the sacred bundles, and told them that they must put an ear of corn on the bundles and must keep a piece of fat in the bundles along with the corn, and that both must be kept out of sight. In the fall they should take the ear of corn out of the bundles and rub the piece of fat over it. Thus they would have good crops and plenty of food.

All these things the people did, and it was a help to them in their living.

HAWAIIAN MYTH

by Padraic Colum

HOW KANA BROUGHT BACK THE SUN AND MOON AND STARS*

Whether or not this story refers to a period comparable to what we know as the ice age is not clear. It does not seem to represent the chaos in Genesis before the Lord created the sun, moon, and stars, since it definitely refers to their previous existence and to their having been stolen.

Once the Sun and the Moon and the Stars were taken away; they were taken away by Ka-hoa-alii, and the people of the world would still be in cold and darkness if Kana and his brother Niheu had not gone to find them and bring them back.

You have been told about Kana, the youth who could stretch himself upward until his body was as thin as the thread of a spider's web, and you have been told about Niheu, his brother, who carried a war-club so great that, by resting one end of it in his canoe and putting the other end against a cliff, he could walk from his canoe to the land, and you have been told about Uli, Kana's and Niheu's wise grandmother.

This story begins with Niheu. Once when he was crossing the Island of Hawaii he heard about Ka-hoa-alii's man and how he kept the people fishing and cooking for him; the people were pitying themselves and complaining when Niheu came amongst them.

Then Niheu saw Ka-hoa-alii's man, and he flung his club at him; the stroke of the great club knocked Ka-hoa-alii's man over. And after he had flung his club Niheu went on to his grandmother's house. He told her what he had done. She was made

* From Padraic Colum, *The Bright Islands*. Reprinted by permission of the publisher, Yale University Press.

afraid, and she told him that trouble would come because of his mischief. "Go," she said, "and find your brother Kana, and bring him here to us, for we shall need his help."

But before he went, Uli made him help her fix a long rope that she had. She took the rope and she tied it to the post of her house, and she brought the end of it down to the seashore, and she tied it to a great stone there. The people wondered, and Niheu wondered at what Uli did. Then Niheu went off to find his brother Kana.

Meanwhile, Ka-hoa-alii had heard what Uli's grandson had done to his man. "I will punish Niheu for this, and I will punish all the people of Hawaii," he said. "Now I will take away the Sun and the Moon and the Stars from their sky. I will leave the people in cold and darkness; only where I am will there be warmth and light."

Niheu found his brother, and he started with him for their grandmother's house. While they were on their way the darkness came, for the Sun was taken out of the sky suddenly. But as they went on, they struck against the rope that Uli had stretched from the post of her house to the stone on the seashore. Holding the rope, they came to the house. Kana did not go within, for no house was high enough to hold him. The two of them saw their grandmother seated by a blazing fire with lights all around her.

"So you have come," said their grandmother to them. "You are the only two in all the world that can bring the Sun and the Moon and the Stars back into our sky. Ka-hoa-alii has taken them away, and you must go to where Ka-hoa-alii is. Before I tell you what to do, do you, Kana, stretch yourself upward, and see if there is any light in the sky."

Kana stretched himself upward until his head was near the sky. He looked around, and he saw a little light in it. He brought himself down again, and he told his grandmother what he had seen.

Then said Uli: "You, Kana, and you, Niheu, will have to go to the country that Ka-hoa-alii rules over. Go straight toward the place that the Sun used to rise in. The fine rain will fall on you and the cold will get into your bones, but go on and on until you come to where an old woman sits at the bottom of a cliff. She is my sister; Luahine-kai-kapu she is named, and she is blind. Tell her that you are Uli's grandchildren, and she will direct you to the country that Ka-hoa-alii rules over."

So Kana and Niheu started off from their grandmother's house. They went in a straight line toward the place that the Sun used to rise in. As they went on, the fine rain fell on them and the cold went into their bones. Kana took up Niheu and carried him on. But still the fine rain fell on them and still the cold crept into their bones. Then, when they came to the place that is called Kaha-kae-kaea, Niheu lay down to die.

Kana left him wrapped in leaves under a loulu palm and went on. He came to where an old woman sat at the bottom of a cliff; she was blind, and he knew that she was Luahine-kai-kapu, his grandmother's sister.

"Whose child are you?" said Luahine-kai-kapu to Kana.

"Your sister Uli's grandchild," said Kana.

"What have you come for?" said she.

"I have come to get the Sun and the Moon and the Stars that Ka-hoa-alii has taken from our sky; I am the only one who can bring them back. Show me the way to Ka-hoa-alii's country."

"I have no eyes," said Luahine-kai-kapu; "I cannot see to show you the way."

"Lie down under this coconut tree," said Kana. Luahine-kai-kapu lay down. Kana picked off the young shoots of the coconut and called out to her, "Luahine-kai-kapu, turn your face toward the sky." She turned her face up as directed; Kana then threw the two young shoots at her eyes.

Then he struck her in the eyes, and she jumped up and cried out with a loud voice, "Oh, I am killed!" Kana then said to her, "Be quiet and rub your eyes." The old woman began rubbing her eyes. After she had done this, she cried out that she was able to see as before.

"Before I send you into the country of Ka-hoa-alii, I shall have to do something to make your hands different," said Luahine-kai-kapu. She took ku-kui-nut and charcoal and she pounded them together and she made a paste. She rubbed the paste she had made on the great hands of Kana. "Now," said she, "you have hands like the hands of Ka-hoa-alii." Then she told him what to do when he came to the place where Ka-hoa-alii lived.

She set a fire before him to guide him, and she set a wind at his back to help him on. And helped on by the wind and guided by the fire, Kana came at last to the borders of Ka-hoa-alii's country. Then the fire died down, and he had no guide to go before him. But still the wind helped him on.

He came to the place where Ka-hoa-alii was. He hid and watched him. Ka-hoa-alii would lift up a great stone that covered a hole in the sky, and take food up in his hands and feast with his attendants. And when they had feasted, they would go into the house and play games. Thus Ka-hoa-alii and his attendants passed the day; they feasted and they played games, and they played games and they feasted.

Kana did what Luahine-kai-kapu told him to do. He watched all they did. When they had gone into the house, he went to the great stone. He lifted it up. He propped it up with his feet. Then he put his two hands down into the hole.

Those below put things into his hands. They were things to eat. Kana flung them away, and put his hands down again. Those below put water into his hands. He emptied the water out. Kana put his hands down again. Those below put birds into his hands; he took them up and let them fly around; they were the birds that cry when darkness is going. Now as they flew around they cried, "Kia-wea! Kia-wea!"

He put his hands down again. Now his hands were filled with Stars. He took them up and flung them into the sky. There they stayed—the Stars that we still see. He lowered his hands again. The Moon was put into his hands. He put the Moon into the blue sky with the Stars, and it stayed there, giving light.

Kana put his hands down again. This time a single bird was put into his hands. He took it up and put it beside him. It was the crowing cock. He put his hands down once more; the warm Sun was put into his hands. He held the bright Sun up. He put it into the sky. The cock beside him crowed.

The cock crew, and Ka-hoa-alii, hearing it crow, came out of his house. He saw Kana standing there, and he saw the Sun shining in the sky. He went toward Kana to kill him, but he saw how tall and how strong Kana was, and he was afraid to touch him. And Kana, seeing that Ka-hoa-alii was afraid of him, demanded from him the Water of Life, the Water of Kane, so that he might restore his brother with it. Ka-hoa-alii gave him the Water of Kane.

Kana then went to Kaha-kae-kaea. His brother Niheu was there, wrapped in leaves under the loulu palm. He gave him the Water of Life, and life came back again to Niheu. Afterward Ka-hoa-alii came to where they were. He gave them a canoe made out of white chicken feathers, and in that canoe Kana and Niheu returned to Hawaii. They went to their grandmother's house, and they saw the Sun in the heavens, and the Moon following the Sun, and Stars with the Moon. And never again were these bright lights taken out of our sky.

INDEX